MW00804284

MY BIG TOE

BOOK 1:

A W A K E N I N G

Section 1
**Delusion or Knowledge:
Is This Guy Nuts, or What?**

Section 2
**Mysticism Demystified
The Foundations of Reality**

The *My Big TOE* reality model will help you understand your life, your purpose, the totality of the reality you experience, how that reality works, and how you might interact most profitably with it.

A half dozen independent test readers of various backgrounds were asked to evaluate the My Big TOE *trilogy and record their impressions of it. This is what they said:*

■ ■ ■

"Eureka! A Theory Of Everything that actually lives up to its name! *My Big TOE* not only unifies physics, but unifies philosophy and theology as well. You will be amazed!"
— PAMELA KNIGHT, PHYSICIST

"Reading *My Big TOE* has challenged my mind and widened my horizon. Expect your worldview to radically expand and your perspective to reach a new level of understanding."
— INA KUZMAN

"*My Big TOE* is utterly original, pioneering and bold. Campbell writes with clarity and humor as he explores and answers the hard questions in this comprehensive work about the ultimate nature of reality and consciousness. Full of fresh and profound ideas, you may be astonished to find that learning how reality works actually improves the quality of your life."
— LYLE FULLER, POWER ENGINEER

"The *My Big TOE* trilogy roared through my comfy no-brainer world like a category F5 tornado that makes you laugh ... when the dust finally settled, I was left with an incredibly clear view of how and why things are as they are."
— PEG ROCHINE, FOUNDER AND CEO, CLINICAL RESEARCH

"This trilogy will profoundly change you .... you will never look at your world in the same way again."
— INA KUZMAN

"Thoroughly challenging, engaging ... a transforming experience. *My Big TOE* marks the end of humanity's childhood."
— LYLE FULLER, POWER ENGINEER

"Unique, profound, and enriching are the words that most easily come to my mind to describe *My Big TOE.*"
— TREVOR GOLDSTEIN, PHILOSOPHER AND FUTURIST

"If you have ever asked the questions: Is this all there is?, What's the purpose?, How am I related to the whole?, *My Big TOE's* logic, grounded in science, provides unequivocal answers that make you think. A profoundly fascinating read!"
— INA KUZMAN

"Finally ... somebody has unraveled the Gordian knot, figured out the whole enchilada, and put the solution in terms that are clear and easy to understand. Now, everything makes sense!"
— PEG ROCHINE, FOUNDER AND CEO, CLINICAL RESEARCH ASSOCIATES

"Grab a handful of highlighters, sit down in the most comfortable chair you can find and prepare yourself for the read of a lifetime."
— KATE VON SEEBURG, BUSINESS OWNER

"If you are a traditionalist, a normal member of your culture carrying all the assumptions that we are taught to never question, the *My Big TOE* trilogy will knock your socks off, unscrew the top of your head, and give you a whole new outlook on life."
— PEG ROCHINE, FOUNDER AND CEO, CLINICAL RESEARCH ASSOCIATES

"New concepts and unusual perspectives. Profound mysteries and ancient secrets. Good science and human ingenuity. Tom Campbell, an unlikely combination of 'Meet Mr. Wizard,' Dr. Phil, and Bill Murray, takes you on a journey through inner space you will never forget.
— KATE VON SEEBURG, BUSINESS OWNER

"These are books that you will want to read more than once. Every read produces an entirely new experience – expands your mind and understanding in completely new directions – because afterwards you are a significantly different person."
— PAMELA KNIGHT, PHYSICIST

"My *Big TOE* finally puts the larger reality, the whole of your experience, on a solid theoretical footing. If you've ever wondered about the ultimate questions of existence you must read this book."
— LYLE FULLER, POWER ENGINEER

"The logic is undeniable and the science is sound ... the *My Big TOE* trilogy represents a 100 megaton scientific bomb blast that will simultaneously rock the foundations of traditional science, refocus philosophy and metaphysics, and panic the keepers of the status quo."
— PAMELA KNIGHT, PHYSICIST

"Has the holy grail of physics finally been discovered? Tom Campbell presents a compelling case. This UNIFIED THEORY OF EVERYTHING is delivered straight up and without caveats. Read and consider the possibilities"!
— INA KUZMAN

"The *My Big TOE* trilogy delivers an entirely fresh perspective, a more general formulation of physics that makes the world, its science, philosophy, theology, and you, all fit together within one consistent scientific understanding of the whole."
— PAMELA KNIGHT, PHYSICIST

"No one interested in science, spirituality, or the nature of reality and consciousness can afford to ignore this important, bold and utterly original book. The 'psi uncertainty principle' alone is one of the most significant ideas ever put forward, period."
— LYLE FULLER, POWER ENGINEER

MY BIG TOE

A TRILOGY
UNIFYING PHILOSOPHY,
PHYSICS, AND METAPHYSICS

BOOK 1:
AWAKENING

BOOK 2:
DISCOVERY

BOOK 3:
INNER WORKINGS

Thomas Campbell

Find the other two books of the *My Big TOE* trilogy:
http://www.My-Big-TOE.com
http://www.lightningstrikebooks.com
Phone orders: 1 – 800 – 901 – 2122

MY BIG TOE: A TRILOGY UNIFYING PHILOSOPHY, PHYSICS, AND METAPHYSICS

BOOK 1: AWAKENING

Lightning Strike Books
http://www.LightningStrikeBooks.com

Copyright © 2003 by Thomas Campbell

All rights reserved – including the right of reproduction, in whole or in part, in any form. No part may be stored in a retrieval system, or transmitted in any form or by any means electronic, mechanical, photocopying, recording, digital, optical, or otherwise without prior written permission of the author.

Printed in the United States of America
First Edition: February, 2003

Book design by Michele DeFilippo, 1106 Design, LLC
Cover illustration by Frank Foster

Publishers Catalogue-in-Publication Data
Campbell, Thomas
My Big TOE: Awakening. Book 1 of a trilogy unifying philosophy, science, and metaphysics / Thomas Campbell
1. Science. 2. Philosophy. 3. Metaphysics. 4. Reality, model of.
5. Consciousness, theory of. 6. Spirituality. 7. Paranormal, theory of.
8. Theory of Everything. 9. TOE. 10. Theology (religion) and science.

ISBN 0-9725094-0-2 (Softcover)
ISBN 0-9725094-1-0 (Hardcover)

To Chris

To Bob & Nancy

To Dennis & Nancy Lea

To Todd, Lyle, Ina, and Trevor,
whose encouragement
was key to success

To those in need of
a new perspective

To all seekers of Big Truth

To Pamela, The One

To love within
A joyous
Heart

■ ■ ■
Synopsis
My Big Picture
Theory of Everything
My Big TOE – A trilogy unifying
philosophy physics, and metaphysics
■ ■ ■

Book 1: Awakening

Section 1 provides a partial biography of the author that is pertinent to the subsequent creation of this trilogy. This brief look at the author's unique experience and credentials sheds some light upon the origins of this extraordinary work. The unusual associations, circumstances, training and initial research that eventually led to the creation of the *My Big TOE* trilogy are described to provide a more accurate perspective of the whole.

Section 2 lays out, logically justifies, and defines the basic conceptual building blocks needed to construct *My Big TOE*'s conceptual foundation. It discusses the cultural beliefs that trap our thinking into a narrow and limited conceptualization of reality, defines the fundamentals of Big Picture epistemology and ontology, as well as examines the inner-workings and practice of meditation. Most importantly, Section 2 defines and develops the two basic assumptions upon which this trilogy is based. From these two assumptions, time, space, consciousness, and the basic properties, purpose, and mechanics of our reality is logically inferred.

Book 2: Discovery

Section 3 develops the interface and interaction between "we the people" and our digital consciousness reality. It derives and explains the characteristics, origins, dynamics, and function of ego, love, free will, and our larger purpose. Finally, Section 3 develops the psi uncertainty principle as it explains and interrelates psi phenomena, free will, love, consciousness evolution, physics, reality, human purpose, digital computation, and entropy.

Section 4 describes an operational and functional model of consciousness that further develops the results of Section 3 and supports the conclusions of Section 5. The origins and nature of digital consciousness are described along with how artificial intelligence (AI), as embodied in AI Guy, leads to artificial consciousness, which leads to actual consciousness and to us. Section 4 derives our physical universe, our science, and our perception of a physical reality. The mind-matter dichotomy is solved as physical reality is directly derived from the nature of digital consciousness.

Book 3: Inner Workings

Section 5 pulls together Sections 2, 3, and 4 into a more formal model of reality that describes how an apparent nonphysical reality works, interacts, and interrelates with our experience of physical reality. Probable realities, predicting and modifying the future, teleportation, telepathy, multiple physical and nonphysical bodies, and the fractal nature of an evolving digital consciousness reality are explained and described in detail.

Section 6 is the wrap-up that puts everything discussed in Sections 2, 3, 4, and 5 into an easily understood personal perspective. Additionally, Section 6 points out *My Big TOE's* relationship with contemporary science and philosophy. By demonstrating a close conceptual relationship between this TOE and some of the establishment's biggest intellectual guns, Section 6 solidly integrates *My Big TOE* into traditional Western scientific and philosophical thought.

Contents

BOOK 2: Discovery

BOOK 3: Inner Workings

SECTION 5
Inner Space, the Final Frontier:

BOOK 3: Inner Workings

SECTION 6
The End is Always the Beginning

Acknowledgements

The One. In a category all to herself, I wish to acknowledge the immeasurable contribution, in all possible forms, given by my most constant, consistent, and challenging teacher: Pamela – The One.

Fellow travelers. First and foremost, acknowledgement goes to Bob Monroe and his wife Nancy who enabled my exploration of the path that eventually led to the *My Big TOE* trilogy. Next, to Dennis Mennerich, my fellow explorer and traveling companion. We pulled each other along when neither of us knew much about where we were going or how we were going to get there. Then, to Nancy Lea McMoneagle who was not only a fellow traveler but also the primary enabler of Monroe's success. All gems, every one – I could not possibly have set out on this strange journey with a better collection of friends and mentors. Finally, to the un-named many who provided me with the opportunities that enabled me to be what and who I have become. I wish I could have made more of the opportunities you offered. In the end it is these tens, these hundreds, these thousands, who made this trilogy possible. Thank you all.

Major contributors. In a more direct and immediate vein, there are a few readers of indomitable fortitude to whom I am eternally grateful. The time and effort volunteered by these remarkable people made all the difference in the world. Together we have tried hard to make all three books as clear and understandable as possible.

Special thanks go to Lyle Fuller, Todd Phillips, Ina Kuzman, and Caroline Lampert for their effort to improve the readability and clarity of *My Big TOE*. All three were quick to point out where I had left stumbling blocks lying on the path to Big TOE understanding. Additionally, Todd's and Ina's questions served as a catalyst to ferret out much interesting material. Many thanks to Chris Nelson who started me writing in the first place. Without their selfless generosity and dedication beyond all reason, this trilogy would be a poor shadow of what you have before you.

In addition, I thank Nancy Lea McMoneagle and Dennis Mennerich for aiding and corroborating the accuracy of my memories of the early years at Whistlefield. Also heartfelt thanks to Lyle Fuller, Joel Dobrzelewski, Trevor Goldstein, and Eric Campbell for their encouragement and good questions. Special thanks to Steve Tragesser for asking questions that became the catalyst for much of Chapter 18, Book 3. Likewise, to Lyle Fuller for doggedly pursuing questions that eventually produced the discussion of free will found in Chapter 11, Book 2 and that added clarity to my exposition of the psi uncertainty principle. Similarly, to Trevor Goldstein whose experience and questions precipitated the discussion of mind tectonics in Chapter 6, Book 2; and to Ina Kuzman for initiating the discussion found in Chapter 23, Book 1 about the nature and practice of meditation. Also, thanks goes to Eric Campbell for precipitating a discussion about the natural constraints of a finite consciousness system. Credit goes to Tom Hand, Zane Young, Rhonda Ganz, and Kristopher Campbell for offering useful suggestions and comments. Finally, I wish to thank Steve Kaufman for being in the right place at the right time with his book, *Unified Reality Theory: The Evolution of Existence Into Experience*. I love it when a plan comes together.

Hired Help. Two ladies of great integrity and competency enabled *My Big TOE* to make the transition from an amateur creation to a professional product. Kate von Seeburg, owner of *K8 & Company*, edited the manuscript while Michele DeFilippo, owner of *1106 Design*, produced the interior and cover designs.

Family. Great appreciation goes to my wife and children, who patiently and cheerfully allowed me to work on "the book" when I should have been paying attention to them. I hope the final result will prove itself worthy of our collective sacrifice.

Non-contributors. Last, and certainly least, I wish to barely mention Kathy Cyphert and Peggy Rochine, who, along with many others too numerous to name, contributed absolutely nothing to this effort but wanted to see their names mentioned in it just the same. Additionally, Boldar, Kiana, Onyx, Joe, Nikki, Chico, Mr. Pickle, Sid, Moe, Sir Maximus, Snuffy, Sir Minimus, Kia, Gabrielle, Isabel, and Kuga-Bear also deserve honorable mentions as outstanding non-contributors.

—Tom Campbell,
Dec. 9, 2002

Preface: Author's Note to the Reader

Yes, you should read this preface.

I understand that many readers have little interest in, or patience for, lengthy prefaces or forewords. The first question is always: Should I take the time to read this ancillary text, or can I skip it without missing anything important?

Most of us are eager to zip past the preliminaries and immediately sink our teeth into the meat of the main text. Anticipation and expectation push us to get on with the real thing. We of Western culture are an impatient goal oriented people driven toward endpoints. In our rush to the finish line, we take little notice of the journey that gets us there. Such a misappropriation of emphasis often squanders our opportunities because, more often than not, the tastiest and most nourishing part of life lies in experiencing the process, not in attaining the goal.

By the end of Section 6, you will no doubt agree that these books are ... well ...different. As such, they require a different approach. The preface and foreword of the *MY Big TOE* trilogy **are** integral parts of the story. Because this trilogy blazes an original trail far off the beaten path, it is essential to include introductory material that can help prepare you for what lies ahead. I know you are eager to get on with it and discover if this trilogy delivers the goods, but rushing off toward that goal too quickly actually reduces the likelihood that you will get there at all.

The function of the preface and the foreword is to maximize the return on your reading investment. The preface provides an overview of the tone, structure, process, and mechanics of the *My Big TOE* trilogy. The foreword establishes a broad view of the trilogy's content and lays out a rough map of where you will be going on this unusual journey. It provides the context and focus wherein the trilogy's content is most easily understood. The foreword and preface together improve comprehension and minimize frustration by providing a global view of the forest before you begin your descent into the trees.

I strongly suggest that you adopt an attitude of patience toward gaining an understanding of the profound mysteries and ancient secrets that are logically unraveled by this new physics. My Big Picture Theory Of Everything (*My Big TOE*) will take you to both the beginning and to the end of time. It will dive deeply into the human heart as well as probe the limits of the human mind. It will define the significance of you, and provide new meaning to your existence. It will help you realize and optimize your potential. It will develop a wholly new scientific understanding of both your inside and outside world.

You may find it more productive to pace yourself by depth of comprehension than by percent of completion. Avoid rushing from concept to concept the way children pursue presents on Christmas day. Take your time. A feast for heart, head, and soul is best ingested little by little, bite by bite, with many thoughtful pauses and much careful cogitation to aid digestion. Genuine breakthroughs must be absorbed slowly as existing paradigms grudgingly dissolve. Familiar paradigms, like a favorite teddy bear, can be extremely difficult to let go.

Every successful journey, regardless of how long or difficult, begins with a single step that is animated by gumption, directed by goals, and repeated as often as necessary by dogged perseverance. On this particular journey, the preface is located at step one, the foreword at step two, followed by the three books: *Awakening, Discovery*, and *Inner Workings*.

I have carefully aimed the content of this scientific and philosophic exposition at a general audience of varied background. You do not need a scientific, philosophical, or metaphysical background to understand the content of the My Big Picture Theory Of Everything trilogy. No leaps of faith or beliefs are required to get to where these books will take you. A determined and tenacious truth seeker – a sturdy, independent intellect that is by nature open minded and skeptical – constitutes the optimal reader. There are no prerequisites. If you have a logical, open, and inquisitive mind – an attitude of scientific pragmatism that appreciates the elegance of fundamental truth and the thrill of breakthrough – you will enjoy this journey of personal and scientific discovery.

Under the best of circumstances the successful communication of this trilogy's content will require much from both of us. This work presents many unique and daunting challenges to the effective communication between author and reader. Worldviews are not casually picked, like fruit, from a vendor's cart: To make the necessary connections, we must dive deeply.

Far beneath the foundation of your intellect, your culture lays out the template for your worldview upon the core belief systems that define your perception of existence. The basic assumptions that support your notion of reality are not seen by you as assumptions at all – they are accepted, without question, as the most solid of all facts. That is simply the nature of culture – belief at the bone and sinew level of awareness. The point is: The concepts presented by this trilogy are likely to challenge the belief systems of your culture – regardless of what culture you come from.

Material within *My Big TOE* may challenge your familiar assumptions, beliefs, and paradigms to the point of serious discomfort. If that discomfort leads to a profitable resolution, I am pleased; if it does not, I am saddened. My goal is to be informative and helpful. I encourage you to take what you can profitably use and leave the rest.

There are enough new concepts and unusual perspectives presented here to support and generate a multitude of books. I have purposely left much unsaid at the periphery in order to stay focused on the central idea of developing a Big TOE. Though the trilogy remains, from beginning to end, tightly focused on its primary objective, I will occasionally take short side trips in the form of asides to add color, explore related connections, and insert topics of special interest and practical value. Hopefully, you will find these side trips so interesting and informative that you will gladly excuse their interruption. Some effort will be required on your part to bridge these asides in order to maintain the logical continuity of the larger discussion. To make sure that you are never confused about whether you are reading an aside or the main text, asides are indented, have their own special font, and are clearly marked (at the beginning and end) with dingbats that look like this: ▶. If a secondary aside resides within a primary aside, it is indented yet again and marked with double dingbats ▶▶. When an aside fills an entire page, it is difficult to judge how much the text is indented, consequently, when this condition occurs, dingbats are placed in the header to let you know that the text is part of an aside. Thus, a casual glance is all that is required to determine if the text that you are reading is part of an aside, and if so, at what level.

You may find the text to be challenging in some places and obvious in others. What is too challenging or too obvious to each reader is mostly dependent on the experience and understanding of that individual reader. It is my intent to never speed through this exposition at such a rate that you cannot appreciate the scenery, nor to wallow about repetitively in the obvious – though from time to time, depending on your background, some may feel that I occasionally do both.

Although the language of American English (the language in which these books were originally written) is decidedly poor in nonphysical conceptual descriptors, it does have the advantage of being unusually rich in communications and information technology descriptors. The latter, oddly enough, is what allows me to convey the former. As strange as that may seem, it is the pervasiveness of modern science and technology, especially communications and data processing technology, that provides the conceptual tools required to produce a model of the larger reality the Western mind – or more broadly, the Western attitude or more accurately, the Western belief system – can relate to, understand, and work with.

Science and technology have advanced to the point where their applications and understanding have begun to mirror some of the fundamental processes of existence. We of the twenty-first century have only recently acquired the necessary concepts to understand and appreciate the nature of the larger reality within the context of our contemporary Western point of view. Previously, knowledge and understanding of the Big Picture and our existence in it was comprehended and described by ancient sages in terms of metaphors that were pertinent to their cultures and specifically created for the benefit of their specific audiences. Today, we find these once practical descriptions to be largely symbolic and irrelevant to a modern scientific view of reality. Philosophy, theology, and science find themselves at odds over what is significant.

I am a scientist. This trilogy is the result of a long and careful scientific exploration focused upon the nature of reality and the individual. Preconceived notions will be more of a hindrance than a help. It is the task of this trilogy to clearly and completely construct your consciousness, your world, your science, and your existence in a general, logical, scientific way that comprehensively explains **all** the personal and professional data you have collected during a lifetime. An overarching Big Picture theory that explains **everything** may seem highly unlikely, if not absolutely impossible, but it is not. Take heart: Good science and human ingenuity have consistently delivered the impossible for at least two hundred years. Be open – history repeatedly demonstrates that the appearance of impossibility is most often the result of limited vision.

Patience will be required. This adventure of mind, science, and spirit is complex and will take significant time to properly unfold. If it were immediately obvious, it would either be old news or you would be reading a short journal article instead of a trilogy. A keen mind that is skeptical and open is the only ticket you need to take this journey.

Based on the feedback from those who have preceded you, I expect that you will find this voyage into the depths of elemental consciousness and fundamental reality to be personally enriching. You will be pushed to think a few big thoughts and ponder a few big ideas, but the conclusions you eventually come away with will be entirely yours, not mine. These are not books that set out to convince you of anything, or persuade you towards a particular point of view. At every turn you are strongly dissuaded from becoming a believer. Data, facts, and measurable results are the exclusive currency upon which this trilogy trades.

Reading the *My Big TOE* trilogy is not likely to be a passive experience. If you decide to seize the opportunity to climb out of the box, you will likely end up doing some difficult work. You will always be encouraged to think for yourself and come to conclusions that are based on **your** personal experience. Despite all the serious cogitation, we are also going to play, laugh, and have some fun as we go.

Much of what you believe to be true about yourself, your existence, and the nature of reality will be challenged. If you are open to exploring a bigger picture, these books will make you think, and think again. Most readers will not consider this trilogy to be an easy read – merely following the logical processes and sequences as they swallow up old paradigms will require some focused effort. On the other hand, significant growth and learning is rarely easy – if easy, it is rarely significant.

Contrary to my best efforts, Sections 2, 3, 4 and 5 remain somewhat conceptually interdependent. Each section will be better understood and make much more sense after reading the other sections. That could not be helped. Reality is a unified whole thing with each of its parts inexorably intertwined with the others.

This trilogy's three books and six sections develop the conceptual content of *My Big TOE* more or less sequentially. Consequently, reading the books or sections out of numerical order provides a less than optimal experience. However, understanding *My Big TOE* is much more dependent upon reading the entire trilogy than it is upon reading it in any particular order.

The nature of reality and of the typical reader is such that we must sneak up on *My Big TOE* one concept at a time. We will examine the Big Picture from multiple perspectives to ensure the design and structure of the whole becomes clearly visible. If things seem to get a little far out every once in a while, hang tough until it all pulls together into a coherent complete picture.

For the reasons stated above, a slow and careful reading will optimize your investment – take your time, and meander through these books at a relaxed and unhurried pace. If you become bogged down, it is better to go on (and come back later if you want to) than to feel as if you must read every word in the order in which it appears. It would be unfortunate for you to miss seeing a part of the forest that may be important to you because you became lost, exhausted, or discouraged wandering unproductively among the trees in another part.

Throughout *My Big TOE*, I have used a seeding technique to sneak up on some of the more difficult ideas. I often plant conceptual seeds (that briefly bring up or introduce an idea) within the sections, chapters, pages, or paragraphs that precede a full and thorough discussion of that idea. I do this because many readers will find the concepts presented within *My Big TOE* to be totally unfamiliar. Comprehension and understanding of this trilogy is significantly improved if the reader is at least somewhat prepared for the major conceptual discussions.

Questions may occasionally leap into your mind as you read. Hold on to your questions, or better yet, write them down as you go. Most will be answered within a few paragraphs or pages. If you have unanswered questions after completing Section 5, these can be productively used as the initial focus of your own quest for Big Truth – a subject that is taken up with gusto in Section 6.

Be careful not to lose sight of the Big Picture as a result of being overly focused on the details. It is easy to get twisted around details that strike an emotive resonance with your beliefs. The winning strategy here is to get a glimpse of the entire forest, not to argue about the color of the moss growing on specific trees. Control your passionate interest in the coloration of moss or you may entirely miss what is important.

One final note before you begin. Those who know me well, along with a few of the initial readers, have suggested that I forewarn you about my sense of humor. If you read something in these books that could be interpreted as humor, sarcasm, condescension, arrogance, silliness, inanity, or all of the above, it is probably only humor, or occasionally, humor with a touch of sarcasm. If you find yourself unsure of how offended you should be, I suggest that you temporarily suspend your judgment of the author's mind-set. I am told that eventually (by the end of Section 4) you'll be familiar with my stealthy humor and informal chatty style. Consequently, a later judgment may be more accurate.

The structural anatomy of *My Big TOE* is laid open like a frog on the dissecting table in the paragraphs below. Most readers will find that this overview provides a helpful perspective on how the book you are now reading fits into the overall *My Big TOE* trilogy.

My Big TOE is designed as a three book trilogy. It is packaged as separate books for those who are not sure of how big a bite they wish to take, and as a more economical three book set for those who are confident they want it all. Each book contains the same dedication, synopsis, table of contents, acknowledgements, preface, and foreword, as well as its own acronym list and two unique sections of content. Though the table of contents displays the contents of all three books a the beginning of each book, the contents belonging to the other two books are cast in light grey instead of black. Although chapter and page numbering starts anew within each book, the six sections are numbered sequentially across the entire trilogy to add a sense of structural continuity.

Book 1: *Awakening* contains the first two sections. **Section 1** provides a partial biography of the author that is pertinent to the subject matter. Its function is to shed light on the origins of this unusual work by providing a look at the author's unique experiences and credentials that eventually led to the creation of *My Big TOE*. **Section 2** lays out the basic building blocks needed to develop this TOE's conceptual foundation. Many of the concepts initiated in Section 2 will be more fully explored in later sections.

Book 2: *Discovery* contains the middle two sections. **Section 3** takes the information gained in Section 2 and develops its implications in more detail and depth while relating it more directly to the reader's personal experience. **Section 4** pulls together the ideas of Sections 2 and 3, while developing the additional concepts required to bind it all together into one consistent whole. Sections 2, 3, and 4 are carefully designed to sequentially work together to produce the fundamental understanding that is necessary to comprehend Section 5.

Book 3: *Inner Workings* contains the last two sections. **Section 5** presents the formal reality model in detail. **Section 6** is the wrap-up that puts everything discussed into an easily understood perspective. Additionally, Section 6 points out *My Big TOE's* relationship with contemporary science and philosophy. By demonstrating a close conceptual relationship between this TOE and some of the establishment's biggest scientific and philosophic intellectual guns, Section 6 integrates *My Big TOE* into traditional Western science and philosophy.

There is a place in cyberspace [**http://www.My-Big-TOE.com** This URL is not case sensitive but the **hyphens are required**] set aside for you to share your experience, exercise your intellect, voice your opinions, vent your angst, or simply hang out with your fellow travelers. You can send email to both the author and the publisher from the **my-big-toe.com** web site, as well as acquire all Big TOE books. There, you can keep up with the latest in Big TOE info, happenings, chitchat, reviews, research, and discussion groups.

— Tom Campbell
Dec. 9, 2002

Foreword: A Conceptual Orientation

Without the proper perspective, clear vision produces only data. The point here is to give the reader an initial high altitude peek at the forest before we begin our trek into its depths. In this foreword, I will describe where you will be going and what you should expect to accomplish. It is always helpful to know where you are headed even if you have no idea of how you are going to get there. This conceptual fly-over is designed to minimize the disorienting affect of totally unfamiliar territory.

Both the structure and the content of your perception of reality are culturally dependent. How a Tibetan Buddhist monk or an American physicist would describe reality is as vastly different as the words, expressions, and metaphors that each would employ to make such a description. What would make sense and be obvious to one would seem to be lost and out of touch to the other. If we can rise above our cultural bias, we have a tendency to ask, or at least wonder: Which description is right and which one is wrong? They seem clearly incompatible – certainly both could not be equally accurate and correct. If we are more sophisticated, we might ask which portions of each description are right or wrong and search for areas of possible agreement as well as define areas that appear to be mutually exclusive. That is a better approach, but it is still wrong-headed.

Neither of the above approaches, though the second is much more expansive than the first, will find truth. Which is right or wrong is the wrong question – it represents a narrow and exclusive perspective. Which works, which helps its owner to better attain his or her goals, which goals are more productive and lead to growth and progress of the individual – to happiness, satisfaction and usefulness to others? These are somewhat better questions because they focus on practical results and on the measurable effects that each worldview has when applied to individuals – as well as the secondary effects those individuals have on others. However, something important is missing. How does one define, realize, and measure the satisfaction, personal growth, quality of life, and fulfillment of individual purpose that is derived from each worldview? What is the standard against which the achievement of these goals is assessed? Now we have a set of questions that have the potential to lead to personal discovery in pursuit of fundamental truth. Big Picture Significance and value have replaced little picture right and wrong as the primary measure of worth. Fundamental truth (Big Picture Truth or simply Big Truth), though absolute and uniformly significant to everyone, must be discovered by each individual within the context of that individual's experience. No one approach to that discovery is the right one for everybody. The significance of "little truth," on the other hand, is circumstantial and relative to the observer.

Truth exists in all cultures. It is only understandable to an individual when it is expressed in the language (symbols, metaphors, and concepts) of that individual. It is the intent of *My Big TOE* to capture the scientific and metaphysical truth from multiple cultures and multiple disciplines and present them within one coherent, self-consistent model that the objective Western mind can easily comprehend. After all, a TOE (Theory Of Everything) must contain and explain **everything**. That is a tall order. A Big Picture Theory Of Everything or Big TOE must include metaphysics (ontology, epistemology, and cosmology) as well as physics and the other sciences within a single seamless integrated model of reality. That is what the *My Big TOE* trilogy is all about.

Truth is truth, but communicating a truth to another is a difficult undertaking fraught with misunderstandings of meaning and interpretation. Big Truth, like wisdom, is not something you can teach or learn from a book. It must be comprehended by individuals within the context of their experience. Each of us comes to an understanding of reality through our interpretation of our physical and mental experiences.

The experience of others can at best provide a useful model – a framework for understanding – a perspective that enables us to comprehend and interpret our experience data in a way that makes good practical sense. The best teachers can do no more than offer a consistent and coherent understanding of reality that helps their students find the larger perspective required to self-discover Big Truth. Such a model is only correct and comprehensive if it accurately describes all the data (physics and metaphysics) all the time under all circumstances for everyone who applies it. The usefulness of a model depends on how correctly it describes the data of experience. A good model should be predictive. It should explain what is known, produce useful new knowledge, and provide a more productive understanding of the whole.

If *My Big TOE* communicates something of significance to you by resonating with your unique knowing, then this particular expression of the nature of reality suits your being. If it leaves you untouched, perhaps some other view of reality will speak to you more effectively. The form your understanding takes is not significant – it is the results that count! If you are prodded to a more productive understanding, you are on the right track. The expression of reality that most effectively nudges your understanding in the direction of learning, growing, and evolving a higher quality of being, is the right one for you. *My Big TOE* is not the only useful expression that Big Truth can take. Nevertheless, it is a uniquely comprehensive model of reality that speaks the language of the Western analytical approach. This Big TOE trilogy fully integrates a subjective, personal, and holistic worldview with objective science. East and West merge, not simply as a compatible or mutually reinforcing mixture, but as a fully integrated single solution.

When some people hear the word "model," they imagine a scale model – a miniature version of the real thing. *My Big TOE* has nothing to do with scale models. A model is an intellectual device that theoreticians use to achieve a more concrete understanding of an abstract concept. Models are often developed to describe an unknown function, interaction, or process (something that lies beyond our current individual experience) in terms of something more comprehensible. The model itself may closely resemble the reality it describes or merely describe its inputs and outputs. In either case, **do not confuse the model of reality with reality itself.** Please repeat that twice before going on.

If you have enough direct experience and a deep understanding of what is being modeled, the model becomes superfluous. With no direct experience, the model enables an understanding that is otherwise impossible to attain. With limited direct experience, the model allows you to place your limited experience within the context of the consistent logical structure of the model. To those with enough experience to incite curiosity and formulate practical questions, the model brings a meaningful interpretation and explanation to data (experience, information, fragments of truth) that otherwise seem hopelessly random and unconnected.

The model of reality developed within this trilogy enables you to understand the properties and characteristics of reality, how you interact with reality, the point of reality, and the boundaries, processes, functions, and mechanics of reality. It describes the what, the why and the how (the nature, purpose, and rules) of the interplay and interaction among sub-stance, energy, and consciousness. You will discover the distinction between the objective physical outside world and the subjective nonphys-ical inside world of mind and consciousness is wholly dependent upon, and relative to, the observer.

My Big TOE describes, as any Big TOE must, the basic oneness, conti-nuity, and connectedness of All That Is. It systematically and logically derives the natural relationships between mind and matter, physics and metaphysics, love and fear, and demonstrates how time, space, and con-sciousness are interconnected – all with a bare minimum of assumptions. Additionally, it describes in detail the most important processes of our reality – how and why reality works. You will find the results of *My Big TOE* to be in consonance with current data – and that it solves a host of longstanding scientific, philosophical, and metaphysical problems.

The model of reality developed within *My Big TOE* is not the only valid metaphor or description of the nature of the larger reality. Nevertheless, this model is perhaps more understandable to those of us who are accus-tomed to understanding our local reality in terms of the processes and measurements of objective causality. A materialistic or scientific defini-tion of reality is sometimes referred to as "Western" because the notion that reality is built upon an inviolate objective causality lies at the core of the Western cultural belief system.

My Big TOE is written to be especially accessible to this Western mind-set or Western attitude. The West does not now have, nor has it ever had, a monopoly on a process oriented, materialistic, and objective approach to existence and reality. We in the West have perhaps pursued science and technology more religiously than others, and have no doubt added a unique cultural slant to our particular brand of consumer-based materi-alism, but the basics of what I am calling a Western attitude are thor-oughly entrenched worldwide and expanding in every direction.

The stunning success of science and engineering in the twentieth cen-tury would seem to prove the usefulness as well as the correctness of this Western view. The result is that many people, whether from the East, West, North, or South of our planet, view reality from an objective and materialistic perspective that often coexists with some culturally based tra-ditional form of religious and social dogma.

Thus, a balance, or standoff, between our inner and outer needs evolves into a practical worldview that encourages Western material pro-ductivity. A pragmatic materialism that depends on objective causality is used to generate the appearance of a manipulatable, rational, stability on the outside, while a belief-system of some sort provides the necessary personal security on the inside. To eliminate the discomfort of conflicting worldviews, the two ends of this bipolar conceptual dichotomy are typically kept separate and do not mix or integrate to any significant depth. Each supports the other superficially as they together produce a materially focused, responsible, upwardly striving worker with a good work ethic, cooperative values, an inclination toward dependency, and a high tolerance of pain.

Because the Western mind-set is growing and spreading rapidly, and because the human spirit often withers on the vine before beginning to ripen in such an environment, it is particularly important to blaze a trail to the understanding of the larger reality in the terms, language, and metaphors of this mind-set. As a product of American culture myself, and as a scientist, I have endeavored to craft a model of the larger reality that not only appears rational to the objective Western attitude, but also provides a comprehensive, complete, and accurate model that Western science can build upon.

My Big TOE provides an understanding of reality that can profitably be used by both science and philosophy – one that provides an original perspective, and makes a significant contribution to physics and metaphysics as well as to several other traditional academic and practical disciplines. By the time you have finished Section 6, you will have been exposed not only to Big Picture physics and Big Picture metaphysics, but also to Big Picture psychology, biology, evolution, philosophy, computer science, artificial intelligence, and philosophy of science. There is even a TOE-bone to toss to the mathematicians – they will find new fractal concepts, and discover why geometric fractals successfully reproduce the likeness of natural objects. You will learn why Albert Einstein and others were unable to successfully develop Unified Field Theory, and why contemporary attempts to produce a successful TOE have been likewise frustrated.

The problem physicists are currently having describing a consistent reality is primarily because of the way they define space, time, objectivity, and consciousness. Their current ideas of these basic concepts contain limitations derived from erroneous cultural beliefs. It is this belief-induced blindness that creates scientific paradoxes (such as wave/particle duality and the instantaneous communication between an entangled pair). As Einstein pointed out more than half a century ago, space and time, as we interact with and experience them, are illusions. Many of the best scientists of the twentieth and twenty-first centuries realize this fact, but did not and do not know what to do about it or how to proceed. Their problem is one of perspective – their conceptualization of reality is too limited (only a little picture) to contain the answer.

Albert Einstein's space-time field (as described in his Unified Field Theory) asserted a nonphysical field as the basis for matter specifically and reality in general, thereby moving science closer to the truth, but he did not appreciate the discrete digital properties of space and time or the role of consciousness (instead of space-time) as the primary energy field. Einstein's student and colleague, the great quantum physicist David Bohm (along with a few of the best Quantum Mechanics theorists including Niels Bohr, Werner Heisenberg, and Eugene Vigner) made the consciousness connection but missed the digital connection and the Big Picture.

Contemporary physicist Edward Fredkin and his Digital Physics movement make the digital connection (quantized space and time) and are heading in the right direction, as was Einstein, Bohr, and Bohm, but they are missing a solid connection to consciousness. Digital physics has not yet discovered that consciousness **is** the computer. All are missing an appreciation of the natural limitations of our physical objective causality and a coherent vision of the Big Picture that ties everything together. You will be shown not only all of the pieces of this both ancient and contemporary reality-puzzle, but will also see how they fit together – philosophy and science, mind and matter, normal and paranormal – into a single unified coherent Big Picture.

You will hear more from the above-mentioned gentlemen of science, as well as many of the top Western thinkers of all time, in Section 6 where I integrate the concepts of *My Big TOE* with the knowledge base of traditional Western science and philosophy.

My Big TOE represents a scientific and logical tour of reality that goes considerably beyond the point where Einstein and other top scientists gave up in frustration. As limitations are removed from your thinking, you will see the source of their frustration clearly, how and why they got stuck, and the solution that they could not find or understand. That this is a non-technical exposition, devoid of the mathematical language of our little picture science, is actually not a weakness at all – even from a strict scientific perspective. How could that be? As you progress through *My Big TOE*, you will come to understand the **natural**, fundamental, and unavoidable limitations of little picture logic, science, and mathematics.

I will show you how physics is related to, and derived from, metaphysics. Additionally, you will find that mind, consciousness, and the paranormal are given a sound scientific explanation that stands upon a solid theoretical foundation. Not necessarily in the way hoped for and expected by traditional science – however, as you will discover, being nontraditional is a necessary strength, not an unavoidable weakness.

Sooner or later, truth must succeed and falsity must self-destruct. Although the consensus of culturally empowered opinion may carry the day, measurable results will carry the day after that. The value and success of *My Big TOE* must be based solely upon the personal and objective results that it produces. Only truth can produce significant consistent results. In contrast, falsity excels at producing assertive beliefs, arguments, and opinions. Open your mind, remain skeptical, pursue only significant measurable results, and let the chips fall where they may.

My Big TOE is in the form of a reality model at a level that is necessarily unusual, but easy to understand. It provides an exploration of the scientific and philosophical implications of consciousness evolution, a subject that holds critical significance for everyone.

Because this material must develop entirely new scientific and reality paradigms, it requires an extensive presentation to shed light upon the limitations of culturally habituated patterns of thought – a goal that cannot be both quickly and effectively reached. Such an in-depth multi-disciplined analysis is better suited to a trilogy than to the condensed formal structure of a traditional scientific paper.

The focus of this trilogy is directed toward the potential significance that *My Big TOE* holds for each individual reader. These books were written for you – you will find their tone to be more personal than general, more of a sharing of experience and concepts, than a lecture by an expert. It is your potential personal interaction with this material that has initiated, as well as driven, its development.

You will find an open, logical, and skeptical mind with a broad depth of experience is much more helpful than a technical background. The details of little picture reality are by nature highly technical, the exclusive territory of modern science and mathematics. On the other hand, Big Picture reality is available and accessible to **anyone** with an open mind and the will to apply it. There are no requirements for formal education or technical credentials in order to understand what is presented here.

There are three main challenges that must be met in order to deliver a shrink-wrapped Big TOE to the general public. First, with shirtsleeves rolled up and the lights turned on, I must turn some portion of metaphysics into physics because I intend to describe the whole of reality – mind and matter, normal and paranormal – not merely the matter and normal part. Consequently, metaphysics is where I must start – our contemporary physics will naturally flow from the metaphysics. The second challenge is to package this unavoidably far-out subject in a way that is interesting, easily readable, intellectually engaging, and non-threatening. To this end, I use the format of a one-on-one, peer-to-peer, informal discussion between the reader and me. The third challenge is to make and keep *My Big TOE* credible – to stay tightly logical while straightforwardly explaining the data of our collective and individual experience.

Culturally conditioned mental reflexes may need to be re-examined, generalized, and expanded. The fact that some of the content of this trilogy is likely to lie far beyond the comfortable familiarity of your personal experience creates a difficult communications problem for both of us. *My Big TOE* not only requires you to think out-of-the-box, but out-of-the-ballpark (if not out-of-the-universe), as well. You will be challenged to overcome deep seated knee-jerk cultural drag in order to climb high enough up the mountain to get a good view.

Modern science and technology are only now providing the combined knowledge by which metaphysics can be understood. It should not be too surprising that science, in its relentless explorations of the unknown, would one day arrive at the roots of existence itself. As it turns out, the nature of reality has both an objective and a subjective component. *My Big TOE* provides a thoroughly scientific description of an objective Theory Of Everything that covers all aspects of reality in an entirely general way. Additionally, it provides a remarkably practical, personally significant understanding of subjective consciousness, and explains how you individually are related to the larger reality. To appreciate and deeply understand the personal or subjective nature of consciousness, you must grow your own Big TOE. One of the major goals of *My Big TOE* is to provide the logical conceptual framework, materials, tools, and direction that you need to independently grow your Big TOE.

My Big TOE will provide the foundation and structure that you need to make sense of both your objective and subjective experience. Your personal Big Understanding of Big Truth must flow primarily from **your** direct experience – not from your intellect alone. This trilogy will bring your objective and subjective experience together under one coherent understanding of the whole you.

Please understand, I did **not** put the "My" in *My Big TOE* to flaunt pride of authorship. Nor does the "My" indicate any lack of generality or applicability to others. The "My" was added to be a constant reminder to you that this reality model cannot serve as your **personal** Big TOE until it is based upon your **personal** experience. On the other hand, personal or subjective experience is only one piece of the reality puzzle. In the objective physical world of traditional science, *My Big TOE* delivers a comprehensive model of reality that subsumes modern science, describes our objective material reality, and is universally applicable. Contemporary physics is shown to be a special case of a more general set of basic principles. After reading the *My Big TOE* trilogy, you will better understand the universal (objective) and the personal (subjective) nature of perception, consciousness, reality, and Big TOEs. You will learn to appreciate the fact that the larger reality extends beyond objective causality, beyond the reach of intellectual effort, into the subjective mind of each individual. **My** *Big TOE* is the launch pad. **Your** Big TOE is the final destination.

A personal Big TOE is necessary because the larger reality, like your consciousness, has a subjective component as well as a collective objective component. The larger reality cannot be fully appreciated or understood merely by studying, or reading about it. You must experience it. Additionally, your understanding of the Big Picture must be sufficient to integrate your subjective experience with your shared objective knowledge or both will remain superficial. To the traditional scientist and other left-brained analytical types, what I have just said sounds suspiciously like a mixing of real science and hocus-pocus, touchy-feely, belief-baloney. It is not, but a properly skeptical mind may need to digest all three books before that becomes apparent.

Arriving at conclusions based upon the assumed infallibility and apparent truth of culturally, personally, and professionally embedded paradigms and dogmas will make it difficult to understand the larger reality. Change and new ways of thinking are often traumatic, difficult to integrate, and generally unwelcome. Resistance to change is automatic at the gut level; we cling to familiar ways for the security and comfort they provide. We do not easily see unfamiliar patterns. You must be willing to overcome fear and rise above self-imposed belief-blindness if you are to succeed in getting a good look at the Big Picture.

In the pages ahead, we are going to explore the reality-wilderness. This trilogy is about the how, what, and why of what is. It is about physics and metaphysics, your world and other worlds. It is about beginnings, endings, mind and matter, point and purpose – it is also about the quality of your personal consciousness.

Your intellectual understanding of the reality you exist within, and are a part of, is only the beginning – a place to start. The most important action, the real fun, begins **after** you have finished the trilogy and begin to apply what you have learned about reality and the Big Picture to the rest of your life – both professionally and personally.

Though you will soon learn there is more to reality than theory and facts, here is one fact that you should consider before you begin: Big Truth, once understood and assimilated, always modifies your intent, and invariably leads to personal change.

■ ■ ■
List of Acronyms, Symbols, and Foreign Words and Phrases Used Within Book 1
■ ■ ■

Acronym	Descriptive Name	Page (First Mention)
AC	Alternating Current	76
AUM	Absolute Unbounded Manifold	250
AUO	Absolute Unbounded Oneness	190
Big TOE	Big Picture Theory Of Everything	9
CEO	Chief Executive Officer	67
CNS	Central Nervous System	241
DNA	Deoxyribo Nucleic Acid	205
EBC	Even Bigger Computer	265
EEG	Electroencephalograph	75
GSR	Galvanic Skin Response	75
Hz	Hertz	75
NPMR	Nonphysical-Matter Reality	80
OOBE	Out Of Body Experience	75
OS	Our System	193
PMR	Physical-Matter Reality	80
TBC	The Big Computer	233
TM	Transcendental Meditation	45
TOE	Theory Of Everything	9

Other Symbols:

C	Speed of light (186,000 mph or 1×10^8 m/s)	259
C++	A compiled computer programming language	270

Foreign Words and Phrases:

gedanken experiment – thought experiment; a logical experiment performed only in the mind.

No problema – No Problem

Section 1

■■■

Delusion or Knowledge:
Is This Guy Nuts, or What?

■■■

1

■■■

Introduction to Section 1

■■■

Beginning with a partial biography of the author may appear to be unnecessary and off the point. Ordinarily, an author's background is adequately covered by a few paragraphs on the inside jacket of the cover. However, understanding the origins of the author's experience is where this adventure must begin. If you do not know anything at all about me, the rest of this effort may wither on the conceptual vine before it is ripe. This trilogy sets forth a Big Picture Theory Of Everything (more concisely known as a Big TOE) that contains, as any Big TOE must, a comprehensive model of reality.

Because *My Big TOE* is so unusual, so far away from the thoughts you are probably used to thinking, it is important that you have some understanding of the seed, soil, and roots from which this unusual exposition sprang. Knowing its origins, the mental mettle from which it has been hammered out, may help provide the context required to assess the genuineness of *My Big TOE.*

This trilogy presents a working model of the larger reality based upon the data I have collected through a lifetime of careful scientific exploration. Section 1 describes how fate sent me down this highly unusual path and then delivered me up to the extraordinary experiences required to formulate the concepts presented in these pages.

The intent is to give you some insight into who I am, where I am coming from, and how I ended up with such an unusual Big TOE. This trilogy is about reality, not a biography about me; accordingly, please pardon my skipping here and there about my life and flying swiftly over things that you might wish I would explain in more detail. For now a quick trip through the formative years is enough. I will not attempt to explain the last twenty years of my becoming, but will instead focus on the ten years before that. That is when the mold was made and the direction of my life set.

Although I have learned much during the preceding thirty years, and have mellowed and gained in wisdom as one typically does with age, I have not changed my basic approach to learning, knowledge, or science since the events that I am about to share with you transpired.

2

■ ■ ■

Hey Mister, You Want to Learn to Meditate?

■ ■ ■

How did a nice scientist like me end up in a strange place like this? My family had no unusual interests – we were normal through and through. Perhaps we were more problem-free than normal, but no strangeness at the roots. I did well at college, graduating with a double major in physics and math. Then on to graduate school where I picked up a master's degree in physics and started working on my Ph.D. I passed the preliminary exams and qualifiers on the first try and settled into thesis research in the specialized area of experimental nuclear physics. It was 1968 and I was your typical twenty-three year old physicist – excessively cerebral, out of touch with my feelings, analytical, precise, curious, and above all, intellectually motivated and driven.

Not a hint of strangeness anywhere. If you have known any brash young physicists, you are probably aware that they tend to be unusual – somewhat skewed off the norm, one might say politely. If you are not that polite and were not snowed or intimidated by their domineering intellectual style, then "arrogant" rather than "unusual" would probably be the adjective that would most naturally come to mind.

On a warm day, late in the spring of 1971, while walking into the physics building on the way to teaching an undergraduate class, I noticed a large poster advertising a free lecture on Transcendental Meditation – or more simply, TM as most people referred to it. As a graduate student, poverty was a normal and given circumstance; consequently, anything free caught my attention. "Control your mind," the poster shouted in large block lettering. "Learn how to relax deeply and lower your blood-pressure."

"OK," I thought, "that's nice, but who cares?" I continued reading. "Improve your concentration and decrease your need for sleep."

What! I read that line again. Now it was interesting as well as free.

A few days later, I attended the free lecture. TM was presented as science – technique and results, stimulus and response. There was no theory. One regularly performs this uncomplicated meditation process and physiological benefits automatically accrue – period. There was no dependency on eastern philosophy, mysticism, or any belief system. I wanted no associations with things that were non-scientific, mystical, or belief based – in other words, goofy. That sort of hocus-pocus was for gullible people with uncontrolled emotional needs.

The two TM presenters backed their claims up with some serious looking research papers and informal studies by reputable individuals at reputable institutions. It seemed straightforward enough – for the special student rate of only $20, I would be taught to meditate in four hours spread over one week. Better concentration, clearer thinking, improved memory, reduced stress, and I would need less sleep – all for $20 and four hours.

I was skeptical but if it worked half as well as the presenters claimed, it would be a good investment for any student. In those days $20 was a lot of money – serious money for a struggling grad student. Still, it was the 70s, I was a student, and a short walk on the wild side – doing something counter to the main culture – seemed almost obligatory. I signed up.

"Just follow these directions," the TM guy said with a friendly smile, handing me a packet of paper as he took my check.

3

The Sacrificial Banana

A week later, I was on my way to the TM Center to pick up my personal meditation sound called a mantra. It would take less than five minutes they promised – stop by, get your mantra, then attend the four training sessions – what could be easier?

As per the directions, on the appointed day I showed up at this seedy little house with a clean handkerchief and a banana. A clean handkerchief and a banana? What a crock! I began to doubt the wisdom of what I was doing and felt more than a little foolish walking up to this house with my banana and hankie. Anybody who needed fresh fruit and a handkerchief to teach me how to meditate was likely to be either goofy or fraudulent. That was the first sign of strangeness. I had seriously thought about showing up without the handkerchief and fruit – just to see what would happen – but realism interceded. I decided instead that humoring them would be a better strategy. Their inane request seemed harmless enough, and more importantly, they already had my $20.

"What's with the banana?" I said derisively, holding my banana up to the first person I saw. "What's fruit have to do with meditation?" I asked. "They never said anything to me about fruit and handkerchiefs at the lecture I attended – this seems a little goofy to me." The person I was addressing evidently wasn't a hard-science type. He was as clueless as I, but questioning the interrelationship among meditation, fruit, and handkerchiefs had evidently never occurred to him. I found that difficult to understand.

His reply had been an exaggerated shrug of his shoulders, followed by a big broad smile. It was now obvious that this guy was doing what he was told without thinking about it. He was probably wondering why I was making such a big deal over a banana that wasn't expensive or much trouble

to get. He seemed a little embarrassed and uncomfortable with my direct-
ness. I looked away, silently wondering how people could be that uncriti-
cal and unthinking about what they were doing. There was something
familiar about that smile – I chuckled silently with amusement, and wondered if he was perhaps related to Alfred E. Neuman.

There were about ten people standing and sitting in the waiting area.
I found a corner to stand in and waited in silence, hanging onto my fruit,
like everybody else. Finally, it was my turn. "What's the banana for?" I
asked at the first opportunity. The initiator explained that they (the TM
organization) had a ceremony of sorts that he was required to do – the
fresh fruit was to represent the traditional offering a student would bring
to his teacher.

"What do you do with all the fruit?" I asked. In my mind, I imagined a
huge pile of rotting symbolic fruit – a sad wasteful testament to the use-
lessness of ceremonial gestures.

"We eat it," he said with a smile.

Now I understood – it was merely a way to get some free groceries. If
they wanted to add on a surcharge of one banana to the $20 price so that
they would have something to eat for breakfast – well, that was all right
with me. Nevertheless, I would have preferred that they had been more
straightforward.

The man standing next to me was about my age, well dressed, soft spoken, and seemed intelligent and serious – he didn't look like a fruit hustler. Maybe it was not them, I hypothesized, perhaps the people who set
this business up knew that they would have a difficult time making ends
meet. I let it go. Having solved the banana problem, I went on to the next
issue – the impending ceremony.

With the intention of being helpful, I offered a constructive criticism
to my initiator. I told him I thought any ceremony was completely irrelevant and that it distracted from the rational image they had carefully presented at the public meeting. He politely nodded, indicating to me that
he recognized the discrepancy, but made no other reply.

"I have to do the ceremony," he said quietly.

It was obvious that he did not care what I thought about his ceremony,
or probably anything else – this was just the way it must be done. He
looked at me for permission to continue. "OK," I said, "no big deal, go
ahead, do your ceremony if it makes you feel better. I will go along as long
as I do not have to profess any beliefs or make any promises." He smiled
at me with amusement and immediately agreed.

At his direction, we knelt, side by side, on a small rug in the middle of the kitchen floor. On the floor in front of us was my banana lying in the center of a clean white handkerchief draped over a small plate – a poor man's alter, no doubt. The instructor chanted a little Sanskrit (at least that is what he said it was) mumbo jumbo for about a minute, then was quiet for about thirty seconds, finally he told me my mantra. I repeated it with him a few times until I got it right. In fewer than three minutes I had been given and had properly memorized my very own personal (probably shared by millions) secret mantra.

I was put in a large room with several others and told to silently practice my mantra so that I would not forget it.

"Just repeat it over and over in your mind for twenty minutes," he told me. "That's all, after that you can leave – but be sure to come to the first training meeting."

"What a crock," I thought, "I paid $20 and a banana for this magic Sanskrit mantra? What could repeating some word-sound do for my mind?"

I expected nothing, but having come this far, I was determined to follow directions and give it a fair try. The twenty minutes of practice went by slowly at first, but then I drifted off into a pleasant nowhere. Suddenly, I became aware that some of the initiates who were far behind me in the queue were leaving. "They must think that it is a crock too, and are not going to stay around to practice," I mused. I checked my watch. "Whoa!" It was way past time to go – I had been practicing some forty-five minutes! I checked my watch again to make sure.

I tried to get up to leave, but I couldn't move. My body simply refused to respond to my will and effort – that had never happened before. My limbs were heavy as if I had been asleep for a long time, yet I was positive that my consciousness had been unbroken – I had **not** fallen asleep. "This is weird," I thought, as I forced my thick, viscous, semi-solid body to slowly stand up and walk. Hmmm, maybe there was something to it, and I was doing it! Or maybe I was merely more tired than I thought. That was not a good explanation – I had gotten more sleep than usual the night before. "This is interesting," I thought, "very interesting."

I had done something strange, or at least goofy, and experienced something weird (my first trip into inner space) all in the same hour. I remained skeptical, which was (and is) my nature, but I also remained open minded. There were four one-hour sessions remaining and my curiosity was growing. I had undeniably experienced something dramatically unusual. That experience, along with my Scottish ancestry and the fact that my $20 was irretrievably gone forever, provided the necessary commitment to follow this TM adventure through to the end.

4

■■■

Watch That First Step, It's a Big One

■■■

Two days later I was attending my first training class. There were about fifteen of us sitting on uncomfortable gray metal folding chairs. I looked around to assess my peers. We were a somewhat motley but otherwise normal looking crew of casually dressed students. I was hopeful that I was about to learn something remarkable and useful, yet at the same time I was a little incredulous, almost embarrassed that I had spent twenty perfectly good dollars to be associated with this Indian meditation thing. The instructor looked like us, except that he had shorter hair, was clean-shaven, and better dressed – obviously not a student. He told us about TM, explained the techniques we should use to maintain the mantra in our minds, and answered our questions.

Everything was process oriented. No theory, no more ceremonies requiring sacrificial bananas, no metaphysical mumbo jumbo – just technique. I liked it that way. I knew there was some Indian yoga-guy with a long name, and beard to match, who was the leader of the TM movement, but no one ever mentioned him. Other than the fact that this so-called guru had sold me this meditation technique through his organization, neither he nor his organization was relevant to what I could do with it. I verified that fact in no uncertain terms as soon as the instructor opened the meeting to questions. The only condition was that I could not give away or sell the mantra to others. I instinctively didn't trust anything that had to be kept secret, but this request seemed reasonable enough. The TM folks were not hiding something from the scrutinizing light of open critical review; they were merely protecting their source of income and fresh fruit. I considered it as a copyright or patent – income producing intellectual property to be protected by secrecy. No problem.

Finally, the last question was answered and it was time to practice our meditation technique. I slumped in my steel chair trying in vain to get comfortable and began to occupy my mind with the sound of my mantra. In a few minutes, I was nothing but a single point of conscious awareness existing in a void of nothingness – floating free, doing nothing – existing as conscious mind without extent or form. No thoughts, no body, no chair, no room, no instructor, nothing. It was a remarkably pleasant experience until a single thought began to violate the expansive peace and quiet: "Uh oh... I am not doing this right; I am supposed to be thinking the sound of my mantra!" That one critical thought interrupted my otherwise thoughtless float in inner space. I needed to get back on task by thinking my mantra. Suddenly, awareness of the outside world rushed in and I was startled to realize that I not only had a body, in a room with an instructor, but it was about to fall out of its chair!

Ooga! Ooga! Emergency! Emergency! My internal alarms went off. Quickly I tried to straighten up. My right leg awkwardly shot forward jerking my body back into balance. "Whew! That was a close one – I almost hit the floor like a sack of potatoes – wouldn't that have been a scene," I thought to myself after it was clear that I had successfully regained my balance. In my imagination, I could see myself thudding to the floor creating a ruckus. My next thought was more practical. "Jeez, I might have banged my head on something – meditation could be dangerous." I made a mental note to be more careful in the future. Almost simultaneously the instructor began to speak.

"Come on back," he said, "practice time is over."

"Great," I thought sarcastically, "he noticed, and now he is going to cut everybody's practice time short because I almost fell out of my chair." I looked up. To my surprise, the instructor was engaged in a conversation with a student sitting on the opposite side of the room. He appeared to be totally unaware of me or my near catastrophe.

"Time's up," he said.

I looked at my watch. What?! That's impossible! I had just lost twenty minutes of my life. What had I been doing for the last twenty minutes, where had I been?

"Any questions?" he said to the group in general.

I raised my hand. "How do you keep from falling out of your chair?" I asked. Everybody laughed. I was serious; it did not immediately occur to me that my experience was unusual. I don't think he had ever gotten that question before because he looked surprised and didn't know what to say.

"What happened?" he asked.

"I started with the mantra, then everything went blank, it was nice, but when I realized I wasn't saying the mantra any longer I almost fell out of my chair and the twenty minutes were already up after only a few minutes." Everybody laughed again, including the instructor. I suddenly realized that what I had said sounded confused, disoriented, or stupid – take your choice – and that no one else had had an experience like mine.

"Two for two – this meditation could be strange stuff," I thought to myself. The question and answer session wrapped up quickly. We were told to practice meditating twice a day for twenty minutes each time. He set the time for our next meeting and we were dismissed. I had meditated (or at least attempted to do so) twice, and both times I had experienced something very strange. What will happen the next time? I wondered. This was exciting – something seemed to be happening. My intellect and curiosity were being tickled. I wanted to experiment; I wanted to know if anything real was involved, would it work as they claimed? If so, then what else could I do with it?

The rest of the training classes resembled the first one, except I sat in a chair next to the wall at an angle so that I could not fall out. "I need to wear a seat belt and helmet, or find a bigger chair," I thought with amusement. I immediately saw a mental picture of myself sitting in a folding metal chair, in front of a big fan. I was in the middle of an otherwise empty room, wearing a seatbelt, a motorcycle helmet, goggles, and with a scarf flapping in the breeze behind me (thus, the need for the fan). I was thoroughly amused and grinned broadly at the bizarre scene. I immediately thought of Ace-Snoopy sitting on the top of his doghouse engaging the Red Baron in battle with his Sopwith Camel. I often saw pictures like that. Some were funny like that one, some were helpful. They never took but a few seconds, and disappeared as quickly as they came.

With each training class, floating in the blank state or existing in the single point of conscious awareness state became easier and more familiar. Shortly I would learn, through trial and error, to combine the blank state with controlled visuals. The two may seem incompatible, but they are not.

Two months later I was meditating twice a day, being careful to put my body in a situation where it would not fall. The point awareness or point consciousness experience continued. It was always pleasant. I usually wanted to stay longer, but did not because I was extremely busy. I also found it invigorating – it seemed to boost my energy. The biggest surprise of all was that meditation could be professionally productive! By adding the visuals, it turned out to be a great place to work.

I could solve physics problems, design experiments, analyze research data, and write and de-bug computer code ten times more quickly, and with better results while in a point awareness state than I could in a normal state of consciousness. Extremely complex matters seemed to become much simpler and clearer in my meditation state. When you work a full week unsuccessfully trying to find a bug in your analysis software, and then go home and solve the problem – not just imagining that you have solved it mind you, but actually solved it – in just ten minutes of meditation time ...well then, you know that you have found something that has real effects – and real value.

This type of illogical yet extraordinarily productive experience was not merely circumstantial; it did not happen only once or twice, off and on – it became a dependable routine. Eventually, I did not wait until all normal methods and efforts were exhausted before turning to meditation. It worked as well when I tried it first, saving a great deal of time and effort by skipping the first three steps of the process. Hard work, long hours, frustration, and exasperation were no longer prerequisites for solving difficult and complex programming and physics problems.

I was surprised and delighted that meditation had a direct objective practical value. That was an unexpected revelation. I tested it and tested it, and then I began to depend on it. I had gotten smarter it seemed, and the other graduate students noticed. They commented on the change in my abilities. Now, more than ever before, they wanted to discuss their research and came to me for help in debugging code.

I told them about TM, but none made an effort to try it. That surprised me. For some strange reason, I had thought physicists would be more open. Meditation appeared to require too big a step out of the comfort zones of their personal and cultural belief systems. "Oh well, it's their loss," I thought. I did not know it then, but I was on my way to becoming strange. I was, at the very least it seemed, unusually open minded. My perspective and reality was expanding.

Up to this time, I believed that meaningful existence was confined to an operational reality. That is, if something can be measured it is real. To be measurable, a thing must interact with our senses or with some device that interacts with our senses. If it is not measurable (can not interact with us or our devices), then its reality or existence (or lack thereof) is irrelevant. It was that simple; things were either operationally real or irrelevant. Things that are not measurable, but can be inferred from other things that are measurable, fall into the gray area of conjecture. All things theoretical or hypothetical fall into this gray basket.

Gray things are acceptable as conceptual constructs or ideals but are not to be confused with real things and are not to be taken too seriously in and of themselves. The primary mission of the academic research scientist is to collect enough valid, repeatable, measurement data to transfer a gray theoretical construct into a real object or effect.

At that time, quantum mechanical wave packets, black holes, quarks, justice, and love all fit into that gray area. It is important not to confuse hypothetical things with real things or you can easily end up chasing your own imaginary tail, or hallucinating the attributes of solidity to smoke. My mind was not closed, I allowed for the possibility of new information. With enough real measured data one might eventually move a thing, such as black holes for example, from the realm of the hypothetical to the realm of the real – but only with sufficient good quality data. That particular attitude has never changed. I continue to feel that way, work that way, and employ that methodology to sort out what is real from what is not.

Now I had to change my philosophy of reality. There were those things that were non-measurable yet functionally operational (including my meditation state, which is properly defined as an altered state of consciousness) that fell into the category of **subjective experience with objective results**. One can use these non-measurable states of mind to operate on real things. (Here, I am using the terms "operate" and "operator" in the mathematical or scientific sense). I had shown that an altered consciousness directed by intent can consistently and directly affect and interact with real things such as my computer code. Complex logical problems could be solved without the intentional application of a rational process. Somehow, a non-measurable subjective experience could be turned into a reliable and effective scientific tool by some sort of consciousness operator. Verrrry interesting!

In contrast to conceptual constructs such as justice and love, altered states of consciousness and their objective results seemed to be measurable, consistent, and reasonably well defined. They were more like the things of science, things that were amenable to research and experiment. If one is in this particular altered state, one can always do these things with it – similar activity will produce similar results for all experimenters.

I was not special; I was the same as anyone else. I wondered if other altered states of consciousness existed and what one could do with them. I was curious – it is my nature to be curious.

My reality expanded. I added the statement: "If a thing is well defined and consistently functional (it can profitably and dependably be used by anyone within the known operational reality), then it must also be real." It seemed reasonable that only real things could be functional operators within and on an operational reality. How could something not real directly affect things that are real? By definition, in an operational reality, things that are not real have no measurable effect, cannot interact with, and have no relevance to, things that are real.

My meditation had a measurable objective effect – I knew it, and a dozen others had clearly noticed it as well, even if they did not understand why. To me, it was as plain as day and totally obvious; this was no subtle effect being misunderstood by some mushy headed non-scientist. This was no hallucination. I knew what I knew. How many others, if any, agreed with me was not relevant. I had confidence in my mind and my science.

I began to analyze other common altered states such as daydreaming. Were daydreams (self-directed imagination or purposeful visual imagery) functional? Of course! Why had I not noticed that before? People have been preparing themselves mentally for all sorts of things since the beginning of time. For example, one might repetitively practice giving a speech in one's imagination – making points and fielding imagined questions. The relevancy criteria are: Is it consistently functional, does it actually help one's performance in objective reality, and are the effects measurable? Our directed imagination example would rate a definite "yes" on all counts.

Ask any top-notch athlete if focused intentional mental preparation is important to his or her success. Mental effort within the context of a particular altered state must represent a real thing because it produces real effects that are universal as well as specific to that particular mental state. "Altered," was defined as different from normal. "Normal" meant wide-awake and focused in the physical world – as you are now while you are reading this book. Each altered state has its functionality. Daydreaming is one specific type of altered state. Of all possible altered states, those with no universal and consistent functionality are, by definition, useless and therefore irrelevant. It was only the useful ones that were welcomed into my newly expanded reality – those were the ones I wanted to know about.

Real things, significant things, must now be either objectively measurable, or consistently and predictably interactive with real things. That was a major expansion of my real world. The word "objective" means that these real things must exist universally and consistently for others as well as for me. They must be independent of me and exist whether I exist or not. Others (potentially everyone) must be able to make the same measurements and find the same measurable functionality. Otherwise, they would be only my private hallucinations, not a part of the larger reality we all share.

When I realized the scope of the reality picture was much bigger than I had previously thought, I wondered if there were other subjective experiences that had consistent objective measurable results. Where were the boundaries? How much more reality was out there that I had missed? What other real and functional processes of mind were lurking beyond my limited awareness? I had been blindly unaware of a significant part of my reality for twenty-some years! That thought was a mind bender that weighed heavily on me.

That I had inadvertently imposed a major limitation on my operative reality out of sheer ignorance was unacceptable, inexcusable, and more than a little humbling. What other significant parts of my life was I missing? I had to find that answer. Being content to accept whatever is given without pushing hard against the boundaries is absolutely foreign to my nature. My mind had been forced open by the indisputable facts of my experience, and as a result, I had become less of a philosophical know-it-all. I realized there was much about life and reality I did not know. Arrogance waned as openness and curiosity waxed.

I have not significantly changed my philosophical approach toward defining reality in the thirty-three years that have come and gone since then; today my definition of what constitutes a real experience remains essentially the same. Any credible conception of reality must include subjective experience that can consistently and universally lead to a useful objective (measurable by anyone) functionality.

Much later it became evident that expanding my reality beyond a certain beginning level would require personal growth. I had to increase the quality of my consciousness to understand the bigger picture. Conversely, understanding the bigger picture helped me grow up. They worked together.

Thus, my journey began innocently enough. Interestingly, though nothing much has changed as far as my overall philosophy goes, the continual flow of incredible learning experiences has steadily accelerated. My understanding of reality continues to actively expand.

5

■■■

Is This Guy Monroe Nuts, or What?

■■■

"Get a job!" intones a popular song of my youth. Everybody must get out of school sometime. I was now almost twenty-seven, and had been in school continuously since I was five. With research completed, I settled on my first real job applying classical physics and mathematics to electro-mechanical and electromagnetic systems simulation. A real job with a real paycheck – imagine that! I continued to meditate more or less regularly, but had found that I did not need the mantra any longer. A little research and experimentation indicated that any two-syllable nonsense word ending in "ing" (a resonant sound) worked as well as any other, including my given super-secret mantra. There was nothing mystical or magical here, only a method of controlling thoughts by filling the otherwise active mind with fluff, nothing but science and technique – no bananas or hankies were required.

Repeating the mantra eventually seemed to get in the way and slow me down; consequently I dropped it. The meditation state was now familiar enough that I could go there in an instant and return as quickly. This level of control was handy at work. I could meditate, find solutions, and return without anyone suspecting that I was doing something strange – to the world I seemed to be deep in thought. That I was disembodied point consciousness adrift in the void – gone completely from their world with no residual awareness of their reality – was my secret. Sometimes people would try to engage me while I was gone. To them, it was as if engaging a dead body. Needless to say, I gained a reputation for being eccentric – with unusual powers of concentration or an unusual ability to sleep while sitting up – nobody could tell which.

My boss, Bill Yost, was a super person. He was smart – no frills, no BS, no hidden agenda, no tact, – an engineer through and through. Bright, honest, and straightforward – that is the personality type that I related to most easily. One day Mr. Yost came by my desk and tossed a book at me. I caught it in mid air and read the title. *Journeys Out Of The Body*, by Robert A. Monroe. "What's this?" I asked, surprised by the strangeness of the subject matter.

"Read it," he said, "and tell me what you think."

When your boss says, "Read it," you just read it, you do not ask why.

I read *Journeys* during the next few days. The book was configured as a diary. It was a "This is what happened to me" type of story wherein Monroe claimed to have collected hard evidence in support of the reality of the out-of-body experience. The experiences, and the evidence of their realness, were laid out matter-of-factly with no theory or belief system attached. It was a wild concept – a more or less independent reality reachable only through the mind. Having prior experience with functional altered states of consciousness, I was probably more open minded than the average scientific type, but not gullible. I knew what was real to me, and my measurement data (experience) included none of that.

"It was very interesting," I told my boss, "but I don't know what to make of it. Is this guy (Monroe) nuts; is he trying to sell books to the gullible; or is he for real?" I asked rhetorically. I continued with barely a pause: "How can you tell where he is coming from? If his story is for real, if you take him at face value, a new aspect of reality opens up that I have never before considered. That would be a definite Wow! But for now, it just sounds wild and I have no way to judge the veracity of it."

Having spit all this out in rapid fire, barely pausing to breathe, I now took a deep breath and waited for the reaction. I watched my boss carefully to see if I had made a fool of myself by being too open.

As a student, I was used to having to get the right answer. Was I supposed to condemn it as foolish rubbish or believe it as a strong possibility? I had no idea where he was coming from. He had given me no hints. I was working as a civilian in a military organization, it was 1972, and the people here were conservative. I was a longhaired, wild-eyed kid-physicist recently out of graduate school. I had about decided that my openness had been a political mistake when Mr. Yost finally spoke.

"I agree with you," he said thoughtfully. "It is a wild concept isn't it?"

"Yes it is," I agreed, "very wild."

"But consider what it would mean if it were true," he continued with an enthusiasm that indicated that he had thought about it seriously. I did not reply. "Think about that," he said. "What does it logically imply **if** it is true – if the evidence is real and not made up?"

"Yeah," I said, "Pretty strange stuff – but how can you ever know if it is true or made up?" He nodded in agreement and changed the subject. That was the end of it. Not another word was mentioned about *Journeys*, at least not for a few weeks.

I had almost forgotten about Monroe's book, having put it out of my mind as something that could never be logically confirmed or denied – and therefore was irrelevant.

"Would you like to go with us to see Monroe?" my boss asked when we were alone.

"Huh?" I muttered, not making the connection.

"There is a group of us from work going to see Monroe – you know, the guy who wrote *Journeys* – this Friday after work. Do you want to go with us?" he asked.

"Where?" I asked in reply.

"Just outside town about forty-five minutes from here," he shot back with some excitement in his voice. "Sure," I said. "I would really like to meet this guy and see if he is crazy or sane, honest or a hustler, delusional or rational." "Me too," said Yost with a twinkle in his eye – "me too!"

6

■ ■ ■

Face to Face with
the Wizard of Whistlefield

■ ■ ■

Late Friday afternoon finally came. While our co-workers headed home
to begin their weekends, twelve of us piled into three cars for the trip
to Monroe's. I did not know these people; I was a relatively new employee
within an organization that employed about five hundred people. We
were a strange crew, male and female; young and old, very conservative –
mostly professional technical types. We were not the sort of people one
would expect to be eagerly converging on Mr. Out-of-Body. I was
impressed there were this many open minded people where I worked. As
always, anything unexpected demanded an immediate reassessment. I
hypothesized that living almost exclusively among hard-core scientists for
the past seven years had inadvertently skewed my judgment of people in
general – clearly, there were bias errors in my analysis algorithms. That
was a serious problem. Within a few seconds I had laid out a tentative
plan for debugging my assumptions and made a mental note to observe
these people more closely.

Most were skeptical, one of the ladies was a little frightened, everyone
was enthusiastic, and nobody knew what to expect. They all jabbered
nervously and endlessly – the scene seemed hyperactive and irrational to
me. As usual, I said nothing. I was not a good mixer. I did not relate to
unfocused bubbling emotion or to anxiety, and I did not understand
these people. Their lives seemed to be driven, or at least animated, by random irrational feelings. They were strangely affected by uncertainty.

At the time, I had no idea that they were the ones who were actually
normal. Years of graduate school and a lack of mainstream social interaction had nudged my vision of normalcy a tad off center. I thought that

Spock was normal while the rest of the Enterprise crew were hopeless, eternally lucky, mush-heads. I heaved a sigh, "This is going to be a weird night," I thought to myself, "with all these weird people, on this weird excursion to see Mr. Weird." As it turned out, except for the people I was traveling with, it was not actually that weird, but it changed my life forever.

Bob Monroe lived on an estate named Whistlefield – five-hundred acres of lakes, forests and fields. A large country manor house elegantly perched on top of a hill, half dozen horses, a barn, and two small lakes thrown in for good measure. It appeared to me that Mr. Monroe was a relatively wealthy Southern gentleman. We slowly motored down the half-mile long driveway that was bordered by a freshly painted white board fence. A few horses trotted along with us. "Whoa, this is classy," I thought. "This guy is no poor raving lunatic – that's for sure." My analysis continued, "Weird books don't pay that well – it doesn't appear that duping the gullible for their money is going to be a likely motivation." Nevertheless, I reserved final judgment on that issue until I could meet the man for myself.

The car finally stopped in front of the house. Several large dogs came bounding out to meet us – two Dalmatians and a large German shepherd were vigorously sounding the alarm that intruders were in the driveway. My riding companions thought it better to stay in the car until the friendliness of the dogs could be verified.

Nonsense! These people were so strange – like frightened children. I wondered what could have possibly happened to them to make them that way. Dogs bark at strangers because that is what they do – it means nothing. I quickly popped out of the car to say hello and rub some ears.

I was immediately mobbed by three wet tongues and wagging tails. It was love at first sight. They acted as if they had not been petted for weeks. It felt good to be out of that crowded car, and to be surrounded by rational beings that knew what they were about. I immediately felt more centered.

I should explain that popping out of that car had been neither brave nor foolish – those dogs were **obviously** friendly. What I did not understand was why that fact was not obvious to everyone else. I surmised that either I happened to be riding with a group of people who were not familiar with dogs, or that one dog-challenged person's fear had influenced the rest.

By now, everyone was getting out of their cars and looking around, wondering what to do next. "Perhaps I shouldn't have changed into these old jeans," one of the ladies said apprehensively – she was obviously intimidated by the classiness of Monroe's estate. All three women present were reflexively fumbling in their purses for fresh make-up. "Why do they always do that?" I wondered silently. "Haven't they figured out by now that it won't make any difference?" I was always amazed and amused when people were internally driven to blatantly irrational behavior.

I had, for many years, been curious about the root causes of "cultural insanity" – those absurdly illogical attitudes and actions that our culture considers normal. Some, including "makeup urgency" are entirely benign; others range from mildly dysfunctional to terribly destructive. I had come to the tentative conclusion that the key motivators of cultural insanity were fear-based and emotionally driven. I could not relate in the slightest to either. Nonetheless, I intuitively knew that this was not a good thing, and it did not speak highly of our society's overall level of rationality. I was curious about it, and took careful mental notes whenever I noticed such a display. I did not feel superior. I had no inclination to make comparisons. I was an impartial observer with an insatiable curiosity – that's all. I was merely different, not better or worse than others because of that difference. I had been born, it seemed, a perpetual outsider – and I liked it that way. Outsiders have a more objective and impartial view. As a scientist, nothing was more important than logical clarity and objectivity. Being different and having an outsider's view had generally been comfortable for me – I saw it as an advantage. It suited me well.

My reverie into the characteristics and causes of illogical social behavior was suddenly upstaged by something more important. The large white door of Whistlefield Manor began to swing open. Conversations were instantly terminated in mid sentence. All heads turned with silent expectation. The one, the only, the Amazing, Out-Of-Body-Man, was about to turn to flesh and blood before our eyes. We would all soon know if this guy was nuts, or what.

Out stepped Mr. Monroe into the doorway. For a second or two he seemed the slightest bit tentative – like a man who clearly knew he was about to be examined and evaluated like a captive alien or a strange animal at the zoo. He gazed out at the crowd of nameless heads staring silently back at him. After the briefest of pauses, he stepped fully out onto the elegant open stone porch with confidence and a solid presence. He was not wearing a white suit with matching hat and string tie like Col. Sanders (the only Southern gentleman I could bring to mind). Instead, he looked comfortable, informal, and friendly – more like the dogs than the house.

Robert Monroe was a heavyset man of medium height; he wore a big smile and had a twinkle in his eye. Just looking at him made you feel relaxed. He greeted us all individually as if he were an experienced politician – making quips and jokes as he went. "This guy could be Santa Claus," I thought with more than a little amusement, "a jolly old elf – passing the summer sipping mint juleps on the veranda of his country estate."

"What are **you** smiling at?" he demanded good-humoredly as his attention suddenly focused in my direction.

He was now looking directly at me with a knowing impish grin. For a moment, I had the feeling that he must have read my mind and was amused by my vision of Santa Monroe.

"Oh nothing," I replied, lamely brushing off the question. Before he could react, I instantly followed that dodge with a question of my own. "How and when did you first go out-of-body?" I asked. Up to this point, nobody had been that direct. I did not know how to be any other way. It suddenly grew quiet and more focused, everybody was now intently listening.

"It just happened," he said. "It just started happening about fifteen years ago for no apparent reason."

"How did you react to that experience?" I continued without pause.

"I thought I might be going nuts," he said. "It worried me initially, but I couldn't help experimenting with it – that's my nature."

He had consulted with psychologists, psychiatrists, and a parapsychologist. All found him rock-solid sane which made him feel better and gave him confidence.

Monroe seemed to have inadvertently stumbled into an altered state of consciousness that gave him access to a larger reality, producing some amazing evidential data under controlled circumstances with the parapsychologist. Because it had no deleterious affect upon his mental soundness and competency, he was encouraged to pursue, record, and eventually control his unusual experiences.

"What sort of evidential data do you have?" I shot back.

"Most of it was in the book," he said, "remote viewing sorts of things for the most part."

"What exactly is remote viewing?" I asked.

"Obtaining information paranormally by going somewhere in the out-of-body state to collect the target information – without taking your body along, as it were."

"Oh, I see," I said sheepishly, realizing that I had asked a dumb question that should have been obvious. My momentary pause gave others a chance to horn in on my private conversation. No one was shy any longer.

Toward the end of the evening Monroe took us to the facility that he hoped to soon turn into a lab dedicated to the study of altered states of consciousness. It was obvious to me that he desperately wanted to legitimize what had spontaneously happened to him. He wanted to remove the stigma of nutty and replace it with the approval of an accepting science. He was earnest, serious, and willing to put his money where his mouth was.

He was not posturing or hustling – he was genuinely interested in real science. He wanted legitimacy, not recognition, money, or fame. He was a successful local businessman. Additionally, he was the CEO of a growing cable company and appeared to me to be totally sane, intelligent, under control, and conservative. Best of all he was a rational type. He had an engineer's personality. He was more straightforward and intellectually precise – less emotionally driven – than most of the technical professionals who were now pelting him with questions. The quality of the questioning was erratic – clearly, he was a polite and patient man. If you did not know he wrote about out-of-the-body experiences, you would never have guessed it from his circumstances, appearance, or demeanor.

Then came an offer I could not refuse. Gazing at the bunch of us lounging on the back deck of the nascent lab, Monroe challenged us. "You folks are technical scientific types, aren't you?" He asked rhetorically. We all nodded our heads and mumbled our concurrence, wondering what was coming next. "I am looking for some hard-core science and engineering types," he continued. "Someone with good professional credentials who could help me do real and proper science that would be acceptable to other scientists." "So that's why we were invited," I thought with mounting expectation, "Great!"

My hand shot into the air – a reflexive act conditioned by over twenty consecutive years as a student – I couldn't help it. I could not, it seemed, respond to a question with my arms at my side. Monroe looked directly at me, amused by my waving hand. Feeling a little stupid, I pulled my hand down out of the air and said, "I am a physicist and I am very interested in your research into altered states. If you will teach me what you know about out-of-body and altered states of consciousness, I will help you do legitimate scientific research."

Almost immediately, from the other side of the deck another voice spoke up.

"I am an electrical engineer and I would like to work with you... if you would try to teach me what you know."

I strained to see who was speaking. It was a young guy, maybe a few years older than me, but not much. I did not know him; he wasn't riding in the car I had come in. Monroe looked at us intently – a long and pregnant pause ensued as he assessed the situation and weighed his options. Everyone was quiet, waiting to see what would happen next.

I think that Monroe would have preferred older, more established scientists to staff his lab. Someone more mature, with an established reputation – instant credibility. But we both knew that those types were not likely to be interested, or willing to work for an exchange of knowledge. If they had established professional reputations, they had reputations to protect and would never allow themselves to become associated with something this far out on the fringe – this far away from the safety of the crowd. Scientists, contrary to their own press reports, are mostly just sheep of a different sort. All credibility flows from peer review and the more notable peers of the scientific community would treat altered states of consciousness and out-of-body as intellectual leprosy. Monroe had run headlong into that brick wall of closed-mindedness previously – which is probably why he craved respectability and acceptability.

He quickly evaluated his chances to do better. Finally, he broke the long silence, "What kind of degrees do you have?" Dennis Mennerich, the other volunteer, had a master's degree in electrical engineering. "OK," he said confidently, "You've got a deal! Call me in a few days and we'll set up a meeting." He rattled off a telephone number. The subject changed. I stopped paying close attention to the conversation. I was as excited as someone like me can get – that is, I felt a mild surge of anticipation.

Where would this lead? What could he actually teach us? How would he attempt to teach us? What scientific protocols would be applicable? What kind of data would we be collecting? What would we be measuring? Question after question poured through my mind. What if it turned out to be bogus? If I found out he wasn't actually interested in real science, I would quickly and politely bow out – that would be easy enough.

The evening had turned out better than I had expected. I was going to be studying altered states – something I had wanted to do for a year or more, but did not know how to start. "This could be a great opportunity," I thought... "Well, maybe, I'll just wait and see what happens, if anything happens at all."

I did not know it then, but my life was about to take a sharp turn. Strange and stranger (all carefully scientific of course) was about to become as common as air.

After a few days passed, I called the number scrawled on the scrap of paper that I had hastily obtained that night on the deck at Monroe's. It had been dark, we were outside – at the time the number seemed clear. I dialed it again. There was no answer. I tried it later, no answer. The next day was the same, as was the day after that. No answer. No answer. No answer. I let it go the rest of the week. The next week I tried again. No answer. I decided that perhaps the three was actually an eight and tried that. No answer. I tried information – Monroe had an unlisted number. I let it rest a few more days. Two weeks had gone by since our visit. I tried it with the "three," then again with the "eight" ... hold on ... somebody began to talk ... jeez, it was just an answering machine! The machine mentioned no names. I left a message. Nothing happened, no one returned the call.

A few days later I decided to try one more time. I was so surprised when a woman's voice offered a polite "hello," that it took me a second to focus on what I was doing – a real flesh and blood person! Wow! I asked to speak to Mr. Monroe.

"What is this in reference to?" she asked politely.

I was on a roll. "Is this Robert Monroe's residence?" I asked.

"Yes," she said, "who is this?"

With immense relief at having made the connection, I quickly explained who I was and said that Mr. Monroe had asked me to call him in a few days and that was two and a half weeks ago.

"Just a minute," she said.

"Finally," I thought, "he'll probably be glad to hear from me." I imagined that he was concerned that I had perhaps changed my mind. He had seemed excited, even somewhat anxious, about getting his lab up and running.

"Hello," the voice said on the other side of the line with no sense of familiarity.

Maybe she didn't tell him who I was, I reasoned. "This is Tom Campbell," I said, "We talked on the deck at your lab a few weeks ago – I am the physicist – you asked me to call."

"What?" he said. "Physicist? What kind of physicist are you?"

What sort of question was that? From his tone it was obvious that he did not know who I was, and that he didn't remember our deal – or he was pretending that he didn't? He was obviously not sitting around worrying because I had not called sooner. I detailed the visit and the offer that we had agreed upon.

"Oh, that physicist," he said with dramatic inflection. "What is your name again?"

I told him my name a second time.

"There was another guy with you, wasn't there?"

"Yes, there was another guy – his name is Dennis," I replied tersely and waited.

"Why don't you two come to the lab next Thursday," he said after a short pause.

"That is good for me," I replied, "I'll check with Dennis and let you know."

"Just come on," he said, "no need to let me know – just come on up to the lab at seven – you and Dennis – is that OK?"

"Sure," I said a little puzzled.

"Do you know how to get here?"

"Yes," I answered, "I can get there. I'll see you this coming Thursday evening at 7 at the lab." I paused to make sure there was no misunderstanding.

He mumbled a gratuitous "OK," sounding mildly annoyed that he had to listen to me repeat the arrangements, and hung up.

"How does he know Dennis will be able and willing to come this Thursday?" I wondered. I sure didn't know that yet. How could he be that sure? I pondered the circumstances. Does he want me to come by myself if Dennis cannot make it? He didn't seem particularly eager to get started. Or... is his mind a little loose? "Now **that** conversation was definitely strange," I mused. In time, I would eventually get used to Monroe being distracted and knowing things paranormally. His mind was not loose, he was always a step ahead and usually right. Unlike me, he did not need to wait for the facts.

I told Dennis the next morning.

"No problem," he said.

I told him that Monroe had seemed to know he would be able to come Thursday evening. We looked at each other and shrugged our shoulders.

"Had you told me this yesterday or anytime last week, I would have told you that I couldn't have made it," Dennis added as an afterthought. "But just this morning, things changed, now I have no conflict."

This was going to be an interesting adventure – I just knew it.

"Who is going to drive?" Dennis asked.

"I planned to take my cycle. Do you want to ride with me?"

"OK," he said, "I have my own helmet – I used to have a bike a few years back."

"I have a big four cylinder Honda – two people won't be a problem."

"Great," he replied, "that should be fun."

"He is pretty courageous," I thought. "I hardly know this guy, he knows nothing about me, and he is willing to get on the back of a motorcycle with me? Maybe only once," I chuckled to myself. I got directions to his house and agreed to pick him up at 6:15 p.m.

7

The Adventure Begins

The trip to Whistlefield was a combination of interstate and country roads. Most of the mileage was on a brand new, and lightly traveled, interstate. I loved my motorcycle. I loved speed. I loved acceleration. I loved the feel of finely controlled and responsive raw power and I loved the presence, the sense of being alive, and the focus in the present moment that you get on a big motorcycle. You, the bike, the environment, and fate – one tightly integrated package – a shared destiny. That was fun. With Dennis on the back, I resolved to be conservative; nothing over eighty-five miles per hour on a regular basis was my plan. It would not be responsible, polite, or friendly to be reckless with somebody else's life.

At 120 mph, my bike was rock solid and smooth as silk. It was made for speed, and I was addicted to it. I had driven cycles ever since I was a teenager. With this particular bike, it was love at first sight – the biggest, the best, the fastest. Dennis was fearless, he never once complained or flinched – except once when the drive chain broke while we were humming along at eighty miles per hour and he almost lost a few fingers. A near miss, but when you are young enough to be immortal and invincible, any miss is as good as a mile – we never skipped a beat. Dennis was always ready and relaxed. Mounted on this trusty steel steed we cut the travel time to Whistlefield to less than half an hour.

Once we got through the initial getting-to-know-you data exchanges, schedules were quickly worked out and routines established. Dennis and I would go to the lab two or three times a week and sometimes on weekends. We would spend the first hour or so setting up equipment, soldering wires, designing and making measurement devices – in general, wiring and outfitting the place to be a lab. After a while, Monroe would join us at the lab and then the real fun began.

Under Bob Monroe's guidance, Dennis and I would begin a systematic exploration of altered states of consciousness. We were constantly working towards consistent repeatable, evidential experience. After a few hours of exploration, Bob would invite us back to the house for discussions, chitchat, planning, or perhaps to meet some other investigators that were working in related areas. His lovely wife Nancy, the ever proper, polite, and most congenial hostess, would often join our discussion. Dennis and I were so bright eyed and bushy tailed in our dogged pursuit of the outer edge of reality that our constant state of total amazement, night after night, amused her to no end.

Bob knew everyone in the country, it seemed, who was investigating, or experiencing anything unusual. They all came to Whistlefield eventually to meet Bob and share the results of their individual efforts. Bob was like a magnet in this disconnected community of leading edge researchers, experimenters, and freelance kooks, because of his no nonsense, straightforward manner and wonderfully open mind. There was no snake-oil being hawked at Whistlefield. Because of Bob's reputation, and the operation and reputation of the lab, there was a steady stream of tremendously interesting visitors. I was impressed there were so many intelligent and sober individuals, sometimes with impressive credentials, who took this area of endeavor seriously. These were not whacked out druggies doing their counter-culture thing. Bob had zero tolerance for that sort – he did not want to tarnish his legitimacy by being associated with drug users. The Timothy Leary types were out. Other than that, Bob was open to almost everything anybody took seriously. However, he was also always skeptical. Open minded **and** skeptical – he wanted to see hard evidence – claims were interesting, but never enough.

Most of the visitors were middle-aged, serious professionals looking for serious answers to serious questions. They, for the most part, were looking for validation and hard evidence. There were the occasional groupies trying to increase their credibility by associating with Bob and his research effort, and a few whose main object was to impress him with their unusual talents. Bob had little patience for either. He politely but firmly sent the pretenders and non-contributors on their way.

8

■■■

The Science of Altered States

■■■

The lab building contained, among other rooms, a control room and three isolation chambers. One chamber had been constructed with complete electromagnetic shielding so the earth's magnetic field and other stray radiation would not wash-out or overpower the effect that carefully controlled electromagnetic fields might have on altered states of consciousness. Each chamber was constructed to provide as much sensory deprivation as possible and was connected to the control room by audio and a host of measuring devices.

I borrowed some unused, sophisticated and expensive electrostatic sensing equipment and audio signal generators and Bob purchased a complete EEG (electroencephalograph) setup and a professional audio mixer. Bill Yost brought in an exceptionally sensitive high input-impedance voltmeter. Dennis and I designed and made a device for tracking Galvanic Skin Response (GSR). Before long we had a reasonably well-equipped lab to work in, even if it did have solder splatters all over the floor.

We measured Bob. He measured us. One key datum Bob had derived from his personal study of out-of-body experience (OOBE) was the perception of a 4 Hz oscillation within his body and consciousness just before exiting his body and sometimes just after returning to it. Experimentation showed that when an instrumented person was caught in that pulsation state in our lab, the EEG indicated the brainwaves collected by multiple pairs of electrodes were unusually coherent (in phase), collectively synchronized, and modulated at 4 Hz. The GSR reading would begin oscillating at 4 Hz as well. Bob intuitively knew that this pulsation state was a key artifact, and we set out to reproduce it – capture it and hold it steady, on demand, and under our control.

A literature search had turned up a few old scholarly studies of out-of-body experience, which was also known as "astral projection." A half dozen highly respected, well-credentialed, medical and technical professionals had been seriously studying out-of-body experiences for decades, mostly around the turn of the last century. A book by Dr. Hereward Carrington and Slyvan Muldoon entitled *The Projection of the Astral Body*, published in 1929 by Samuel Weiser of New York, suggested the pineal gland was somehow involved. *Astral Projections: Out of the Body Experiences*, by Oliver Fox and *The Study and Practice of Astral Projection* by Dr. Robert Crookall (University Press, 1960); agreed that the pineal gland was perhaps a key organ affecting the out-of-the-body experience.

We were in the cut and try mode of operation and would try anything at least once. Dennis and I always applied any unusual experimental devices to ourselves first. Only after we tested how it affected us, and became convinced of its worth and safety, would we try it on others to gain a wider sample – friends, visitors, passers by, anyone, we were not picky. We were looking for something that would work with anybody and everybody.

For example, one of the things we tried was to shake the pineal gland at 4 Hz. We built a huge capacitor with 2-ft^2 plates to generate a uniform and strong electric field. We were committed and dedicated to the pursuit of our quest – risk taking was not an issue. With something like a 250,000 volt, 4 Hz AC signal being fed to the plates, I stuck my head between them and tried to reach a working altered state. I stayed there about an hour or so experimenting with different voltages and frequencies against different altered states, hoping for a resonant effect to occur that would have a dramatic effect on the state of my consciousness. Suddenly I began to feel woozy. My head started to wobble dangerously between the exposed metal plates. The experiment was stopped. I had a terrible headache for about three weeks.

We worked with negative ion generators to provide controlled backgrounds, and used ultra-high impedance input voltmeters to study the changing electrical potentials generated by a body in an altered state vs. a normal one. We measured the dynamic buildup of static charge around our heads with borrowed equipment as we eased in and out of various brain-wave configurations measured by the EEG.

It may seem a little like mad scientists toiling in their hilltop laboratory at the midnight hour but we were as serious, sober, and straight as our counterparts working traditional problems in universities everywhere. We were careful about our science. Our methodology was good. Were we cautious and conservative? No, we were not cautious. If there was **any** reasonable chance of gaining knowledge, we took it. We were hard driven to find honest answers – real, verifiable, repeatable results. We wanted to know, and this was the chance of a lifetime to find out. We were fearless in our pursuit of truth because the risks were totally invisible to us – sometimes, the naiveté and brash enthusiasm of youth has its advantages.

Meanwhile, while Dennis and I were working in and on the lab, Bob was leading us and teaching us to experience and explore the nonphysical. He would first lead us into a deep relaxation state, then using visualization we would begin to focus our thoughts, center our attention – let go of our bodies and the environment. These exercises produced various states of consciousness that were similar to the meditation state I had learned to achieve with TM. Bob thought that perhaps there was opportunity on the boundary between being awake and asleep. We practiced hovering on that edge. Put the body asleep and keep the mind awake simultaneously. Eventually we got good at it and it did not take us long to get there. After developing a basic competency in defining and establishing willful repeatability of a half dozen altered states of consciousness, we began experimenting and exploring the functionality of each state. Each mind-state had its own unique functionality – things you could do, abilities you had, while in that state.

9

Breakthrough

One day while I was at work, Dennis dropped by and showed me an article he had found in the October 1973 *Scientific American*. It was a short article, by Gerald Oster, titled "Auditory Beats in the Brain" that described a phenomenon called "binaural beats." Simply put, if a pure tone of say 100 Hz was put in one of your ears, and a pure tone of 104 Hz in your other ear, you would perceive a 4 Hz beat frequency along with the 100 and 104 Hz tones. Dennis waited while I read it. "Let's try that at the lab," he said. "Sure, why not?" I replied. Dennis had been gathering information on the binaural beat phenomena for some months and had created a binaural beat audio-tape for us to experiment with. Our hope was that the beat frequency, occurring in the corpus callosum between the brain's hemispheres, would drive the brainwaves.

Dennis' intuition was correct. The binaural beats obviously affected our state of consciousness. During the next week we begged, borrowed, and bought the necessary equipment to expand our experiments. Bob had gone out of town for a week or two; subsequently, we experimented with the effect of binaural beats on altered state of consciousness on our own. After a week of trial and error experimenting, we were more excited about the possibilities. The effect was powerful. Using the binaural beat to entrain brainwaves as measured by the EEG was a fact. The effect on one's state of consciousness was dramatic. Bob came back and we started testing what this technology could do. The good news was that by trial and error we were able to significantly optimize the effect we were looking for. The better news was it seemed to work as well on everybody as it did on us. Now we had a technique for putting people with no training into specific altered states of consciousness, at will, on demand, with consistent results.

We focused on the 4 Hz beat and created a set of audiotapes that guided the listener into what Bob called "Nonphysical Matter Reality" (NPMR). "Physical Matter Reality" (PMR) contained my body, the lab, the house where I lived, and my daytime job. Once in NPMR, the fun began. Now we had the potential to collect evidence that would be based on a much larger sample of subjects. As we gained experience with more people, we continually improved the effectiveness of the audiotapes. In about eight months we were ready for the world to give us a try. Bob put out the word that we needed a limited number of guinea pigs to try out our binaural-beat brainwave entrainment techniques for facilitating the projection of one's consciousness into the nonphysical as an aware operational entity. The response was overwhelming.

Soon, Bob was booking every room at the nearby Tuckahoe Motel. The Tuckahoe management, having seen better times, agreed to let us string wires throughout their facility. Dennis and I had a lot to do before the big weekend when we would discover if our methodology was as effective as we thought it was. We expected about twenty totally naïve subjects – and we planned to keep them that way by telling them nothing. We did not want to lead their reactions and experiences by giving them any expectations.

Building mobile measuring equipment and audio equipment for large groups was a challenge. We barely made our deadlines by working evenings and weekends for three weeks, but with the help of Bill Yost and Bob's stepdaughter, Nancy Lea Honeycutt, we had the equipment installed, checked out, and ready to go late in the afternoon of the last day. What a panic! In a parallel activity, Nancy Lea, who had joined our research team after her graduation from college, orchestrated and administered all the necessary arrangements. Somehow, at the last moment, everything pulled together. It was worth it. During Friday night, all day Saturday, and half of Sunday, the attendees had the time of their life. There were so many paranormal happenings that weekend that we had a difficult time getting them all recorded. These naïve subjects were reading numbers in sealed envelopes, remote viewing, manifesting lights in the sky, visiting their relatives, reading next week's newspaper headlines, and much more. It was a circus! Fun, but exhausting. Dennis, Nancy Lea, and I ran the show, with visits from Bob off and on throughout the weekend.

We collected lots of solid evidential data – the results were more dramatic than we had expected. Things were never the same after that. When word got out about the effectiveness of Monroe's program, Bob was swamped with requests from people of all sorts wanting to participate. Bob began to see the makings of a business and Dennis and I, along with Nancy Lea, became trainers more than researchers.

10

But Is It Real?

Let's slip back in time and view the whole from a slightly different perspective. My association with Bob Monroe presented a fantastic opportunity. With those years of practice, Dennis and I could easily differentiate among the various altered states of consciousness and get to them, shift between them, and come back to a normal state at will. However, it was not that easy to begin with.

We worked hard and modified the rest of our lives to accommodate our work. I had decided that while I was working at the lab, I would take no mind-altering drugs of any sort. It was going to be confusing enough without that variable floating around in the equation. I had never used any illicit drugs as a student because it did not seem rational. I lived out of my mind, it was my ticket to success – I didn't want to mess anything up. But now I swore off even an occasional beer. Not a drop – socially or otherwise. I became a devout tea-totaler for the cause of clarity.

A few years later, food additives, preservatives, caffeine, and sugar were permanently banished from my diet. I reasoned that subtle natural effects might be washed out by the impact that these substances had on consciousness. I was right – the difference was dramatic. The success of our research hinged on the clear perception of subtle shifts in consciousness, anything that could potentially muddy those waters was dropped by the wayside.

We logged thousands of hours exploring and probing the limits of reality, produced a huge pile of measured data, and filled up boxes full of audiotape that recorded every word of our sessions. The mental space we practiced in was nonphysical – bodiless. Unlike my previous TM meditation, we were active, willful, autonomous agents within this larger nonphysical reality. We went places, did things, communicated with nonphysical beings.

It was fun, but neither of us could take it too seriously. Bob was careful to never lead the witness. He played the part of neutral observer – never hinting at what we might experience or how we might experience it. He didn't want his experiences to influence or bias us. As far as we could tell, he had no expectations of what we could, or would, accomplish.

Bob knew that if we were to experience the larger reality as he did, we would have to get there on our own. He could guide, but not lead – that would ruin the independent quality of our effort. He wasn't looking for an echo – he wanted to accomplish real science. Initially, Dennis and I had the same problem. "Is this stuff real?" we would ask each other. How could we tell if what we were experiencing was inside (we were imagining it), or outside (had its own existence independent of us)? That was the burning big question for both us – and for Bob as well.

Eventually we gained enough mental control and facility in working with altered states that Bob thought that we were ready to begin collecting some evidence to determine the operational significance of what we were experiencing in NPMR. Dennis and I were excited about the possibilities, and willing to accept the facts however they came out. We had been eager to objectively test the operational significance of our subjective experiences for some time. Bob had wanted us to wait until he thought we were ready. Neither of us was particularly optimistic or pessimistic – we wanted to know the truth. We were in the discovery mode and open to all possibilities. As long as our methodology was sound, we were confident that eventually enough results would accumulate to tell their own story.

One of our first experiments was for Dennis and me to take a trip (experience) in the nonphysical together. Our independent descriptions of what we were experiencing should correlate closely if the experience were real and independent of either of us. From the beginning of our training, we had learned to give real-time descriptions of whatever we experienced. A microphone was suspended from the ceiling above each of our heads. What we said was recorded on tape. Dennis and I could not hear each other because we were in separate soundproof chambers.

Dennis and I quickly achieved the appropriate altered state, left our bodies, and met in the nonphysical as planned. It was a long adventure. We went places, saw things, had conversations with each other and with several nonphysical beings we happened to run into along the way.

Bob had let us go a long time before he ended the session and called us back. We pulled off our EEG and GSR electrodes and stumbled out of the darkness into the hallway of the lab.

In the control room, Bob was waiting for us. After a quick exchange, we knew that this would be a good test because we both had experienced many specific interactions. But were they the same interactions? Bob looked at us deadpan. "So, you two think you were together?" he asked, trying to sound disappointed. We looked at each other and shrugged our shoulders.

"Maybe," Dennis said tentatively, "at least we perceived meeting each other."

"Listen to this!" Bob said emphatically. The tapes, rewound as we disconnected electrodes and climbed out of our chambers, began to roll forward. We sat down and listened. The correlation was astonishing. For almost two hours we sat there with our mouths open, hooting and exclaiming, filling in the details for each other. Bob was now grinning. "Now that tells you something, doesn't it?" he exclaimed beaming. He was every bit as excited as we were.

I was dumbfounded. There was only one good explanation: THIS STUFF WAS REAL! My mind searched for some other more rational explanation. "Perhaps only one of us imagined the trip and the other was reading his thoughts telepathically," I said trying to cover all the possibilities. That was almost as far out as the first explanation, but not quite.

The undeniable fact was: We had seen the same visuals, heard the same telepathic conversations, and experienced the same clarity. "This stuff might actually be real," I said aloud to no one in particular. Dennis and I sat there wide-eyed, incredulous, and at a loss to explain it any other way. I said those same six words: "This stuff might actually be real," over and over to myself fifty times during the next few days. I could not believe it, but I had to. I was there. This was my own experience. I was not reading this in a book about somebody else. In the vernacular of the times, I was blown away. You cannot understand the impact something such as this has until it happens to you. One more data point was in. My reality was about to get broader and stranger.

We repeated that experiment with similar results. It wasn't a phenomenon that depended on the two of us. Nancy Lea and I shared equally astonishing joint experiences. We tried other things as well. We read three and four digit numbers written on a blackboard next to the control room. Somebody would write a random number and we would read it while our bodies lay asleep. Then they would erase it and write another one, and so on and on. We went places – to people's homes – and saw what they were doing, then called them or talked to them the next day to check it out. We traveled into the future and into the past. We tried to heal people's illnesses with our minds and intent because that was a good technique for interacting evidentially with the energy of others.

We designed, generated, and tested intent focusing tools for our use in the nonphysical. We diagnosed illnesses in people we never met, but that somebody else knew well. The evidence poured in. Now there were hundreds of data points; later evidentiary experiences tended to be more clear and often more dramatic, than the initial ones. We began to discern subtleties of the altered states where things worked well and where things did not work well. We refined our processes and improved our efficiency slowly during the next three years – it was a painstaking trial and error process.

Dennis and I were the same demanding and skeptical scientists that had started this adventure, but we had stopped asking if it was real. We now knew the answer. We also realized that one has to experience it oneself to get to that point. Nobody else can convince you. You simply must experience it yourself. All the data in the world, regardless of how carefully taken, become suspect if you are not there to participate and know the truth of the matter first hand. Old beliefs must be shattered before you can begin to imagine a bigger picture. Until the inescapable logic of unambiguous first hand experience hits you squarely between the eyes, the truth does not sink in deeply. That is the way I was, and so is most everybody else.

I suppose by now, Dennis and I were certifiably strange. We were strange because of what we knew to be true by our carefully evaluated experience. We could not deny what we had seen, heard, and measured – even if it was incredibly strange. We knew how careful, skeptical, and demanding we were. We knew how high our standards of evidence were. We also knew that nobody else could possibly understand unless they experienced these truths for themselves. Once you find true knowledge, ignorance is no longer an option – and if the knowledge you find is unusual, then strange becomes a way of life.

Our activity was not entirely internal. For example, Dennis and I were encouraged to volunteer for some remote viewing experiments at a well-known sleep & dream lab. The object was, under controlled conditions, to describe pictures being displayed in another room. As it turned out, being able to describe all the pictures correctly was not the most remarkable thing that happened.

When the EEG scrolls were returned from Duke University (where they had been sent for more detailed analysis) a higher level of strangeness was evidenced. We were told that Dennis's EEG results produced the highest levels of alpha-waves ever recorded at Duke. Mine exhibited strong simultaneous levels of alpha and theta unlike anything they had ever seen before. Both were singular events previously unseen by the Duke researchers because of the narrowness of the peaks. This was particularly meaningful because during the 60s and 70s, Duke University was recognized worldwide as the leader in parapsychological research.

Our brainwaves were, it seemed, tightly focused to specific, nearly single frequencies. We were not particularly surprised by the tight focusing, but duly noted with interest that out of thousands and thousands of EEG analysis results, ours stood out as blatantly unique ("Your data blew them away at Duke," we were told by the researcher). We had for some time felt that what we were learning and developing was uniquely effective at producing specific altered states, but now we had corroborating evidence – an independent lab at Duke had substantiated a physical manifestation of this uniqueness.

Once the mental door of indisputable fact is pried open, the light begins to flood through. The old questions returned with new meaning. Now my reality, my picture, was bigger than I could have previously imagined. Nevertheless, I continually wondered if there were other subjective experiences that could produce consistent objective measurable results. Where were the boundaries – how much more reality was out there that I had missed? Could there be other operational states of consciousness hiding in the darkness of my ignorance?

I was driven to understand how everything was related, how it all worked together. Surely, there was some sort of science at the root. We had lots of data, but no self-consistent model to explain the how's and why's of it all – to define the interactions. How did reality function? What were the processes, the limits, and the rules? Is this the way it is, or only the way it seems? What did the Big Picture look like – where all the data are consistent and makes sense? How could any self-respecting physicist not ask these questions?

Bob, Dennis, and I would discuss it down at the house after the work at the lab was done. We informally came up with some "the way things were" and "the way things seemed to be" statements, but they lacked deeper understanding. We surveyed the existing models – mostly a mishmash of emotion laden, belief focused, unscientific balderdash with little or no hard evidence that was reproducible. That was not what we were looking for. This was a scientific inquiry, not a new-age gathering of the faithful.

Finally, we ran across a candidate model – a place to start. Though imperfect, it was more or less rational, consistent, and coherent most of the time – that made it much better than the rest. Its explanations and descriptions were not complete, nor necessarily a place to end up, but it did provide a theoretical basis from which to tentatively and skeptically begin. This model came to us in the form of *Seth Speaks*, by Jane Roberts. That the material was channeled was not a problem for us. By then, we were all personally familiar with the nonphysical and its host of sentient beings. In fact, it was a plus. Would you ask a fish about mountain hiking trails? No, not if you expected an accurate or useful answer.

We began to spend much of our training time at the lab testing and interpreting Seth's concepts, and procuring information from our own nonphysical sources. We worked on these issues for several years, slowly gaining ground. It was sometimes confusing, sometimes clarifying, but always interesting and always evidence was required.

I worked harder at these particular models of reality issues than the others. I was the theoretician of the group (what you might expect from a physicist), Dennis was more into applications (what you might expect from an engineer). Bob was a practical man focused primarily on whatever worked and upon gaining and maintaining objective credibility. Bill Yost contributed his engineering insights, management skills, encouragement, and support. Nancy Lea did much of the daily support work, and became a full partner in our explorations of nonphysical reality (as had her sister, Penny Honeycutt, a few years before). It was a good team.

We were all aided and abetted all along the way by our families (who for the most part participated in our research from time to time) and many unmentioned others. The research flowed in whichever direction seemed most productive at the time. Bob did not direct as much as he facilitated. Having perfected the wise and knowing smile of all good teachers who know how to let their students figure it out for themselves, he managed to float above the day to day effort and let our individual research take us wherever it would.

11

■ ■ ■

If This is Tuesday, I Must Be
in Physical Matter Reality

■ ■ ■

Meanwhile, back at the lab, Dennis and I were putting in about fifteen to twenty hours a week. After I would get home from the lab, often at two or three in the morning, I would lie in bed practicing what I had learned or continuing that evening's experiments. After two or three hours of sleep, I would get up and go to work. The evenings I didn't go out to the lab, I would continue experimenting after everyone else fell asleep until a few hours before getting up and going to work. I was putting in forty-five hours a week studying altered states and the larger reality while simultaneously putting in fifty hours a week at my day job and raising a family.

My son Eric was about five years old at the time. Like most kids that age, he had frequent spontaneous out-of-body-experiences (OOBE). We would go out-of-body together – I would go by and join him – we would have a blast. One time we were exploring the oceans together when a huge whale approached us. As our bodies slipped easily through the whale, Eric's head for some reason bumped against each of its ribs, one after the next. It frightened him a little; typically we did not interact with our surroundings. We came back immediately.

Eric usually had total and clear recall of our nightly adventures. We would often discuss them in the morning – it was great fun for both of us. Exploring the larger reality turned out to be an excellent father and son activity, though perhaps somewhat unusual. Do not misunderstand me. I was not warping Eric's tender perspective, or jerking him out-of-body. At about five years of age, most children naturally and **spontaneously** have lots of OOBEs. I was merely joining him so that we could go together. It was comforting and reassuring to Eric to have me along – he was going with or without me. I was able to structure the experiences to be both fun and educational (such as exploring the oceans).

Instead of denying and discarding his experiences as foolish dreams (typical parental reaction), I was shaping and sharing them with him. He thought it was cool and looked forward to our outings. Eventually he was no longer a natural, and our forays into the wilds of nonphysical matter reality (NPMR) ended as easily and naturally as they had begun. He, by the way, now has an advanced degree in aeronautical engineering and to this day clearly remembers bumping his head on those whalebones.

I have always been a sleepy head – nine to ten hours a night is about right for me. Yet by spending so much time in altered states where my body was deeply relaxed, if not officially asleep, I got by on two or three hours of sleep per night – night after night after night – year after year.

At work, I was exceptionally productive, but becoming stranger. I was spending almost as much time in NPMR as I was in physical-matter reality (PMR), and it showed. I soon earned a reputation for being an absent minded professor. PMR and NPMR seemed to blend into a continuum and I found I could live in both realities simultaneously; it was no longer a matter of leaving one and going to the other. Now, it was merely a matter of shifting and splitting my focus – I lived and was continuously aware, sentient, and conscious (except when sleeping) in both reality systems simultaneously and permanently.

At first, I could only sequentially (albeit quickly) switch between them. Then I learned to engage mentally in NPMR on one thing while carrying on a conversation **and** driving a car (or motorcycle) at the same time. Most of the time there was no confusion between reality frames, but now and then, for a few seconds, until I forced myself to differentiate between them and get my bearings, I was occasionally not sure which reality I was in. Both were equally real, they were just different and had different functions. I began to marvel at the mind's capacity for parallel processing.

For one relatively short (about six months) period, I was spending more time in NPMR than in PMR. I was a space cadet and obviously needed a keeper. Luckily, being a physicist, and maintaining high professional productivity, I could get by with being eccentric. Nevertheless, I soon realized that I needed to regain a better balance. With a little experimenting, the optimum balance was obtained. I remained eccentric, but didn't need a full-time keeper to remind me of what was coming next in PMR.

With the two realities so completely inter-mixed, I began to notice connections between the two. One spring day while walking back to the office after lunch, I noticed that golden-white foam was draped over the trees in a nearby park. A quick reality check indicated I was solidly focused in PMR. "Wow," I exclaimed with mild surprise, "that is really pretty, but what is that stuff?" By now I was so used to being amazed by the larger reality that what was normally strange had become strangely normal. I studied the white foam; it had the texture of cotton candy. It connected all the trees into one large luminescent mass. It reminded me of a grove of cypress trees along the Gulf coast loaded with glowing Spanish moss.

I thought it was very interesting but had no idea what it was. I wondered if other people could see it. I made an effort to be obviously looking at something. A few passers-by turned their heads to see what I was looking at and then went on about their business without any noticeable reaction. I knew that they must not have seen what I saw because what I was looking at was not ho-hum in the least. It was massive and beautiful. If others could see it, there should have been a crowd forming.

I went back to work, and looked out of my third-story window to see if the light-foam was still there. It was. I closed the door to my office and began to study the phenomenon I was experiencing. I discovered that I could make it disappear and reappear by adjusting the state of my consciousness. Within a few days, I noticed that everything living had this fuzzy light around it, and that there were strands of this nonphysical cotton candy connecting everything to everything. What about inorganic matter, I wondered. I moved my attention to buildings, telephone poles and power-lines.

To my astonishment, there was a smaller more uniform close-cut off-white light around everything! The light around the power-lines was in motion and bushier than what was around the poles. I was incredulous and I looked repeatedly to make sure. I shook my head, then closed my eyes and opened them again. What I saw remained the same. I had hypothesized this odd light as some representation of life energy. Buildings, telephone poles, and wires with life energy? I knew I had to throw that idea out. The light around the wires danced. I immediately wondered what I would see around an electrical appliance. Would inside things have an aura too, or was it related to sunlight? I looked at the clock on my wall. It not only had light around it, but the light was highly structured and in steady motion. I looked at my programmable calculator and saw a finely structured complex pattern. I turned it on and set it to work – the patterns changed and scintillated as it worked. Now I was amazed all over again. What was I looking at?

Within a few days I noticed that people had auras around them that changed and scintillated as their owners talked to me about important things in their lives. A movie theater not only contained ordinary people, but also rows of swirling colored forms. I could turn all of it, or any of it, on or off by shifting the state of my consciousness. Years later, I would only need to shift my intent.

The connections linking living things became visually obvious. I could literally see that everything was connected. Even inanimate things such as clocks and computers had their complex moving nonphysical energy pattern. This same experience did not happen to Dennis. Perhaps he did not immerse himself in the exploration of NPMR and its theory to the extent that I did. I was extreme in my dedication to the effort. We often grew in different ways at different times and had usually, eventually, ended up with similar experiences. We were in this thing together and I had discussed my experiences – seeing energy forms – with Dennis as they happened.

One day he brought me a group photograph of five people and dropped it on my desk.

"These are all Soviets," he said, "one of them is supposed to be leading research in psychic activity in the Soviet Union. Which one is the psychic?"

I had never looked at pictures in this way before, but with focused intent, their auras blossomed up exactly as they did with flesh and blood people. "That was fascinating!" I thought. Conscious intent is everything – space and time are not fundamental. Wow!

"Which one is the psychic?" Dennis asked again.

I looked back at the picture, sure enough, one had a much more developed energy body – particularly around and above his head – than the others. "This one is different from the others," I said pointing to one of the men in the picture. "I am not sure what the difference means yet," I cautioned, "but this one is definitely different from the others." Clairvoyance was still a new experience and I did not know the significance of much of what I saw. At this point, I was more into formulating basic connections and had not thought about auras having unique meaning.

Dennis looked at me and grinned. "That's the one," he said with enthusiasm.

I was surprised. Dennis knew the answer – this was a test! I didn't mind; actually, I was pleased, another data-point was in and I had learned something valuable and amazing about time and space being a subset of a larger reality. "I have so much to learn," I thought to myself, suddenly overwhelmed by the unfathomable depth and complexity of reality. Dennis went back to his office. I took a deep breath and wondered what would happen next, where was all this going, what else was out there waiting to be discovered? I felt small, humbled by the enormity of my ignorance. It was clear that I had barely begun to scratch the surface of something so immense and fundamental that I could barely imagine it.

At the same time, I was excited by the possibilities and determined to discover whatever I could about the nature of reality. I am a physicist and science and discovery are my passions – I was born wanting to know why and how. After twenty-two years of continuous education, I realized that I had studied only one small subset of the natural world. I was young, my learning seemed to be accelerating, and reality was far cooler, more complex, and more interesting than I could have ever imagined. To someone like me, it doesn't get any better than this – I was energized to discover any truth that would yield to my experimentation.

12

End of an Era

Back at the lab during the middle to late 70s, running the seminars dominated everything. We were overwhelmed with demand. People from all over were clamoring to experience Bob Monroe's tapes – and all from word of mouth. Bob saw an economic opportunity on the horizon. He was a businessman, and this business (supporting the lab facility) had been a constant financial drain. Perhaps, he thought, he could get two birds with one stone. He eventually succeeded, but basic research was the first casualty for a few years.

Eventually he was able to add the basic research back at a much greater level than it had been before, as well as provide a life changing and enriching experience for thousands of people. But all that took time, and the era of Bob, Dennis and Tom working until the wee hours of the morning, trying to make science out of the strangeness they discovered, was gone. Its time was rightfully over, fate had been extraordinarily kind, and we ended on a long sweet high note. We were each ready to broaden the scope of our efforts in our own way. It was time for us to soar, coast, or crash on our own.

In the end, Bob was proved right, as usual. He captained his ship flawlessly from the initial tentative launch, through the tricky undercurrents of close-minded rejection by the larger society, while at the same time skillfully avoiding the shallows of easy, safe, generally acceptable answers. With Bob at the helm, high standards of proof drove off pirate charlatans who wanted to co-opt his success and commandeer his hard won credibility. Through dedication to honest science, personal integrity, and an intuitive knowing that was steady and reliable, Bob optimized his gifts for the greater good.

I do not wish to leave the impression that Bob, Dennis and I were the only explorers at Whistlefield Research Laboratories during the early seventies; there were others as well who made important contributions to Monroe's overall effort. A few became regulars making extended connections of various durations, while others were merely passing through trading knowledge like bees pollinating wild flowers. Nancy Lea had joined the research effort with Dennis and me after her graduation from college and soon became an integral part of the team, collecting evidence, testing concepts, participating in singular as well as joint explorations – even soldering wires on occasion. She began to carry more and more of the workload as Dennis and I reached and passed our limits of available time. Eventually Dennis and I needed to go home to our families. Nancy Lea took over the seminar operations and after a few years of successfully building and managing the business, she became the director of The Monroe Institute of Applied Sciences. The truer picture is that the overall effort at Whistlefield was a joint one. It was a busy place with a lot going on and many talented, interesting, and dedicated players.

The end of any era must necessarily share time's stage with the beginning of a new era. With the demands of the activities at Whistlefield winding down, I had more time to integrate and assimilate the continual whirlwind of extraordinary experiences that I had encountered. The nature of reality, a Big Picture that brought coherency to the wealth of collected data, began to take form in my mind. Any model or theory had to consistently account for, and accurately contain, the entirety of my experience – the roots of which ran deeper than I had previously imagined.

13

Once Upon a Time, a Long, Long Time Ago

I have often told people who were inquiring about the possibility of learning what I have learned that if a bone-headed physicist like me could do it, anybody could. I would point out that I began from a cold start with no particular natural talent and learned everything from scratch the hard way. If I could, they could – and probably with less trouble. Dragging Spock from the deck of the Enterprise into the Twilight Zone, with logic fully intact and uncompromised, was a slow and tedious process. Most people could probably learn more quickly than I, even if they did not have the time or inclination to thoroughly immerse themselves as I did.

The point made above remains fundamentally true – anyone can learn what I have learned – but the picky fact is the previous statements contain one little white lie. My start wasn't as cold as I first thought. After I became familiar with the out-of-the-body experience and familiar with NPMR, I realized that I had done this sort of thing before. Old memories returned clear as crystal now that I had the knowledge and perspective to understand them.

When I was between five and eight years old, some friendly nonphysical beings helped me get out-of-body. It was not a random prank. They had a purpose. At first I played with it, slipping out through the wall of my second story bedroom and whooshing around the yard. They would get me out and I would play and soar. I well remember the first time I found myself outside floating a foot or two above the yard, gliding toward this monstrously thick hedge and realizing that I did not know how to steer or stop. I grabbed my head and curled up into a ball expecting a terrible and painful crash. To my utter amazement, I glided right through it and out the other side without interacting with it. Wow! Neat-o! That was fun!

> ▶ A short aside follows to help you find the proper perspective. Most children, particularly those younger than seven, have spontaneous, fully conscious out-of-body-experiences. Their parents tell them it is just a meaningless dream and they forget about it. These experiences are usually non-threatening and fun for the kids. You may recall some of your out-of-body-experiences if your memory is good and the experiences were dramatic.
>
> Most adults have spontaneous out-of-body voyages as well, but they are typically **not** fully conscious and therefore do not qualify as experiences. Out-of-body, as a phenomenon or happening, is much more mundane and common than it is strange. OOBE seems strange because the limitations we place on our concepts of consciousness and reality force us to reject many of the mental functions that are naturally available to our species and to misunderstand the purpose of the mental activities that take place while we are asleep. It is as if we are born with two good legs, but never learned to walk because the ability to crawl precedes the ability to walk, and because everybody is completely adapted to crawling around within a social structure that stigmatizes non-crawling non-conformists as wackos. ◀

Eventually these helpful beings and I became conversant. "How can I do that (get out-of-body) whenever I want to?" I wanted to know. They taught me several techniques. I practiced diligently and got results. Each time I would lose consciousness for a few seconds, regaining consciousness in the out-of-the-body state. "I want to be conscious the entire time," I complained, thinking that I would prefer to be more self-sufficient.

"You will not like it," they said, "We black you out for a short time during the transition to make the process more comfortable."

"I want to do it anyway," I protested.

They finally agreed. I immediately started applying one of the techniques they had taught me. As the here and now began to fade away into oblivion, a much fuller and richer awareness took root and began to blossom. Abruptly my body began to vibrate. The amplitude of the vibrations steadily grew larger and larger – my body had become plastic and was being shaken like a loose canvass awning flapping in a strong wind. Whoa! The violence of the oscillations had startled me. I immediately returned to a normal physical reality lying still in my bed. "OK," I said, "let's try that again." The same sequence repeated itself several times – I would pop back into physical reality after the oscillations became large, fast, and violent. "OK," I said, "you do it." I was almost instantly awake in the out-of-body state.

They won. I never bothered them anymore about doing it my way. Now I realize that I had been had. Those violent oscillations were not necessary. They simply did not want me to become too independent. I noticed that when I was out-of-body, I was an adult, not a little kid. That was neat. When I came back, I was a kid again. I hung out with my nonphysical mentors almost every night. They loved to teach and I loved to learn – we had a great time.

One night my adventures in inner-space took an unexpected turn that subsequently left nothing the same. Unknown to me, phase one was over and phase two was about to begin. Without forewarning, I was set up to begin a battery of exams that would determine the quality of my being. How evolved an entity was I? How much had I learned and grown with the help of my mentors? What was the limit of my understanding? The questions, or more accurately situations, presented me with multiple choices that became progressively more difficult. The first question was mostly verbal. "Would you rather have this treasure (I got a picture) or learn something new?" The answer was obvious; knowledge was far more valuable than goods. It was so blatantly obvious in fact that I decided to make a joke. "Just gimmee the loot," I said sarcastically in my best gangster voice, "I can always learn something new on my own." At the time, I did not realize that this was the first question on a long and especially serious test. My world exploded.

BZZZZZT!! Wrong! I was instantly transported to an entirely different place.

"He failed the first question!"

"He is not ready!" I heard someone exclaim with surprise and disappointment.

"Send him back!" someone else shouted, "he failed the test."

"Test?" I said, feeling a little like Alice at the Queen's castle. "I didn't know this was a test. I was joking, I knew the answer, I thought someone was playing around with me – making up goofy choices – so I was being goofy to get them back." The panel of judges that were to administer and evaluate my exam slipped back in time, inspected my mind for my true motivations – they evidently weren't expecting a smart aleck.

My advocates approached the bench vouching for my readiness. I was relieved that somebody was taking my side. I did not know who they were, but I was glad they were there. The tone had suddenly become heavy as if something terribly important was going on. Two judges said "Failed was failed – send him home," while the other three said "Continue the test, let's see what he can do." A higher level judge was consulted. It was decided. I was to be given a second chance. It was obvious there was some serious hardball politics involved that I did not understand.

The tension was thick as tar; these judges did not like each other and there was a strong competitive hostility between the two groups. I knew this was very serious business, but I didn't know what I was doing in the middle of it. It was clear that whatever was going on was important to me and important to others for reasons I did not understand. I was thankful for the chance to show what I actually knew. My advocates who had evidently been working with me for a long time to get me ready for this first test were almost apoplectic. Their relief at my second chance was immense but they remained worried. It was as if their most important plans, careers, and reputations hung in the balance – and there I was, a somewhat unpredictable embodied bone-headed human.

Instantly, I was back in test-space. The first question was repeated – it was a precise replay of what I had previously experienced. I surmised that this was a fixed or standardized set of questions and that they had to restart the series from the beginning even though the first question and its answer had been revealed. Question after question, situation after situation, was put before me. I evidently did well because when you get one wrong, it's over. There were problems that tested ego and desire with sexual enticements – some of which were bizarre. There were choices between helping others and pursuing your personal path. They played to my emotions and ego, tried to instill fear, and probed how well I truly understood love.

Eventually, I was clueless as to how to approach the problem – I went with my best guess and the test abruptly ended. I was back in my body, turning into a young kid again though my mental space retained its adult nature while in the altered state. "Jeez," I thought, "what was that about?" As a kid, I often retained a clear memory of what happened, for a short while at least. But, I did not relate to it. At least five times since then I have been hauled in front of panels of judges because of my unpredictable quirky human nature. Thus far, I have prevailed. I must, as they say, have a rap sheet a mile long.

Some twenty-three years later, the event that had jogged this childhood memory occurred. I was at Bob's house one weekend afternoon when he began to comment on a training exercise I had been involved in the night before. Regular training sessions designed to develop my effectiveness within NPMR began again in earnest shortly after I resumed sentience within the larger reality. Bob had been in the audience watching my performance. He was telling me about what I had done. I was surprised, not that he could know, but because usually he was not involved in my OOBEs.

He knew every move I made and started kidding me about a show-off display I had performed at the successful end of a particularly difficult series – the way football players sometimes dance in the end zone. We were laughing about it, when he told me about an especially difficult test he himself had recently been given. He started to describe it. After he described the third test in this long series, I stopped him. He knew something was up. Now it was my opportunity to puzzle him.

My experiences of twenty-three years ago had come flooding back in a gushing torrent as he described the first three tests. I made him wait until I had collected my thoughts. I told him what the fourth test was. His jaw dropped. I had never seen Bob speechless before. I described the fifth test. He was dumbfounded. We went through the rest of the test, alternating who would give the description of the presented problems. Oddly enough, we had bombed out at the same place but with different answers. Evidently neither one was right, or that was the last question. Without a doubt, that **was** a standardized test. Since that time I have run into several others who have experienced some sequence of events while in NPMR that were **identical** in form, function, and content to events I experienced.

Back to the early 1950s. Immediately after that first big test, I was put in regular training classes. Every night for most of a year I was run through situations, given jobs to do, and further tested by my trainers. I was never told what I was being trained for. I worked hard. After that first major evaluation almost turned catastrophic, I was serious. It was more work than fun. I was learning to control my mind, to manipulate non-physical energy, to make the right choices for the right reasons, to think fast, and act fast. I was learning to follow directions and to break old PMR conceptual habits. I was becoming effective and efficient in NPMR – I was learning focus and control. Eventually, after much practice, I began to feel competent and strong, like an athlete ready to walk into the arena.

One night there was no more training. I would not resume the effort until some twenty years later, but I didn't know that then.

14

This Kid is Weird Enough

I did not know it, but my learning time in the nonphysical was about to come to an end for a long time. My mind would typically shift into adult mode as I drifted on the boundary between awake and asleep. It had been a week or more since my instructors had been by to take me to class and for some reason I had not gone on my own. It was time to get back to it. I began to slip out-of-body, unassisted by my instructors. Now it was easy. I wondered where my teachers were – why hadn't they come?

"Oh well, this will be fun," I thought with great anticipation. I paused for a moment, "Where should I go, what should I do?" My training had been highly structured; I wasn't used to this much freedom. "Perhaps they want to see what I will do on my own," I thought. I felt that they were probably watching.

Rather suddenly, someone stopped me cold in my tracks, forcefully shoving me back into my body.

"Hey," I said, "what are you doing – you can't do that to me!"

"Yes I can," the reply came back in a firm authoritative tone. "In fact," he continued, "I have been instructed to seal off this passage. You will no longer be allowed to exit your body."

"If this is a test, I don't get it," I thought to myself as I struggled to find the correct response. It was not a test. There were two of them but only one spoke – workers sent to close and seal the door on my experiences in NPMR. "Are you sure you have the right person?" I challenged, "This must be some mistake." I waited while he checked out that possibility.

"No mistake," he said looking at his work order, "you are the one."

"But why?" I pleaded.

"You are a young kid aren't you," he said.

"Yes, but just my body," I replied. "That has never been a problem before."

"You have completed what you were doing," he said matter-of-factly, "and now they don't want you to grow up too weird. You know what I mean – you need to grow up like a normal kid, develop a healthy personality. Too much of this other-world experience would make you strange and not fit comfortably into the world you will grow up in."

"I can handle it," I protested, "I haven't had any problems so far."

"You have no choice," he said emphatically. "Trust me. It may be easy now because you are only in one reality at a time, but as you get older, it would become a problem for you to juggle multiple realities simultaneously."

I did trust him, and I intuitively knew that he was right. I also had no choice; he was much more powerful and knowledgeable than I was. I knew I could not slip thoughts into his mind. I didn't try. "Will I ever be allowed to get back out again? Will you ever unseal this door?" I asked hopefully.

"I don't know," he said flatly as if it were none of his business.

"Can you find out for me?" I pleaded, "Please look and see." I don't think they were supposed to do this sort of thing, but I must have sounded desperate and sad. Neither worker said anything, but they both looked far away into the distance. It was a long and intense look. Suddenly, they both gave a loud gasp – as if they were simultaneously surprised and shocked. They were momentarily stunned, and remained quiet for a few seconds.

"What is it?" I asked. "What do you see?" I strained to see the picture that was in their minds, but could not. "Will I ever get through this door again? Tell me, please." Both workers now had the demeanor of someone who has inadvertently blundered into something they were not supposed to know about. Both had become tightly focused on what they were doing and were now non-communicative and in a hurry. They glanced at each other with concern. I could sense that they were more than a little worried. I could feel their feelings and could pick up a few surface thoughts, but the startling events they had witnessed were securely and purposely unavailable.

How could the information they had inadvertently found out about **my** future put **them** in a jam? I was dumbfounded. My concern and overall puzzlement was growing rapidly. They had a sense of impending personal jeopardy. After some quick discussion they briefed higher authority on the situation – a few others who were somehow connected were brought in. Security was tight. Decisions were made quickly – a plan B was set into motion and everyone but the two workers immediately disappeared.

The problem was not that the two workers had broken a rule by looking ahead for me – that was a relatively small issue that could be, and was, quickly forgiven. The problem was that now they knew something that they were not supposed to know. I was perplexed, and could not even make a wild guess at what was causing all the concern. "What did you see... what is the problem... what's going on?" I asked the workers in a quiet and serious tone trying to sound as if I were a team member who had, for some unavoidable reason, just happened to miss the preceding conversation. They took a few seconds to finish what they were doing and then slowly turned toward me, paused, and stared with quizzical amazement for a few moments. They looked at each other for a brief moment, then back at me. Saying nothing, they slammed the door hard. I was shut out.

As it turned out, I was not shut out entirely. There were no more out-of-body experiences, to be sure, but I still had friends. In my mind, I could easily communicate telepathically with my guides. I did not call them that but that was their function.

15

■■■

With a Little Bit of Help From My Friends: How's Your Love Life?

■■■

I always knew growing up that there were nonphysical entities available to help me. They looked after me and I knew it. They were nonphysical friends who were older and wiser and knew what was coming. I think that many people have this sense of having helpers. Whether you interpret it as a religious manifestation (God, or guardian angels perhaps), or simply let it exist unnamed within your imagination seems primarily to be a function of your cultural belief system and temperament.

When in need, I intuitively sought out my guides and depended on them. When I did not need them, I forgot about them. Whether I was aware of them or not, they were always with me, they were at times my intuition, my luck, my counselor, my pals – and they made a special effort to keep me alive. Risk and daring had always been two of my favorite playmates and most steady companions – I was not an easy case.

Several times in particular these guides provided detailed information about my future. Both times were in response to questions of relationship that contained strong emotional and intellectual content. Once, at fourteen while waiting for the school bus to take me home, I asked in frustration about the possibility of ever having a successful love life. Instead of being amused at my pathetic pubescent condition, they proceeded to lay out the relationship map of the rest of my life. Every significant relationship with pictures and detailed description followed in rapid succession. I repeated it over and over in my mind so that I would not easily forget it.

To this day, I remember most of the conversation clearly. Accurate predictions were made that penetrated twenty years into the future! How could they do that? I do not know for sure – I must be an exceptionally predictable person. In particular they predicted that "the one," the final lasting connection (significant other) would be with a woman who was now only two years old!

"Two," I blurted out, "you have got to be kidding! I am paired with some two-year-old baby! Come on guys, I can't wait that long! This must be a joke! Right?" It was no joke. At fourteen, this was not what I wanted to hear. "That is so far away, how can you predict that?" I asked. They did not answer. "Do I know this baby?" I asked.

"No," they said, "she is not in this state."

"Great," I thought, "a monk forever!"

"There will be others before her," they said in consolation.

"Yeah, sure, but what's the point, they are not 'the one'," I shot back with obvious disappointment.

"No, they will not be 'the one', but they are important and necessary," my guides replied with great patience.

I heaved a sigh of resignation. They never kidded around and were, as far as I could tell, always right. Arguing with your guides was even more futile than arguing with your mother.

I paused and turned inward. I began to remember an experience I'd had a few years earlier, when I was twelve. I had sneakily taken a look at the foldout of the month in a girly magazine at a news stand while the owner was busy ringing up sales. Being exceedingly impressed with what I had seen, I wondered if I would ever have a woman like that to have and to hold.

To my surprise, a reply began to stream into my mind.

"Yes," I was told, "you will have one that looks very much like that one... she will meet all of your desires," my guides added with a hint of amusement. "She will really love you – the two of you will be tightly connected." I was given a sense of the quality of the relationship.

Wow! I thought. I was excited – the luckiest guy alive – because my guides always knew what they were talking about. They were always sure and confident and never guessed or speculated. "When?" I asked excitedly; "when do I find her?"

"When you are thirty-five years old," they said flatly.

I was totally devastated. "Awww man, that's really old – I mean **really, really** old! Do you have any idea how far it is to thirty-five when you are only twelve? It's forever!" I whined.

"That's the way it is," they said with no trace of emotion. I had the sense that they were ever so slightly amused at my reaction.

As that memory poured into my consciousness, the connection was immediately obvious. That two-year-old baby and my foldout-princess were one and the same. "Interesting, but totally useless," I thought. The immediate romantic future that I was most interested in looked as bleak as ever.

Another instance occurred when, at twenty-one, I was about to get married after graduating from college. I was having second thoughts, when a similar experience took place. The future was outlined. Again "the one" was described and predicted. The problem was, it did not happen to be the person I was about to marry! Yes, I was supposed to get married. Yes, I would have a son. No, it was not going to last forever. "But why do it now if this is not 'the one'?" I argued, and then continued with, "It is not fair to her or the child."

The answer came back clear and strong: "It is what you are supposed to do; it is part of a larger plan. Marry her. It is the next step for you, and will be the best thing for everyone including her. Everything will work out." I did. It did.

Everything they said happened as they said it would, except for a few items at the far end of the given timeline that have either changed their probability of occurrence over the years (which is what I think) or they are still in the queue.

In the event you are curious, at the age of thirty-five (I am writing these words in the year 2000 at the age of fifty-five) I began a relationship with "the one" who is twelve years younger than I am (was two when I was fourteen). We have three children (exactly as foretold) who adore their big half-brother Eric. Life is good.

As you see, it is not exactly true that I had a cold start with TM at the age of twenty-four. Life had been good to me and I had completely forgotten most of what I just told you. To an exceedingly skeptical, young, bone-headed, hard-science-type who had made a concerted (and relatively successful) effort to purge his system of all beliefs, and who was naturally wary of anything he could not directly measure, it certainly seemed as if it were an ice-cold start at the time.

16

■■■

Here We Go Again!

■■■

By the early 70s, that door to NPMR that had been slammed shut 20 years earlier was thrown wide open again. I was back in NPMR with a mission to understand it all – from a scientist's perspective this time. By the end of the 70s, Bob and the lab were doing their thing, and I was doing my own thing independently. I had learned that the so-called phenomena or powers (paranormal events) were only an artifact of a path well taken, not the objective or destination. Becoming too enamored of paranormal phenomena can distract you from more important issues and retard or prevent your further development.

I also learned that the bigger picture was centered on the quality of your consciousness, the evolution of your being, and that my experience could be scientifically explained. Eventually, it became apparent that the rate of learning accelerates. The more you know, the faster you learn. Up to 1980, I was on the launch pad, getting ready, learning, training. Then things really took off. The pace has never slowed and my interest and dedication have never waned. More data points continue to pour in today.

From another point of view, nothing exceptionally strange happened. Many children around the age of five to seven have unusual experiences in their dreams. I was able to later remember mine and understand them within a larger context. Likewise, many people have nonphysical guides or advisors. In our culture, this sometimes occurs within a religious paradigm. I was given an unusual opportunity to work in a fascinating field with a good teacher and I took full advantage of it by working hard and being dedicated and conscientious in my effort. That was simply good fortune (or good planning) – being in the right place at the right time with the right credentials, the right interests, and the right attitude.

What I learned was more by virtue of hard work and a focused interest than by anything fantastic, amazing, or strange. There was no magic, no bump on the head, no aliens from outer space, no near death experience, and I did not find deep mystical secrets hidden in a golden urn buried under the rubble of an ancient monastery in Tibet. It was good science and dedicated effort applied to an opportunity – that is all. I essentially worked my way to where I am today and I have no regrets. Indeed, I feel extremely lucky to have found the path that I am on. The word "strange" is a relative word. Anything not mundane must, necessarily, **seem** strange to those who have not experienced it.

Today I work as a physicist in an engineering services company specializing in missile defense research and development, and if you saw me or worked with me you would not think that I was the slightest bit strange. Yet, in another environment, away from the workplace, I help guide the development of a small group of students and other people interested in increasing the quality of their consciousness. I have learned to work harmoniously with the environment I find myself in. Because most of my real work has been focused in the nonphysical, it has been easy to maintain a low profile in PMR.

I have been strongly encouraged to share some of the results and conclusions of my explorations of the reality we live in. That is what *My Big TOE* is about. I hope that by knowing how I came to have the somewhat unusual knowledge and experience that makes this book possible, you will be able to view the unusual concepts you are about to delve into with a broader perspective. Having been faced with the same dilemma of analysis (is this guy nuts, or what?) that faces you now, I fully understand your position.

There is no easy or satisfactory way to judge the quality of the information upon which this trilogy is based without knowing me personally. Nevertheless, I hope the above account at least helps a little. Those with your own experience will find familiarity in what I have to say. Good luck, I hope you make out as well as I did, or at least learn something useful. Remember, the evidence, as well as the key to understanding, lies within your own experience – and nowhere else.

Section 2

■ ■ ■

Mysticism Demystified:
The Foundations of Reality

■ ■ ■

17

■■■

Introduction to Section 2

■■■

What we call mystical is relative to the extent of our knowledge and understanding. If some process, phenomena, or conceptualization **appears** to lie beyond our potential ability to explain it within the context of PMR (physical-matter reality), we describe it as mystical. Much of what was considered mystical a thousand years ago is considered science today and much of what is considered mystical today will be clearly understood by a future science.

As our current accumulated **objective** knowledge reaches its limits and begins to dissolve into the seemingly unknowable, what lies beyond our **presumed** theoretical reach is defined as mystical. Such presumptions well up from our beliefs about objective reality; thus, what appears to be mystical or unknowable from the view of Western culture simply reflects Western cultural beliefs and the limited understanding of contemporary science. Consequently, it is a double dose of ignorance (cultural beliefs and limited scientific knowledge) that defines what appears to be beyond our serious consideration. Think about that the next time you roll your eyes and snicker because you universally associate the concept of mystical with ignorance (other peoples, not yours), foolishness, and unscientific blather.

For an individual, the process is more personal. What may be perceived by an individual to be mystical is relative to the individual's understanding, knowledge, and ignorance. It is our personal beliefs that determine what we consider to be mystical. Whether individuals know little or much about either PMR or NPMR (nonphysical-matter reality), what lies beyond the reach of his or her personal understanding and knowledge may be: 1) interpreted by that individual as mystical, 2) construed by belief to be something that suits the needs of the individual, 3) regarded as a temporary ignorance of something theoretically knowable, or 4) regarded as a permanent ignorance of something theoretically unknowable. An individual's conclusions regarding what lies beyond his objective reach are necessarily belief-based unless, of course, the conclusion is that there can be no conclusions. Nevertheless, most of us embrace a multitude of both culturally given and personally derived belief-based conclusions with a degree of certainty that only a deep bone-level ignorance could sustain.

Belief is a conclusion based upon a mystical premise. Scientists might **believe** that what is unknown must be contained within the PMR data-set and follow ordinary objective causality, but that **belief** or article of faith simply expresses a more accepted form of mysticism. Mysticism that supports our cultural beliefs is accepted as obvious fact. By definition, such a **belief** necessarily appears to be the most reasonable assumption that a rational person (within that culture) can make. This is how ordinary mysticism expressed as cultural and personal belief is transmuted into an unquestioned philosophical foundation. We see that the objective causality of Western materialism must necessarily spring from a foundation of mystical assumption. Voilà! Faith becomes science, or at least an integral part of the scientific attitude.

The results of this illogical transformation continue in chain reaction. Next, science becomes truth – or at least the sole judge of truth – and is given the job of defining reality. Thus, from the Western perspective, the world of ideas and concepts bifurcates, with science and truth on the one hand and philosophy and conjecture on the other. Though science is important because it produces a marvelous array of useful physical products, philosophy is marginalized because it produces nothing but useless arguments. In the final act of this farce, we see that science, unable to overcome the barrier of its ancient, no longer useful, faith-based paradigms, becomes imprisoned by the limitations of its core beliefs. As science struggles with its self-induced myopia, philosophy tries in vain to mimic science's illusion of objectivity in order to appear relevant. Does this not remind you of some preposterously convoluted French farce?

Ahhh, but wait...the action isn't over – there is a surprise ending! However, you will have to take this journey with me and My Big TOE – from here to the end of Section 6 – if you want to discover how this drama plays out.

> ▶ No doubt about it, I am putting you off. Why? Because, if I told you the ending now, before thoroughly discussing some of your current beliefs and paradigms, you would

not, could not, "get it". I know that you are experienced and brilliant, but that is not the point. Seeing the Big Picture requires more than intellectual capacity. It also requires transcending ingrained belief systems. That is something that many people are not willing or able to do – at least not quickly or easily, if at all. That is why a trilogy is required instead of a technical paper.

Academic papers provide a media for communicating something of value only if one is working within the accepted cultural and scientific belief systems. Consequently, significant new knowledge is typically generated by meticulously taking countless tiny steps of ever expanding detail toward some specific goal. Digging out details requires a totally different mental process than discovering Big Picture paradigms. Today, almost all scientists remain focused on prying details from a reality exclusively circumscribed by traditional scientific belief. Fact is: You will never be able to see the Big Picture as long as you focus on individual politically correct pixels.

Because *My Big TOE* must go beyond traditional belief systems to introduce an entirely new understanding of reality, much of this trilogy must necessarily be spent broadening your perspective. Have patience and resist the urge to come to what appear to be obvious conclusions before you have consumed the entire trilogy. Transcending old paradigms and belief systems is as inherently difficult a process to facilitate as it is to undergo. ◀

Will *My Big TOE* come to the rescue and re-energize this languishing drama of stultified science and marginalized philosophy by dissolving the Gordian knot of limiting belief that condemns both to little more than picking the bones of the past (simply taking the next logical step or digging ever deeper into the detail of yesterday's discoveries)? Can *My Big TOE* successfully raise science to the next plateau of understanding while simultaneously returning philosophy to its rightful place leading the parade of human progress with meaningful and useful insight? Stay tuned!

What I hope to accomplish in this section is to develop the basic concepts necessary to support a rational theory of existence – a conceptualization that provides the foundation for a reasonable Big Picture Theory Of Everything (Big TOE). In the process, I hope to push your mystical edge (where knowledge meets ignorance) back to a point where the residual unknown has no potential significance and is of no practical interest.

A TOE that does not reach beyond PMR is only a little TOE (Little picture **T**heory **O**f **E**verything) confined to PMR and limited to a local causality. Can you imagine the elements and limitations of a Tiny TOE from the perspective of bacteria living in your intestines? Would a seemingly complete and comprehensive (from the view of the bacteria) Tiny TOE be concerned with the nuclear fusion taking place within our sun or the density and composition of our atmosphere? No, of course not; these things have no **direct** significance to the bacteria in your intestines. Although all things that live upon the earth depend on the sun's energy and the composition and density of earth's atmosphere, the bacteria in your intestine cannot directly experience either – their Tiny TOE needs only to describe everything that is potentially knowable by the bacteria.

To a given awareness, the **practical** definition of the word "everything" means: everything knowable, important, meaningful, or significant that can directly interact with that awareness. Thus, what constitutes a comprehensive and complete Big TOE is relative to your perspective, knowledge, and limitations. That Tiny TOE would seem complete from the view of the bacteria, even if it neglected to include the money in your bank account, the light bulb in your refrigerator, or the car in your garage. However, these items may **indirectly** have a profound effect on the current intestinal environment.

Money, refrigerators, light bulbs, and automobiles are too far removed (far beyond the practical, functional, or theoretical scope of a bacterium's Tiny TOE) to be comprehended by the bacteria, or to be of any **direct** importance to them. To the bacteria in the intestine, the source of digested food descending from the stomach would seem mystical. The economic, social, and physical circumstances and processes that indirectly result in a particular food being deposited in the stomach would be beyond mystical. The causal mechanisms that drive and order these apparently mystical events and processes are necessarily invisible to even the most brilliant intestinal bacteria. The forces and relationships that govern the growing of wheat as well as the making and marketing of bread falls beyond a bacterium's theoretical ability to imagine, and therefore forever lies beyond the largest reality it can possibly comprehend. Do not be too surprised to find Homo sapiens in a similar situation.

This is a difficult pill for many, especially scientists, to swallow. The concept that there may be a natural practical limit to the extent of our knowledge – a limit beyond which our perception cannot penetrate – is based upon the notion that we are only a very small part of a much greater reality. This humbling thought runs counter to the significance and self-importance we humans place upon ourselves. If our experience is limited to a small part of a larger reality, it is only reasonable to assume that beyond the limit of our possible knowing there may well exist a host of phenomena, interactions, relationships, and ordered happenings upon which our reality and existence profoundly depends, but of which we cannot **directly** perceive. Allowing the outside theoretical possibility that our beloved PMR may be a local reality (a subset of something larger) is the first step toward comprehending a bigger picture.

This possibility breaks the conventional paradigm of PMR being all there is and replaces it with a more expansive paradigm that forms a logical superset – the limited little picture concept is fully contained within a more general bigger picture concept. If the larger and more general paradigm provides a better and more concise understanding of the available data as well as produces valuable new knowledge, approaches, and processes, then the more general conceptualization is also a more accurate, productive, and truer representation of the whole. An improved reality paradigm is one that broadens and deepens the available solution space relative to existing data and problems in a way that is practical and useful.

It is as easy to understand the limitations of a bacterium's perspective as it is difficult to understand the limitations of our own perspective. That is natural enough. We cannot be aware of what is beyond our awareness. However, we can be open to learning new things, and in the process, expand the scope of our awareness – and therefore our reality – to its outer limits.

At the top level, where any Big Picture must first be clearly drawn, *My Big TOE* will attempt to encompass everything known and knowable. What lies beyond *My Big TOE* will remain practically unknowable (forever mystical) because of the inherent limits of our vision. Nevertheless, both the mystical and the beyond mystical will be explored as we have some fun with logical extrapolations that reach well beyond our capacity to comprehend.

▶ "Encompass everything knowable? Derive physics from metaphysics? Explain the paranormal scientifically? No way! Even at the most general theoretical level that's completely impossible – what's the catch? Is this guy nuts or what?"

I know the idea of encompassing or bounding "everything known and knowable" sounds unlikely at this point – as does the rest – but it is not as far fetched as you may think. *My Big TOE* is not presented at such a high level of generality, nor is it so off the wall as to hold little direct scientific or practical value to the real world. No catch, no megalomania, no hypothetical wackiness, no goofy beliefs – just straightforward science that better describes the measured data and provides a wealth of practical results and new understanding that can be applied personally and professionally by scientists and nonscientists alike. By the end of this trilogy you will be able to assess the accuracy of these seemingly impossible, unsubstantiated statements. Until then, open minded skepticism is the only approach that retains the possibility of success for either of us. ◀

Let us begin to explore the outer limits of our reality and see how far we can push back the boundary. We are generally somewhat smarter than bacteria and are theoretically limited only by the capacity of our minds. Unfortunately, we are limited by much more – beliefs, pseudo-knowledge, preconceived notions, attitudes, fears, desires, needs, and cultural biases. For this reason, we must talk about some of these first.

The biggest picture must cover everything – everything objective, everything subjective, everything normal, and everything paranormal. Mind and matter, consciousness and concrete, all the true data and the facts of existence (the personal as well as the scientific) must be accounted for, compatible with, and contained within this single Big TOE – **if** it is a comprehensive and correct Big TOE. If it is only a little TOE, or incorrect Big TOE, it will not support or explain **all** the data. It is your job to assess the extent to which this Big TOE explains **your** experience and knowledge. However, before reaching conclusions, it is important to understand the difference between knowledge and belief. In the chapter after next we will thoroughly explore that subject. To set the stage for that challenging epistemological adventure, we must first take a look at our collective beginning. It is always a good idea to start at the beginning.

Let's get started on this strange journey. Oh yes, it will need to be strange or it could not possibly be a correct Big TOE. Trust me, unless you have invested many years of experience in this area, what you are about to read will greatly challenge the elasticity of your mind. To make things worse, my insistence that this Big TOE is primarily derived from and based upon carefully evaluated scientific data, rather than theoretical conjecture, will require your sense of my credibility to stretch even further than your mind. Unfortunately, a reader with a simultaneously stretched mind and stretched sense of credibility puts me on thin ice from the beginning, but that is the way it has to be. Such is the nature of this topic, the facts of my experience, and the results of my research. Something less strange or more widely credible would be easier to convey, find a wider audience, and be more acceptable to almost everyone, but it would not be correct.

People generally **believe** that they know **almost** everything that is knowable, that the final few things to be figured out will constitute small steps compared to the distance already come. For example, scientists toward the end of the nineteenth century often lamented the **obvious** fact that everything important (in science and technology) had been discovered. Little more than a century later, that claim is laughable. By definition, it is clear that you cannot be aware of what you do not know. Yet, we almost always let our egos trick us into believing that we are much less ignorant than we actually are. It is often said there is nothing as outrageous or strange as the truth. The truth of that statement, clearly demonstrated by modern physics, demands an open minded approach.

Hopefully *My Big TOE* will stimulate you to consider some important things in an entirely new and beneficial way. Take from it whatever you can. The picture and perspective may be very big and initially the credibility (for those who do not know me) may be very thin, but if you **feel** your way through it with your **intuition** as well as think your way through it with your intellect (all the while collecting and applying the data of your experience), it might just make some sense to you.

Appreciating and understanding the Big Picture is always the first step in focusing and directing the effective investment of the resources you have at your command. The point and purpose of this work is to offer an expanded view of reality and of your relationship to that reality that is **useful** and helpful to you in a direct and practical way. In *My Big TOE*, you will find a reality model that provides a unique perspective which can be profitably applied to your professional and personal life.

One final caution. Section 2 lays down the conceptual foundation for much of the rest of the trilogy without explaining how these concepts link up later to complete a meaningful pattern. It may be difficult to get a firm grip on some of this material because it is predominately abstract and may be relatively distant from your common everyday experience. Understanding and validation will accrue slowly as you digest the next four sections and bring your own explorations of Big Truth to bear on the conclusions drawn.

Though there are many abstract tunnels to explore in Section 2, there is precious little light to be seen at the end of any of them initially. Nevertheless, a logical approach requires many of the conceptual building blocks to be defined and set out before Big TOE construction can be initiated. Delay final judgments until these concepts are more fully developed and applied in subsequent sections. If you can hang tough, the method to the madness should become fully apparent by the time you finish Book 3.

If *My Big TOE* entices those who are open minded and intrepid explorers to explore the far reaches of their reality on their own, I would be delighted. To be optimally effective, my discovery must lead to your discovery. I must not only help you to objectively understand the nature of your reality, but must also help you discover it in personal terms. In the end, if these books have no effect other than to cause you to reassess your beliefs, concepts, knowledge, and attitudes, regardless of what the outcome of that assessment is, my effort will have been worthwhile. Have at it. Good luck on your journey – may you find value of lasting significance.

18

■■■

In the Beginning...
Causality and Mysticism

■■■

Beginnings are always difficult. Wherever one starts, there is always the question: "What was before that?" This question comes from our sense of objective causality – that everything must be preceded by its cause. Must everything have a cause? If "no," then one leaps immediately to invoking mystical beginnings. If "yes," then the beginning is a logical impossibility. There can, by definition, be no beginning if everything must have a cause. By the logic of causality, beginnings are illogical. The logic of causality requires (because we **do** exist) the **initial** existence from which we are derived to erupt spontaneously from nothing. Clearly, the notion of objective causality must violate its own logic in order to get started.

The other alternative – there is no beginning, existence is **somehow** infinite and perpetual, is itself a mystical assertion that comes from nowhere and goes nowhere. Such an unbounded mysticism offers its supporters no possibility of either answers or clues. Beginning with a premise that our ignorance of beginnings is total and perpetual is not a particularly clever way to begin an analysis of beginnings. Easy perhaps, but not useful. This logical alternative provides a trivial solution that leaves no foundation upon which to build a reality.

Thus, the logical result of invoking an objective causality is a mystical beginning. Likewise, the logical result of denying an objective causality (our beginning began without prior cause) is also a mystical beginning. Although the logic of our objective causality would seem to indicate that our beginning **must** be mystical, that is not necessarily so. It depends on the reality in which such a beginning is taking place, and the reality from which we are viewing it. Causality is system specific – the logic of causality (the logic of PMR physics for example) holds within a given causal system. The logic of causality only requires that a given system's beginning appears to be mystical from a point of view that lies within that system. The logic of causality can say nothing about the beginnings of its own system because those beginnings lie outside that system – beyond the reach of its own causal logic. Beginnings belong to the next higher level of causality and are beyond the purview or scope of a subsystem's own causal logic. Imagine a hierarchy of causal systems, each being a subset of the next. Thus, mysticism may be removed from our own beginning if we can obtain the perspective of the superset to which we belong.

I am not saying that our objective causality should be tossed out. The logic of our objective causality has been, and remains, the philosophical foundation of our science. It has motivated us to ask: "How does this work?" or "What caused that?" It has led to the technology and understanding that is now begging us to take the next step beyond the purely material. I am not putting down the logic of our objective causality. I am a scientist – I live and work by it. I am simply putting it into the proper perspective. I am pointing out its logical limitations, the boundary of its meaningful application, the fact that it requires its beginning to violate its own logic.

Thus **our** beginning, from the point of view of **our** objective causality, must be indefinable, or equivalently, mystical. If you do not logically equate "indefinable" with "mystical," that is fine. Given that the subject is the creation of our reality (our beginnings), the terms "necessarily undefined" and "unknowable" quickly morph into "mystical" in the minds of many – thus I use the word "mystical" to generally describe the unknowable. By the time you reach the end of this trilogy, the veil of mysticism will be logically removed from our beginnings and you will clearly understand the roots of our existence and how and why those roots came into being.

Once we realize the causal logic that gives us science also limits our understanding of the larger reality (and its beginning), we are free to begin exploring the larger truth. Without this realization, our perspective and capacity to understand is trapped in a conceptual prison (a belief trap) of our own making.

The erroneous belief in a universal causality (as opposed to a local causality) is used repetitively to make those who would dare rationally tackle the questions of beginnings appear to be ignorant and incorrect. The repeatedly and iteratively asked question "What was before that?"

inevitably must end with a confession of complete ignorance existing at the foundation of an otherwise rational discourse. The position is taken that logical arguments built upon a foundation of ignorance are highly suspect and can be dispensed with immediately as foolish or unsubstantiated conjecture.

Our physical space-time causality **is** local and simply does not apply to "what was before that" – otherwise we would either be stuck with no beginning, or we would have spontaneously popped out of nothing. Either of those alternatives lead to mystical beliefs that are not scientifically or logically productive – neither makes good sense, nor provides a rational foundation from which to build a scientific Big Picture Theory Of Everything. A major paradigm shift described within this section provides another alternative (necessarily mystical from the PMR point of view) that is **not** belief-based, that **does** make good sense, and that **is** scientifically and logically productive.

Our beginnings appear mystical to us because of the limitations of our logic and because of the limitations that our belief-based perspectives impose upon our minds. If you raise science, as well as your vision and understanding, to the next higher level of causality – to the supersystem that contains PMR as a subsystem – the ever-present mysticism will recede to the outer edges of your newly acquired knowledge.

If your picture (worldview or understanding of reality) is significantly bigger than your neighbor's picture, your neighbor may see you as a mystic. Indeed, you will always appear to be a mystic from a viewpoint that is greatly limited in its understanding regardless of how rational, complete, or scientific your understanding is. A mystic appears to be animated by unknowable interactions that lie beyond rational understanding. Perhaps your dog thinks that you are a powerful irrational mystic. If your neighbor also finds you to be a particularly good, loving, wise, productive, successful, and capable person, he should try to understand what you seem to understand. If, on the other hand, you appear arrogant, condescending, manipulating, or begin proselytizing and asking for donations, he would do well to keep his door locked and avoid you.

The quality of your being expresses the correctness of your understanding. Think about that a moment. What does the quality of **your** being say about the correctness of **your** understanding?

19

■■■

Beware of the Belief Trap

■■■

Most of us are awash with beliefs of all sorts. We are steeped in the common sense and prevailing wisdom of our culture, traditions, communities, profession, family, and friends. Because belief is very personal for each of us, I will approach this discussion of belief and knowledge from many different directions. Hopefully, at least one of these approaches will connect with your unique experience, intellect, and inner-self.

When encountering something complex and unfamiliar, repetition is usually required before we feel comfortable with it. Likewise, reiteration is often needed to punch through deeply held and ingrained ways of thinking and being. Most of us have deeply held and ingrained ways of thinking and being whether we are intellectually aware of them or not. What is deeply ingrained in us is nearly impossible for us to notice – it becomes part of the invisible inner core of our being. It is a fact that subtle belief systems circumscribe our personal reality. It is also a fact that most of our beliefs lie beyond the easy reach of our intellects. Outside our awareness, they literally define, and thus also limit, what we allow ourselves to perceive and interpret as reality.

I am sure that you can process Big Picture information intellectually without difficulty, however, because your core beliefs are profoundly ingrained, it is far more difficult for you to successfully integrate that information into deeper levels of understanding. Because you find certain material to be **intellectually** easy to understand or conceptually obvious and repetitious, does not necessarily indicate that the **significance** of that material has actually sunk in to deeper levels of knowing.

What passes for intellectual understanding is often shallow and incomplete because we have no means to accurately assess the extent of our ignorance. The logical result of an awareness of our ignorance relative to some very important issue is an uncomfortable anxiety – the anxiety of not knowing what you desperately need to know. We generally feel compelled to produce an **apparently** solid assessment of the problem regardless of how much we know or do not know. In order to ensure that our assessment appears solid enough to significantly reduce the fear-based anxiety brought on by our ignorance, we make assumptions about the degree, quality, and completeness of our knowledge that invariably lead us to interpret "shallow and incomplete" as "sufficient and conclusive." The resultant intellectual judgment, regardless how ill conceived, will always produce a conclusion that appears (to its creator) to be reasonably certain as well as obviously correct. Presto-change-o! The discomforting anxiety disappears as pseudo-knowledge is manufactured by the ego to deny ignorance its due.

Do you see how the fear of not knowing thus assuages itself by creating a believable self-satisfying story that provides an alternative to acknowledging and accepting ignorance? That the story may be false is invisible to its author because it is based upon assumptions and beliefs designed to meet the author's pressing needs for reassurance and security. Have you ever wondered how **other** people can come to the strangest conclusions about all manner of things? From religious fanatics to your sometimes exasperating manager or significant other, it works the same way. Be careful that **your** intellect does not trick you into believing comfortable and seductive conclusions that are primarily designed to reduce your anxiety, reassure your ego, and maintain your current self-satisfying worldview.

Whenever you feel reasonably certain that you are obviously correct even though you have no real data to back it up, you should at least consider the possibility that you may be stuck in a belief trap of your own creation. Only open minded skepticism will allow you to assess that possibility.

Big Truth must be understood deeply to be effectively applied. Wisdom resides more in the heart and soul than in the intellect. Your intellect can only take you so far in your exploration of Big Truth; it can direct your search but cannot cause you to learn anything of deeper significance. On the other hand, your intellect can cause you to squander every opportunity to know Big Truth.

To focus our discussion of belief traps, let me give you a more precise and clear understanding of what I mean when I use the words "belief" and "knowledge." Beliefs may be cultural, religious, scientific, or personal. Belief is generated and necessitated by ignorance. If you know for sure, belief is not required. In that case, you have real knowledge. Knowledge is derived from knowing what is true. If your apparent knowledge is false, you only **believe** that you know. In this situation, belief is masquerading as knowledge. Belief posing as knowledge is pseudo-knowledge, not real knowledge.

▶ Because many are now wondering how you can tell pseudo-knowledge from knowledge, I think a short aside is in order. Throughout this trilogy, you will find discussions of how to discriminate between the wise and the foolish, between the real and the apparent, between falsehood and truth, between knowledge and pseudo-knowledge (belief). We will approach this issue from several directions over the course of Sections 2 through 6.

This is a pudding thing and a science thing. "The proof of the pudding is in the eating" implies that truth and knowledge can be evaluated by the objective results of their application. Science is the primary tool and process that enables you to avoid belief traps while assessing objective results.

Typically, it boils down to the fact that you need personal experience (knowledge must be **applied**) and measurable results (you must taste the pudding) to become a discriminating connoisseur of reality. If you are not careful, you can be deluded about the results, as well as the experience. That is why you must be a good scientist in your explorations. Being a good scientist requires only that you have the right approach and attitude – no degree or formal scientific training is required. You must wait until you have collected enough high quality evidential data before converting potential possibilities into actualities or knowledge. These potential possibilities, with their associated probability of being true, must always be reassessed and recalculated as new data come in. Apparent knowledge remains potential and tentative – truth is absolute.

Your list of potential possibilities will, for a very long time, if not always, be a much, much, longer list than your list of absolute truths. If you are careful to remain simultaneously open minded and skeptical, you will be unlikely to inadvertently make a major investment in false knowledge. On the other hand, you might pursue a hypothesis or potential possibility to a dead end – or to the conclusion that your hypothesis is wrong. That is how good science works. There is no way to guarantee that your hypotheses will be proved correct. Proving a hypothesis wrong also produces useful information.

Always remain skeptical and open minded so that you won't wander too far down too many blind alleys. It is those who abandon the open minded skepticism of the scientist, in pursuit of easy and quick answers, who end up leaping into belief traps. They lose their way and unwisely invest their time and energy moving in non-optimal, unproductive directions based on pseudo-knowledge. The truth is not delicate; it will stand up to vigorous testing.

However, you must be careful that your tests are valid. This is not as easy as it first appears. The inherent difficulty scientists have in validating concepts and results reflects a standard problem of science. By definition, it is always difficult for you to design tests to evaluate something that you do not understand. Exploring NPMR is in many ways the same as exploring PMR. Research in NPMR requires, more often than not, a long, slow, sometimes frustrating and tedious process to find tentative new knowledge. There, as with serious research anywhere, dogged perseverance, careful analysis and steady effort yields results better and more surely than any other method.

If you repeat your questions about how to separate knowledge from pseudo-knowledge while at the same time pretending that you are talking about the knowledge of PMR instead of the knowledge of NPMR, most of the same obvious answers will apply. Science is science, in both PMR and NPMR. Scientific methodology has the same difficulties and attributes in both "places." The primary difference is that in NPMR (as viewed from PMR), science is a personal or **subjective** activity with **objective** results. This contrasts with PMR (as viewed from PMR), where science is a directly shareable objective activity that likewise produces objective results. For the record, NPMR science, as viewed from NPMR, is also a directly shareable objective activity that produces objective results.

This discussion will be continued in much greater detail, and from several different perspectives, at other places within the *My Big TOE* trilogy. In this aside, I simply want to point out there is no magic formula or short cut for finding and assessing truth. **Believing** what I say, or what anyone else says about NPMR or the nature of reality is tantamount to jumping to conclusions without doing the science or investigative work oneself.

Belief is not a shortcut that will actually take you to a significant destination. Believing what others say is a risky business. You must discover truth and knowledge for yourself or it will not be your truth or your knowledge. Your truth and knowledge lives deeply and vibrantly within your being while someone else's truth and knowledge can penetrate no deeper than your intellect.

Listening to others may greatly improve the efficiency of your journey, or send you off to wander aimlessly. In either case, you must make the trip and experience, assess, and validate the reality you find.

I do not wish to imply that you must accomplish everything by yourself. Including others on your journey to a greater understanding is generally a good idea. Interacting with others, if wisely chosen, can help you develop a broader perspective and provide much needed encouragement as well as guidance and direction. But others cannot learn and grow for you – you must do that for yourself. Wisdom, maturity, and the capacity to love are all personal attributes that dwell within the core of your being.

Some may be wondering how you go about collecting, evaluating, validating, and applying data in thought-space or how you can experience the reality of NPMR. These are good questions. I am talking about the subjective experiential data you gather while you carefully explore the realm of interactive consciousness within inner space. I am also talking about clear, objective, evidential results. At the boundary, where NPMR activities influence and modify PMR activities and vice versa, evidential data can be collected easily.

At this boundary, being aware in NPMR is somewhat like participating in a narrowly focused mental activity (somewhat like a totally absorbing interactive day dream) that has a strong causal (evidential) connection with PMR and a dynamic existence that is independent of you and your conscious or unconscious mental processes. Your mind must be calm, clear, and steady without unruly chatter or noise or you cannot differentiate between what your mind creates and what exists independently of your mind. That is why finding (and learning to exist and operate within) the calm unperturbed center of your consciousness is always the first step.

To a clear, low-noise, operative consciousness, collecting data in NPMR will be like moving through an unusually clear daydream. An exploring consciousness should initially busy itself doing experiments and looking for evidence of NPMR activity creating effects in PMR (and vice versa). One day, after enough hard evidence is gathered through personal experience, it will become clear that NPMR is both independent of you and causally connected to PMR. Realizing that fact will be your first, biggest, and most amazing discovery!

I still clearly recall my feelings of incredulous amazement when Dennis and I first began sharing identical simultaneous experiences while exploring NPMR (see Chapter 10 of this book). After consistently verifying the accuracy of remote viewing experiments and experiencing first hand the efficacy of dramatically affecting the health of a physical body with a focused mind, my reality was forced to broaden. As the paranormal becomes normal, one has no rational or logical option other than to seek a bigger picture that contains the whole of one's carefully evaluated evidential experience.

You can always assume that **other** people are lying or confused but when your own experience, consistently and on demand, carries you to a logically and scientifically inescapable conclusion, the truth of that experience will demand a larger and deeper understanding of the reality within which you exist. Simply labeling the paranormal as something experienced by the delusional, the diabolical, the weird, and the wacky will no longer provide an easy way out of dealing with the existence of a reality that flies in the face of your deepest beliefs and assumptions.

When the experience is yours, and the processes used to gain and evaluate that experience have been careful and scientific, you must deal with the **objective** facts of what you have discovered – denying them is to cling to ignorance and limitation out of habit, insecurity, and fear. To deny such experience is to give up difficult knowledge for the comfort of a mindless dogma.

Allowing ignorance and fear to define the possibilities eliminates opportunities for growth and squanders potential. That this is true is obvious when applied to others whose ignorance and disadvantage we understand, and nearly impossible to see in ourselves.

After the collection of evidential data (NPMR-PMR psi effects) becomes routine, one generally moves on to determine the culture, laws, and physics of NPMR by careful experimentation and observation of cause and effect. Imagine that you are an alien scientist from another dimension teleported to earth to learn what the earth, and its life-forms are like: exploring NPMR is like that, but without the limitation of a needy physical body. ◄

▶▶ Let's take a short break to define the word "psi." Psi is a familiar term among parapsychologists and others who are engaged in studying and exploring the capabilities of mind. Psi events generally refer to unusual artifacts of consciousness, specifically to paranormal events associated with mental abilities or altered states of consciousness. Psi is often used as a synonym for Parapsychological – thus the term "psi phenomena" refers to measurable physical phenomena that are produced by some characteristic or ability of mind that is presently beyond traditional scientific explanation. For example, telepathic communication, precognition, and remote viewing are a few commonly experienced and researched psi events. The terms "psi energy" and "psi forces" are often used to imply some unknown theoretical causal mechanism that is assumed to lie behind psi phenomena. ◄◄

▶ Because I exhort you at every turn to collect your own experience data, I suppose that I should tell you how to go about accomplishing that task. To this end, in Chapter 23 of this book, we will discuss techniques that you can use to reduce the mental noise, gain mastery and control of your mental energy, and begin exploring NPMR and the inner-space of consciousness.

However, before we get to that, it is imperative that you first discover how your beliefs limit your reality and learn to appreciate the difference between your knowledge and pseudo-knowledge. Otherwise your attempt to explore NPMR could end up exploring nothing more than your own ego.

Exploring your own ego might be a productive first step if it leads to a better understanding, and thus dissolution, of the fear and belief systems that limit your natural potential, but it is not at all the same as exploring NPMR – a reality that exists independently of your belief systems and personal mind.

There is a natural and necessary order to any developmental growth. Skipping steps almost always leads to frustration and blocks, not to rapid advancement. You must first deal successfully with your fear and limiting belief systems before you can productively explore NPMR. Conquering all fear is not required – far from it – but some minimum threshold of competence in managing your consciousness is a prerequisite.

The required basic competence is usually developed through meditation, courage, and an energetic dedication to the discovery of truth. The underlying principles and mechanics of meditation are discussed in Chapter 23 of this book. Though there are many ways to meditate successfully, fear can only be overcome by courage and determination.

I do not have a special weird science that can help you cut corners and find truth in giant leaps of intuition. Discovery and science are all about making steady progress by taking one small tentative step after another, all the while "tasting the pudding," checking the evidence, and producing **objective** measurable results. There are, as far as I know, no "worm holes" that let one tunnel through to enlightenment, or sign posts clearly defining the best route for each individual to take. The choice of path and the effort applied must be the result of your own volition.

Think deeply about how the material in this chapter applies to you – though it may get intellectually repetitive, this discussion of belief, fear, and knowledge represents a crucial step that must be assimilated at a level much deeper than the intellect. It is as difficult to over-emphasize the subject of fear, knowledge, and belief, as it is easy to speed through it intellectually without digging in too deeply. The concepts themselves are deceivingly simple and thus, repetition quickly becomes tedious. However, their implications for each and every individual are extremely difficult to grasp fully.

What fears lurk deeply hidden that push me this way, and pull me that way, like a small boat on an angry ocean? What beliefs limit my reality? What can I do about them? These are difficult and complex personal questions that many egos are all too eager to sidestep.

Typically, those who most need to answer these questions are also most likely to zip by without taking much notice. As these folks skim over the surface, they may find this chapter to be as tedious and annoying as a parental lecture. On the other hand, those who have little difficulty in this area will eagerly review the issues once again because they understand the importance, are not discomforted by the process, and do not fear the results. They too may notice the intended repetition, but will use it to improve their mastery rather than suffer through it. ◀

Everyone understands the terms cultural belief and religious belief, but some may be wondering what is meant by scientific belief and personal belief. Scientific belief is the belief that the larger reality and **all truth** must be solely defined by, and limited to, objective, repeatable-on-demand, consistent, PMR hard-science measurements. This is the narrow view of the scientific method cast as an exclusive PMR-only dogma. Though this belief holds true and is wonderfully productive for a certain subset of reality, it does not hold in a bigger picture that contains consciousness – much as classical mechanics fails in a bigger picture that contains very high velocities (which requires relativistic mechanics) and very small sizes (which requires quantum mechanics).

Personal belief encompasses all those things you believe about yourself and other people, places, or things – your apparent reality extrapolated beyond your certain knowledge. Personal beliefs, if not correct, are often distorted by hope, fear, guilt, need, desire, misinformation, and misunderstanding. Personal beliefs contain many personalized versions of your cultural beliefs as well. Many are derived from the beliefs of your parents, peers, and associates.

Cultural beliefs represent those beliefs that you assume true because everybody around you assumes they are true. Racism, for example, is an expression of a cultural belief. Belief in a universal objective physical causality or beliefs that conclude that telepathy, mental or faith healing, psychokinesis, or precognition are all totally impossible are also culturally derived.

Religious belief, on the other hand, is a belief in the creed, dogma, and articles of faith of some organized religion. Scientific belief is like religious belief. It is a belief in the creed (PMR causality rules all), dogma (only PMR exists), and articles of faith (the subjective contains no fact, only opinion) of "objective" Western science.

This discussion about belief traps is relevant to all belief – religious, scientific, personal, cultural, political, economic, and any other category you might conjure up. These categories of belief do not have distinct boundaries and, in many instances, overlap greatly. Some people associate belief primarily with religion and are unaware of the pervasive and significant role that belief plays outside the typical religious context. Neither I nor *My Big TOE* is particularly picking on religious belief. It is the characteristics and properties of belief itself, rather than any particular type of belief, which is being scrutinized in this chapter.

Sorting knowledge from belief is the function of science – both objective and subjective science. Knowing the difference between knowledge and belief relevant to any particular piece of **subjective** information is called wisdom. Knowing the difference between knowledge and belief relevant to any particular piece of **objective** information is to know the facts.

Many feel compelled to either believe or disbelieve all information they come in contact with and quickly pass a judgment on everything accordingly. Such a process leaves little room and little time for actual knowledge and shows no particular interest in truth. For these individuals, pseudo-knowledge is good enough, especially if it also happens to reduce anxiety and be widely accepted. This approach to information is unfortunate and produces a tendency to jump to conclusions based upon erroneous feel-good assumptions.

The result of understanding, appreciating, and accepting the limits of your knowledge is that you neither believe nor disbelieve much of the information that **initially** lies **beyond** your knowledge. Judgment should be suspended until **sufficient** data are collected. That method of approaching information is called open minded. The quality (rigor) of the conditions and processes that define "sufficient" is dependent upon how scientific your exploration is. Good science produces actual knowledge whereas bad science produces only pseudo-knowledge.

Knowledge, ignorance, truth, falsehood, good science, bad science, wisdom, foolishness, fact, fiction, open mindedness, and closed-mindedness almost always exist simultaneously in differing proportions as they pertain to developing (as in creating this trilogy) or evaluating (what you think of this trilogy) any piece or set of information. Rarely are knowledge and science perfect and pure. It is more a matter of degree and proportion. Perhaps all public thoughts, ideas and published papers need to be clearly marked by the Federal Knowledge and Belief Administration: "This concept contains 80% knowledge, 20% belief." An amusing thought with frightening overtones. Obviously, the only valid assessment is yours and you must make it as correctly as possible – the quality of your mind and being hangs in the balance.

You should **not** depend on experts, professionals, or anyone else to distinguish knowledge from belief for you – even if you trust them more than you trust yourself and are **willing to believe** what they say. Conversely, you can only discriminate between belief and knowledge for yourself, not for others. Think about it: How do you discriminate actual truth tellers from those who only believe they are telling the truth? Hint: Comparing their beliefs to your own is not the answer.

You should take responsibility for separating belief from knowledge for yourself (and only for yourself) because you will reap the rewards of being correct or suffer the consequences of being wrong. Herd instincts – going along with others who are themselves simply going along with others – are counterproductive. There is no safety in numbers with regard to discovering Big Truth. Failing with the majority provides no consolation because all successes or failures are personal. No one can drag you along to success by thinking or experiencing for you. On the other hand, you may allow others to retard your progress by not thinking for yourself.

It is true that to trust and assume the truth is often necessary at a mundane level and can be a useful shortcut in a world of ideas where we are time and experience limited. Nevertheless, you must be careful not to inadvertently absorb limitations on your mind's ability to expand or modify what you initially trust to be the truth. Be forever watchful for, and open to, new data. Do not block out or creatively reinterpret information that conflicts with your beliefs or what you desire or need the truth to be. Good science starts with honesty, and honesty is most easily applied in an ego-free and fear-free environment.

Belief is created when one who lacks scientifically evaluated knowledge puts faith in the premise that things actually are as he or she supposes them to be. Dogma is a fixed set of beliefs that must be accepted on faith in order to join the ranks of the believers who share that particular dogma. Dogma can be cultural, religious, scientific, or personal; it is an integral part of any category of belief. Knowledge that **appears** to be scientifically or objectively evaluated (to a given individual) may actually be incorrect. This is because we are not omniscient (our knowledge and data are limited), and because we each create our personal reality (objective and subjective) by **interpreting** our experience.

Belief and knowledge can be either false (incorrect) or true (correct). Both (in either state of correctness) can strongly motivate action. If you are presented with new information, new ideas, or new concepts that you think **may** possibly have merit, it is far better to maintain open minded skepticism while collecting your data on the subject (even if it takes a lifetime) than to jump to conclusion based on some previously held belief or by adding a new belief. Hold on to **all** the possibilities, old and new, until you have produced the knowledge that **correctly** evaluates the issues by means of direct experience. The important thing is: You need to get out there and collect the data. Laziness or fear of incompetence on this issue produces high-risk results and dramatically reduces the possibility of significant gain or progress.

The proof of correctness of any piece of knowledge lies only in the results its **application** produces. That is true of any knowledge (objective or subjective) offered up from any source about anything – including any astute cerebral gems that you may find in this Big TOE trilogy. If knowledge cannot be applied, or its application produces no practical results, that knowledge is, by definition, useless and irrelevant.

Before drawing your sword of truth and hacking away at pseudo-knowledge, let me remind you of something. If you cannot productively apply a particular piece of knowledge or a new concept, then that knowledge or concept **may** be pseudo-knowledge **or** you may be ignorant and basing your evaluation of that knowledge or concept upon belief or pseudo-knowledge. For advice on how to deal with this logical dilemma, re-read the aside at the beginning of this chapter.

Results can be objective, subjective, complex, obvious, abstract, or concrete but they must be real actual results – they must eventually produce

objectively measurable effects or changes by interacting with something that is real. **Knowledge is only as significant as its effects**. The proof of the pudding is in the eating – you will hear more about how to apply this results-oriented truth-testing concept in Sections 3 and 5. For now, it is enough to understand that "tasting the pudding" refers to testing the value of your experience, truth, or knowledge by evaluating the objective measurable results it produces. If what you consider to be truth cannot honestly produce objective measurable results, then remove it from the truth bin and put it back into the interesting possibilities bin. Continue collecting pertinent data and always maintain high scientific standards when evaluating results.

If the results are not clear and obvious to yourself and others, you are either shooting blanks or playing with a toy gun. You should always keep in mind that results need to be measurable and meaningful. Here, "meaningful" includes advancing your personal development, increasing the quality of your evolving consciousness, and improving the correctness and depth of your understanding.

Most of us are thoroughly dominated by beliefs, most of which lie outside of our intellectual awareness. How should we go about reexamining our beliefs? The proof of correctness of any belief lies in first removing the ignorance that necessitated the belief in the first place and replacing it with knowledge or open minded skepticism. Whenever sufficient knowledge has been accumulated to support logical scientific conclusions, apply that knowledge and observe the result. If the ignorance that defines the belief and upon which the necessity for the belief is based cannot be replaced by testable (or, using our pudding metaphor, tasteable) knowledge, then the belief simply remains a belief and its falseness and correctness remain unproven. No intelligent comment can be made either way and you should remain skeptical as well as open minded until enough data are collected to provide testable knowledge.

Beyond the edge of your knowledge and the outer boundary of your 3D PMR understanding lies your personal unknown. Some of the potential knowledge that remains unknown to you may appear to be beyond the theoretical reach of your knowing (mystical), and some may appear to be only a lack of information. In either case, you can leave the unknown alone, ignore it and accept it as the forever unknown, or you can probe it and explore it with the intent of eventually converting at least some of it into knowledge. Most people do a little bit of both, typically choosing a small part of the comfortable unknown to explore using objectivity and belief as tools and ignoring the rest. They pick the low hanging fruit and convince themselves that anything that isn't relatively easy to reach isn't worth the effort or the social risk.

Using subjective experience tightly coupled with objective results is not often explored because it is more difficult and because it is an individual rather than group experience. Those who cannot take a step without the reassurance of others are frightened away. These individuals erroneously believe that what remains naturally mystical to them is forever beyond their reach. The companion belief is that what remains naturally mystical **to them** is forever beyond **anyone's** reach. This soothing belief is manufactured to absolve themselves of the responsibility of mustering the courage and making the commitment to do the hard work required to turn the unknown into knowledge. Because of its absolving nature of this belief, it is held most passionately and is a great closer of minds.

Another serious error is to intellectually and emotionally deal with that naturally existing (what lies beyond your knowing) mysticism by assuming a dogmatic set of beliefs. Dogma and belief are straightjackets on the mind, blindfolds to the awareness, limitations on the thoughts you are capable of thinking and the understanding you can obtain. Dogma creates a small, usually incomplete and distorted perspective that cannot be expanded beyond the confines of the belief.

Let us look at disbelief for a moment. Disbelief typically represents a negative reaction to a competitive belief. Whether you **believe** something is true, or **believe** it is not true, you are using belief to smooth the discomfort of ignorance. Whether believing or disbelieving, the ignorance is shared. It is only the jumped to conclusions that are different. Most vocal non-believers and close-minded skeptics are as wrapped up in their beliefs as those they ridicule or disagree with. The main difference is that they are more apt to deny that their beliefs are beliefs.

The more you are **committed** to your belief, the more that belief appears to be knowledge and represents absolute truth. Pseudo-knowledge can be passionately held if it meets a powerful need or stems from a powerful fear. The relationship linking need, the discomfort of ignorance and fear, and the faux salve of ego is established in Section 3.

The statement, "I know that what you believe is untrue" most often expresses a conflict of differing beliefs and pseudo-knowledge, not a statement of truth. How can you tell which is which? Here is how most people tell. If **someone else** is saying those words ("I know that what you believe is untrue") to us, **they** obviously are suffering from delusionary pseudo-knowledge. On the other hand, if **we** are saying those words to someone else, it is again **they** who are obviously confusing pseudo-knowledge with knowledge. This is an easy rule to remember: If others agree with you, they possess real knowledge but if they disagree with you, they are afflicted with delusion and pseudo-knowledge.

If you want to stay in the mainstream and play it safe in the center of the well-beaten path, applying the above rule is the standard technique for discriminating real knowledge from pseudo-knowledge. What rule could be more simple or satisfying to apply? Other people are always the idiots!

The fact is, disagreement on Big Picture concepts is most often the result of a conflict of beliefs regardless of who is talking, pretending to listen, agreeing, or disagreeing. If you are to avoid jumping to conclusions in the absence of knowledge, you must maintain the state of open minded skepticism – there is no other reasonable or logical alternative. Anything else is a trap.

By now, you may be wondering if there is such a thing as good belief. I can best answer that question with another question. Is there such a thing as good ignorance – is there any situation where ignorance is better, more valuable, than knowledge? If there is, then wherever and whenever ignorance is best, that is where you will find a good belief. In the short term and in the little picture you might find some advantages to ignorance in a few special cases. Ignorance is perhaps not so bad if the problem is of little significance and of minimal importance, or one you can do nothing about. If you are trying to trick, use, or manipulate others to your advantage, **their** ignorance is always very helpful.

In the long run and in the Big Picture, if you are not trying to manipulate others and your ego is small, ignorance has little to no value. If the issues are significant, the stakes high, or the outcome important to you, then ignorance and belief will leave you vulnerable and looking like an ostrich with its head in the sand. In substantive matters of long term significance, there is no good belief.

The main use and function of belief or pseudo-knowledge is to deny the existence of ignorance, sugarcoat fear, and to manipulate others. Knowledge, on the other hand, provides you with the opportunity to optimize your given potential in any situation. A head in the sand may make you feel better in the near term, but it prevents you from going anywhere actually helpful or productive, and it lets your you-know-what stick out unprotected.

If what you happen to believe is Big Truth, you will be saved by the good luck of being born into the **correct culture**. A correct culture would necessarily, by definition, be composed almost entirely of impeccably wise individuals of stellar quality. Does that description resemble the culture in which you are immersed?

Because the quality of your being expresses the correctness of your understanding, it is easy to determine if you and the members of your culture or sub-culture (including those who share your religion, profession, association, gang, or neighborhood) are enlightened. Simply taste the pudding – look at the people around you. Look at the **average** people in **your** culture and look at yourself. If you primarily see goodness, wisdom, wholeness, and love everywhere, then your belief system needs no further adjustments and you are spared growing the quality of your consciousness in order to **appear** grown.

If that is, by some unfortunate circumstance, not your situation, or if you are more interested in actually being grown than in appearing to be grown, then temporarily suspend any limiting beliefs (that is to say **all** beliefs) at least long enough to ponder a few big thoughts. If you succeed, you will have greatly raised the probability that you will figure out how to improve the quality of your being.

Don't worry; these unusual concepts cannot stretch your mind beyond its elastic limit. Your mind has an almost unlimited capacity to take in, as well as shut out, new information and new relationships between pieces of information.

Some individuals believe that their belief systems are perfect – that their only problem is an imperfect implementation of those beliefs. No way! You are who you are. You absolutely reflect your **actual** beliefs completely and accurately. The quality of your being necessarily reflects the quality, the correctness, of your beliefs and understanding. Perhaps you don't know what your actual beliefs are (the real ones, not the intellectual ones you talk about). That is normal enough. Cultural, religious, scientific and personal beliefs can be extremely subtle and are often invisible to the individuals and to the members of the group that share them.

Religious, personal, and cultural truths are typically so ingrained and so obvious that they appear to define reality itself and thus are never called into question. Therein lies a major limitation of belief – when you believe that you have the right answers, there is no need to continue to seek truth or ask questions.

▶ People who continually question the obvious truth are annoying to those of us who know the answers. If we could only find an effective technique for reeducating the problem people who don't understand the **real** truth as we do, the planet would be a much better and safer place for everyone and everything. Gentle and kind terminations of the blatantly uneducable would clearly be justified and would go a long way toward making our world a better place for our children and future generations. We could ensure a continuing bright future for all by finally and effectively neutralizing the most undesirable and negative elements that are the root cause of all the trouble. God is counting on us to manifest his will. We will be the heroes of all future generations! Are you with me comrade?

If you found this book laying on top of the john in a public restroom or abandoned in an empty subway seat and opened it to this page, the previous paragraph was meant to be sarcastic. I have attempted to use a little generic religio-politico-historical humor to make a deadly serious point about the siren song sung to one's ego and fears (the bait), and the uncompromising iron jaws (peer pressure) of the belief trap – and the debilitating effect it can have on the common sense of **someone else.**

If **ego** (I must be right, my needs, opinion and beliefs define the truth), **fear** (of the unknown, being wrong, disapproval, imperfection, failure, God, or of the unholy enemy), and **peer pressure** (this is the way everybody else thinks, therefore it must be right, or at least safe) have influence or veto power over what thoughts you can honestly and seriously entertain, then you are caught in one or more belief traps – even if you don't want to terminate those degenerates who are screwing it up for the rest of us.

On the other hand, if one actually thinks it is a good idea to terminate the unredeemable degenerates among us, then such an individual is not only caught in a belief trap, but is potentially dangerous as well. Violent or forceful interdiction as a solution to a problem almost always produces the opposite of the effect intended; it usually makes the original problem much worse while greatly reducing the credibility of the forceful individual's viewpoint. ◀

Unfortunately, the wisdom and intended meaning of the ancient sages necessarily seem obscure from the viewpoint of those who share neither their culture nor their experience. Additionally, such wisdom and meaning are easily lost and twisted by the belief systems that others quickly establish around these individuals in order to express their ideas at the lowest and widest level of understanding. Furthermore, the self-serving concept of "holier than thou" often dilutes the significance of such knowledge further as a movement or ideology forms to codify and extend what is essentially an individual quality of understanding and being to a more marketable group-certification.

No group, regardless of how small or large, can possibly create and bestow experience-based understanding, integrity, and personal growth (the basis of wisdom) upon an individual. The individual must accomplish that. However, there are some things that groups and organizations **can** create and bestow – power, influence, wealth, and prestige come immediately to mind. These attributes, delegated primarily to the group's leadership, are created by recruiting and maintaining large numbers of members or supporters. The group's members find mutual support, approval, status, political power, and security.

The power of numbers is so compelling that groups spring up and are organized around every conceivable interest or idea that can support a viable membership. Large groups, movements, and organizations – from science to religion to professional societies to politics – often end up being about ego, power, money, prestige, and influence, regardless of what their original intentions were. Guilt, fear, intimidation, tradition, security, acceptance, identity, shared values, socialization, and acculturation become the tools of choice to grow, maintain, and strengthen the organization and its power.

In contrast, it is the **personal** science, philosophy, and quality of the **individual** that must supply the fire at the creative core of human existence. Only the individual can bring content, direction, quality, and value to the power of numbers. Though *My Big TOE* is about science, philosophy, and the general organization and mechanics of reality, it is simultaneously about you – the individual. You are a vitally important element of the Big Picture because your individual consciousness plays a key role at the core of reality.

20

■ ■ ■

Causality in Every Dimension can Potentially Transform a Mystic into a Scientist from Inner Space

■ ■ ■

Scientists often believe that everything must have an objective cause. This, as it turns out, is not a fair or reasonable expectation. It stretches the concept of our PMR causality beyond the bounded intellectual or logical region to which it applies. A more limited statement is: Everything that we can objectively understand from our PMR base of knowledge must have a cause. We can clearly agree with that one, fully understanding the limitations implied by "objectively understand from our PMR base of knowledge" which is based upon measurements made exclusively within PMR. From this viewpoint, it is only those things that we can assess from our limited PMR perspective that logically must have accessible causes. What is beyond PMR may seem mystical to us and can, within the causality of its own dimension, logically violate our 3D objective causality resulting in **measurable** PMR effects that we often label as paranormal. Paranormal essentially means acausal – beyond the normal cause and effect relationships defined by our limited PMR physical science. Once the limitations of PMR science are surmounted, what was once defined as paranormal becomes a normal part of a larger scientific understanding that answers to a higher (more general) level of causality.

▶ Does the concept of "beyond PMR" seem strange, unscientific, and reek of non-provable goofiness? If it does, you are probably in the majority. The assumption that nothing exists beyond PMR is a normal, self-fulfilling, self-perpetuating, illogical belief. I intend to examine this belief thoroughly over the next four sections of *My Big TOE* and provide a rational alternative that more fully, accurately, and consistently explains the available measured data. The unfolding of something as unusual and complex as this TOE must necessarily be slow and methodical – for this reason it may be a while yet before you can begin to see the Big Picture come into focus. If you can maintain an attitude of open minded skepticism until the end of Section 6, you will be in an excellent position to apply your own personal data and specific knowledge to verify the value of this model and develop accurate conclusions. Unfortunately, the paradigm busting and rebuilding process must necessarily introduce concepts that seem dubious and are initially incredibly difficult to fathom – it can appear no other way. ◀

Normal events and interactions within NPMR must take place within the constraints of a uniform causality. There is well-defined action and reaction – similar processes must consistently produce similar results for all experimenters. The major difference between the causality that is local to (and defines science in) NPMR and the causality that is local to (and defines science in) PMR is that within NPMR the range of possible causes is far less restricted. PMR and its causality is a subset of NPMR and its causality. The rules that govern NPMR physics and the interactions between NPMR beings are of a higher order (more general, less restrictive). Thus, NPMR can interact with PMR in ways that violate PMR's causality (such an interaction may produce paranormal activity from the viewpoint of PMR), yet maintain NPMR's own causality. Stepping up a level, beyond-NPMR also has its own unique causality and answers to a yet higher order of less restrictive rules. Similarly, beyond-NPMR can interact with NPMR in ways that violate NPMR's causality, but maintain beyond-NPMR's causality. And so on and so forth as each larger dimension of existence supports, and is a super-set of, the next one down.

▶ Eventually we will come to understand that whether a reality appears to be physical or nonphysical is relative to the observer. The property of being physical or nonphysical is simply the result of one's perspective and has no real significance of its own. For the time being, the concepts of PMR and NPMR provide a useful conceptualization of the larger reality from the perspective of a PMR resident who has experienced no other reality save the physical one in which he or she is now reading this book. ◀

From our viewpoint, PMR appears to be the final downhill stop for this inter-causal reality train (unless one counts the fictional *Flatland* as the next dimensional stop below us). The book *Flatland*, by E. A. Abbot, provides a wonderful understanding of the scientific, philosophic, and social difficulties involved in perceiving higher dimensions. Anyone can easily understand the limitations of the dimensions that exist **below** their normal perspective; at the same time, looking upstream reveals nothing but mystical confusion. Though *Flatland* deals only with geometric or spatial dimensions, the difficulties encountered in perceiving and understanding a dimensionality that is different from one's native perceptual construct are much the same.

▶ The second revised edition of the book *Flatland* was published in 1884 by E. A. Abbott and is currently available from Princeton University Press. The book describes, in a light-hearted and humorous manner, the fundamental technical, epistemological, social, and political difficulty in expanding your awareness of reality beyond the dimensionality of your physical perceptions. If you have not yet read this book, I strongly urge you to do so. It will help you understand how the apparent logic of your reality and the analytic quality of your thinking process is limited by the dimensionality you **believe** you live in – and, it is a hoot. *Flatland*, in its entirety, can be accessed on line at: **http://www.geom.umn.edu/~banchoff/ Flatland.** ◀

Perhaps beyond-NPMR is the outermost layer, or perhaps beyond-beyond-NPMR is outermost. I will describe and discuss both in great detail later, as well as explain what dimensionality actually is and how it is generated. Hold on to these thoughts. We will pick this discussion back up and continue to peel the reality onion after we have more thoroughly developed the conceptual foundation required to support the construction of a Big TOE.

Though I have not yet explained the origins and nature of dimensionality, it is not too early to discuss a few of its properties relative to causal hierarchies or reality subsystems. We see that beginnings belong to, and are governed by, the rules of causality of the next higher dimension. Each dimension of existence births and nurtures the child dimensions it spawns. A child can (but is not required to) become a parent. One parent can birth many children. Each child exists within their own dimension. Dimensionality is like your family tree, it has the property of breadth as well as depth. However, in this discussion we are only looking at depth – the creational hierarchy. From the perspective of the child, its birth (beginning) must appear mystical. To the parent, the process and circumstances of the child's birth are well understood and not the slightest bit mystical.

From the viewpoint of the child's own local objective causal system, the child's reality logically requires a mystical beginning. In other words, any system of objective causality is insulated from other causal systems by the

local logic through which it defines itself. Reality subsystems, each with their own local causality, can be likened to the software components and subroutines of a large complex simulation – all run interdependently within the same computer as long as they have self-consistent rule-sets to define their internal and external interactions. There may be relationships and interactions between causal systems, but comprehension and understanding normally flows in only one direction – from the superset to the subset. The subset does not have what it takes to understand the superset. To understand the superset, one must first become a member of it.

If you have read *Flatland*, it will be clear that the ordinary residents of a given reality can only observe and understand interactions within their own reality and the interactions of residents of realities that are more highly constrained than their own. Residents of a more constrained reality cannot comprehend a less constrained reality because it lies beyond the limits of their normal perception.

Each dimension of reality has its own rules that define its objective science. Additionally, each dimension of reality experiences the next higher (less limited) dimension as subjective and mystical. Consequently, your mysticism may be another's science: It depends on how big a picture you live and work in, and the degree to which constraints limit your perception. The perspective from the next higher dimension provides a bigger picture with a more complete understanding. This more comprehensive, complete, and less restrictive knowledge is only accessible to lower dimensional beings (those with a more constrained awareness) through the experience of their individual locally-subjective mind.

Consequently, a mystic could be a scientist from a higher dimension, or a delusional fool hopelessly caught in a distorted web of belief. How do you know which is which? A good question! We will go through the differentiating process in great detail in Section 3 (especially Chapter 14, Book 2). First, read *Flatland* to help you appreciate the problem of understanding higher dimensions. Second, carefully and scientifically gather your experience as you progress, step by step, along your path toward increasing the quality and capability of your mind, consciousness, or being. Then simply taste the pudding to separate the wise from the foolish. If you can't tell a high quality consciousness that is wise and loving from one that is not (you have uneducated taste buds and cannot correctly interpret your experience), repeat step two as often as necessary. To some extent, it takes one to know one, and you may need to develop (evolve) your consciousness before you get good at discrimination.

   The notion of local realities within separate dimensions and of a hierarchy of dimensional existences is probably a difficult concept to grasp. Have patience – the seed has been planted and later we will learn where these dimensions come from, what they mean, how they are created, and what love, wisdom, and physics could possibly have to do with any of it.

21

■ ■ ■
Cultural Bias
■ ■ ■

Objective causality is the fundamental philosophical underpinning of PMR science. It has been extremely useful to us in understanding and manipulating the material realm. Unfortunately, we PMR beings of limited comprehension have become so committed to our belief in a physical objective causality that we force everything into the PMR causality straight-jacket. Why do I love you? Why do I enjoy music? Why do fractal images look like natural landscapes? Why am I obsessed with frogs? There **must** be some good reason that falls within the PMR causality model. Even if there is no cause within PMR (my feelings and behavior simply erupted spontaneously, mystically, or from some interaction or association with a larger reality that constitutes a superset of PMR), reasons will be hypothesized and rationalized in order to make our PMR causal model appear inviolate (no doubt some unknown neurological or psychological function or dysfunction explains all but the fractals). Invoking the unknown to serve as a logical explanation for some difficult to understand event is not logical or even particularly rational in most circumstances.

▶ We routinely adjust our interpretation of events and our scientific theories to satisfy the dogmatic requirements of our beliefs. Theories that violate our cultural and scientific beliefs are preposterous by definition and are not taken seriously by the majority of scientists. Our beliefs set the boundaries and define the limits of our science — they always have and any reasonably accurate history of science will verify that fact. Most scientists, from pre-history to the present day, feel that though belief obviously blinded their forbearers, it does not seriously inhibit their own clear vision. As time passes, the belief-blindness of those who came before appears more and more ridiculous yet current belief blindness remains as invisible as ever. If you think that we of the modern world – we who have come so far in our understanding and knowledge – are no longer seriously and dramatically limited by our beliefs, you are mistaken.

Major conceptual breakthroughs in science and philosophy must always lie outside the solution space defined by what is generally accepted. If you wish to leap ahead, be prepared to transcend your present notions of reality and possibility and to rip old limiting beliefs and paradigms up by the roots.

Thinking that you can effectively live and work in the middle ground between bold leaps and dogmatic limitations is no more than a comforting delusion. **To get out of the box, you first must step over its edge** – an act too frightening and intimidating for most box dwellers who will always find plenty of good reasons why it is actually better to stay safely in the box. It is a mistake to let the fear of going from the frying pan into the fire prevent you from ever getting out of the frying pan. Open minded skepticism, careful science, and a willingness to work and learn can enable you to get out of the box (or frying pan) without getting hurt, burnt, or deluded. ◀

We **believe** there are always objective causes for every effect and every event whether we know what they are or not. Determining what those causes are and discovering their rules is what we call science. Given an effect, if we do not perceive an objective cause we believe that our science is simply incomplete. Our belief in the supremacy of our local causality will not allow us to consider there might not be an objective **local** cause – that the effect may have at least one component that lies beyond PMR objectivity. Such an effect would be called paranormal and would appear mystical when viewed from a PMR perspective. This possibility is immediately rejected because it conflicts with our cultural and scientific **beliefs** about reality.

The Western commitment to the universality of our **local** objective causality is a dogmatic (non-negotiable belief) attitude which is culturally ingrained at a deep level. As we have seen (Chapter 18 of this book), this belief **requires** our reality system to have a mystical beginning. At the same time, the Western cultural and scientific belief in universal objective causality condemns every effort to investigate that mystical beginning as irrational, illogical, and superstitious – an objective Catch 22. Science simultaneously logically demands and rationally denies a mystical beginning.

The problem is our belief that objective causality is universal (applies to all reality) instead of just local to PMR. When one sees the bigger picture and realizes that PMR is a subset of a larger reality, the logical and operational difficulty of our beginnings appearing to be mystical immediately disappears. Now our beginning is simply the result of a more general causality working within the rules of its own science – better yet, it is amenable to our analysis and open to our understanding **if** we can gain the perspective of that more general causality. Ahhh ha! A solution and a plan to effect that solution begins to emerge from the logical possibilities.

In other less technically focused cultures, what appears from the PMR perspective as mystical is not necessarily associated with, or defined as irrational, illogical, or unscientific. However, to most Western ears the phrase, "Assume the existence of an apparently infinite absolute unbounded oneness" sounds less credible than the phrase "assume the existence of a spherical chicken."

We have shown it to be logical that if there is such a thing as higher, more correct and complete knowledge that reflects the science of the "place" of our beginning or beyond, then it must necessarily appear mystical to us. We have also shown that such knowledge is only available to us through the expansion of our perspective into the next higher dimension of existence, where our origins are ordinary, mundane and well understood. Nevertheless, a material-based Western culture steadfastly labels mystical (from the PMR viewpoint) thought and experience as unsubstantiated useless blather that is beneath serious consideration because it cannot be understood within the purview of our limited (applies to PMR only) scientific method.

It is a goal of this Big TOE to take what appears to be mystical and beyond knowing, as seen from the PMR-only viewpoint, and, through the use of impeccable logic applied to two reasonable assumptions, turn it into hard science in broad daylight under your watchful and properly skeptical gaze.

A more general science is believed not to exist because it cannot be derived from a portion of science that limits itself exclusively to local, physical, objective phenomena. Do you see the logical inconsistency of this cultural belief? Is it clear that the self-referential circular argument that is primarily responsible for closing twentieth century minds to the possibility of a bigger picture is simply the result of being caught in a belief trap?

Such belief-based, circular, non-logic posing as obvious truth within Western cultures severely blinds and restricts the growth options of those who are caught in that particular trap. The only remaining logical possibility is that although there must have been a mystical beginning, now for some unknown reason, the substance and intent (force) behind that mystical event has disappeared leaving nothing else to exist beyond the local objective measurable reality. Do you find this a plausible, **objective** explanation, or does it seem more like limited thinking desperately trying to justify its limits? A logical possibility perhaps, but it leads to an irrational conclusion.

The intent and the implementing power behind our seemingly mystical origins must represent a source more capable and powerful and more fundamental in its existence in order to give birth to our local reality. Our parent reality must necessarily be operational at a higher (more general) level of existence or dimension. It must necessarily represent a superset to which our local physical reality belongs. Assuming that this creative source has somehow disappeared is like the ice-cubes in my automatic ice-maker bucket believing that the compressor responsible for their freezing must have stopped working years ago. Those delusional ice-cubes obviously do not understand the bigger picture.

Does it seem likely that this higher level creative force, for unknown reasons, just dried up and blew away, leaving us to exist alone like deserted orphans? That premise assumes we could exist independently from our initiating source. As it turns out, our source is both initiating and sustaining – we cannot exist independently from it any more than our internal organs can exist independently from our body. Does this assumption (the source of our mystical beginning no longer exists) appear to be the result of scientific analysis – or does it seem more like one of those mystical beliefs that are considered credible because they support the accepted individual, cultural, and scientific dogma? Popular pseudo-wisdom says if we (our individual selves, our culture, and our science), with our impressive understanding and knowledge do not understand it, cannot clearly grasp it much less measure it, then it must not and cannot exist. Does this appear to you to be a scientific conclusion, or the expression of a little picture belief?

Coming to the logical and rational conclusion that a larger reality within a bigger picture could **possibly** exist beyond the confines of our present physical reality defines what I have called open minded skepticism. Simply allowing this possibility (regardless of how remote you might **believe** it to be) and having the gumption and commitment to explore that possibility honestly and scientifically is all that is necessary to grow your Big TOE – a **personal** Big TOE that has the ability to accelerate the evolution of your consciousness.

I have mentioned the terms personal growth, consciousness evolution, and improving the quality of consciousness several times without defining what they mean. These presently vague terms will be precisely defined after we have more fully developed the conceptual basis required to support their meaning.

Should you expect our collective mystical (only from the view of PMR) origin, which is necessarily initiated and sustained from a higher level of organization and a higher dimensional existence, to be obvious, easy to understand, and just like us? Do our machines, computers, pets, designer viruses, intestinal bacteria, and internal organs have a difficult time understanding human experience and motivation within the context of their existence? They cannot begin to comprehend anything but a shallow one-dimensional sense of us. The knowledge, understanding, and intents that animate our actions and fuel our seemingly awesome power are unfathomable to them.

If the understanding of the larger reality that contains our beginning is so difficult and beyond the tools of our objective science, is it any wonder that many people, having seen a fleeting glimpse of Big Truth (derived from their own experience or, more commonly, delivered to them by others), have anthropomorphized all manner of beliefs and gods to fill the void created by ignorance and fear?

▶ Deep ignorance and deep fear produces a long and varied list. Sun gods, Tree gods, Moon gods, Fire gods, River gods, War gods, Fertility gods, Tribal gods, Ocean gods, Storm gods, Animal gods, even Booze, Sex, and Party gods (Bacchus) – to mention just a few of the probably thousands of gods people have conjured up for their own needs, in their own image, or in the image of their fear. What else would account for the myriad of false gods that other people believe in?

Do you realize that people from every religion of the world will agree with the preceding sentence! Wow! Question? Does unanimous agreement from such a contentious group constitute a miracle? ◀

Left with a total unknowing of something so fundamental and important as the circumstances of their beginning, the nature of their reality and purpose, we can forgive other people for anthropomorphically projecting what they did know into a plausible (to them, at the time) answer. That is a typically human, if not rational, response. Unfortunately, it also sets the stage for much mischief, agony, guilt, intolerance, fear, confusion, and violence.

Undeniably, a little knowledge can be a dangerous thing. That is particularly true of knowledge gained from others when the recipients do not have the personal quality to have derived that knowledge on their own, thus guaranteeing that misunderstandings will occur and that it will be impossible for the recipients to make distinctions between knowledge and pseudo-knowledge. In matters of Big Truth, you cannot teach, much less force, someone to get it.

As a teacher, it is better to wait until your students are ready than to push Big Truth into an apparent position of mystical misconception within their minds. As a student, it is better to wait until you are ready (have grown up enough) to understand Big Truth at a profound level than to leap headlong into a belief trap, thinking that you have taken a short cut to knowledge and wisdom. You cannot access understanding and wisdom that is beyond what the quality of your consciousness can naturally support. Every individuated unit of consciousness must develop in its own unique way, powered by the free will that drives its intent.

Given an **important** question in any dear-to-the-heart subject, it seems that humankind (this is true for individuals as well as groups and cultures) vastly prefers any plausible (at the time) answer, even if it is likely to be wrong, to no answer at all. When knowing seems to be important, the only thing worse than a wrong answer is no answer. It is far easier and more rewarding in the short term to calm anxiety with pseudo-knowledge than to face ignorance with open minded skepticism. Unfortunately, growth over the long term, which is what is important, is severely stunted by an almost universal preference for the short term feel-good solution.

If faced with no answer to an important question about almost anything, we humans tend to make up an answer that suits our emotional and intellectual needs and then believe in it with a force of conviction that is equal to the power of the original need. That is how we humans are – fearful of what we do not know or understand – ill at ease with not knowing, uncomfortable with uncertainty. This is why open minded skepticism, as an approach to learning and growth, is rarely implemented. Though open minded skepticism is obviously and logically the most correct, beneficial, and productive approach to evaluating new ideas and experiences, it does not provide the immediate closure and false confidence of a believed in conclusion – and it requires further work. Jumping to conclusions, particularly if they are widely held and therefore a socially safe short jump, is much easier and immediately more satisfying than doing the long difficult work of honest scientific research.

It is these tightly held beliefs, fantasies, and delusions of convenience that drive the day-to-day behavior (dysfunctional and functional) of most of us. There is almost nothing more important to us than our fantasies or beliefs. Beliefs appear to make life easier, less work, and happier, at least in the short run. Without them we must face our ignorance, our uncertainty, our inadequacy, and our fear – anything is better than that. The unfortunate fact is that in the long run, from the perspective of the bigger picture, beliefs and fantasies almost always have an effect that is opposite to what is intended. The process of denying a fear generally causes what is feared to manifest in your reality.

The richness, importance, and meaningfulness of our **subjective** existence directly conflicts with the notion that if you cannot measure or **physically** experience it, it is either non-existent or irrelevant. Likewise, the abundance of reputable scientifically collected data documenting paranormal happenings also flies in the face of our limited reality. Given the accepted scientific facts of wave particle duality, paradoxical entangled particle pairs that instantaneously communicate, and statistically based material existence, modern physics itself is pushing the notion of our cherished objective reality into the subjective mind-space of the experimenter.

If you are thinking that "subjective" and "rational" are mutually exclusive concepts and wondering what reputable data or modern physics I could possibly be referring to, it might indicate you need to assess your beliefs (spot the traps), open up, look around, and get out (of the box) more often. Credible information speaking to these issues is out there by the basketful and not difficult to find.

▶ Examples of reputable data are available in *Mind-Reach – Scientists Look at Psychic Ability* by Russel Targ and Harold Puthoff, Delacorte Press, 1977 and *The Conscious Universe: The Scientific Truth of Psychic Phenomena,* by Dean I. Radin; Harper Collins, 1997.

As far as modern physics goes, an excellent **non-mathematical** description of the theories of relativity and quantum mechanics written especially for the non-scientist is *The Evolution of Physics* by Albert Einstein and Leopold Infeld, published by Simon and Schuster in 1961.

These are only a few of a large selection of books that you might use as a starting point in broadening your knowledge of the boundary between physics and metaphysics. From these books, you will learn that the material reality that you think you live in is actually much stranger than you ever imagined. You will also gain an appreciation of how little science actually knows about the fundamental characteristics and properties of reality. The one thing that most modern physicists agree on these days is that what we generally take for our local 3D time ordered causal reality is merely a perceptual illusion. Some sixty years after quantum physics destroyed the widely accepted material foundation of physical reality, what lies behind this persistent perceptual illusion remains as mysterious as ever to a traditional science trapped in the little picture by limiting beliefs. ◀

The reality paradigm is shifting under our cultural feet. East and West, North and South, are increasingly exchanging information and inextricably intermingling their cultural and philosophic values as information and communication technologies continue to link and integrate the mind-space of our planet. This is an especially propitious time to ponder these issues and to figure out what is real, productive, and non-delusional.

It will be important to maintain solidity and balance as the cultural ground shifts and shakes beneath you. It is also important to filter out the truth from the inevitable cacophony of conflicting concepts to which everyone is about to be exposed in the coming cultural implosion (a spin-off of the information-computer-networking revolution). To achieve the most efficient personal evolution and growth, you must find an optimal synthesis of the available concepts and then add to or customize this information to suit yourself. Having a correct and comprehensive Big TOE has never been more timely or important to your future growth than it is right now at the dawn of the Information Age.

That some individuals refuse to make any effort to explore subjective truth says something about those individuals and the limiting power of their belief systems. Those who seriously take up the challenge of exploring reality and growing their awareness rarely come home empty handed. They inevitably find a greater reality beyond objective PMR, and it is almost always worth far more to them than the considerable effort required to access it.

Again, the proof of the usefulness and quality of any pudding you cook up is in the tasting, evaluating, experiencing, and sharing the results of that particular batch of pudding. You can start anywhere. Be skeptical, be open minded, and demand measurable objective results after a reasonable effort. If there are no obvious measurable results, try a different recipe. Assess the results, adjust the recipe, and go make some more, slightly better, pudding. Repeat the cycle continually. Before long, you will be winning prizes at the county fair for the quality of your consciousness.

It is important to be aware of how your cultural biases and beliefs can severely limit the scope (breadth, depth, and quality) of the thoughts you are able to think, as well as the size of the picture you are able to comprehend. The struggle to reach beyond a belief-limited perspective is usually immensely difficult and only determined and serious explorers doggedly pursuing the truth down whatever path it takes are likely to be successful. Unfortunately, the belief-limited blindfold we all wear feels so natural and is so obviously correct, deeply ingrained, and widely held that we are not aware of it, and may vehemently deny it exists.

A **belief** that PMR is "all there is" is extremely limiting and makes some very important and interesting questions absolutely impossible to answer without invoking additional limiting belief systems. The argument between science and belief – a more general version of the argument between science and religion – is a self-energizing, endless loop of non-logic bouncing uselessly in endless debate back and forth from one limiting belief system to another. The illogical excesses of each create the rational necessity for the other. These arguments violate the Rule of Rationality by forming a perpetual wasted motion machine within a logical black hole! Campbell's Third Law of No Motion (otherwise known as the law of inaction-reaction) accurately describes these arguments: For every irrational rationalization there exists an equal but opposite irrational rationalization.

Certainly, most religions do not **believe** that PMR is all there is, and religion, as well as science, is a significant part of our cultural heritage. Nonetheless, the organization and codification of mysticism into various religious doctrines and dogmas is of little value. That we as a culture permit a limited and narrowly focused mysticism (various religious dogmas) to coexist and blend with our scientific dogma serves only to confuse, distort, and restrict our ability to deal with the real issue of consciousness quality.

Science and religion, each in their own way, preach the gospel of hope and promise deliverance to the Promised Land of good and plenty. However, as a general rule, neither provides a significant boost to the inner quality of an individual's life. The quality of your consciousness must grow as an independently evolving entity in the shadow of both. Consciousness quality is a personal achievement that can only be developed by an individual – it is not a group endeavor. It has absolutely nothing to do with creed, dogma, or belief. An individual's quality cannot be increased one single iota by any belief, or by accumulating information about anything, or by doing good deeds that are not properly motivated, or by talking to others or reading books.

Again, I seek your indulgence – horses must remain in front of carts and an orderly process takes time to unfurl. The concept of consciousness quality and its relationship to spiritual quality will firm up later when it is more precisely described and given a technical definition. In the mean time, let me say this: Spiritual growth, personal growth, improving the quality of your consciousness, evolving your being, increasing your capacity to love, and decreasing the entropy of your consciousness are all essentially synonymous and equivalent. Many readers have a good idea (or at least think they do) about what these terms mean, but there are some who are not at all sure, and some of those are now becoming a little worried.

This is as it should be – properly skeptical minds need logical clarity. Establishing logical scientific connections that interrelate physics, spirituality, consciousness, and love is not as goofy or impossible as it appears – in fact it is something that a comprehensive Big TOE must necessarily accomplish. Hang in there with me – these ideas are more logical and rational, than you might guess.

Do not misunderstand me. I am not denigrating the potential spiritual quality that can be found within religion by **individual** seekers of truth. When I use the word "religion" here, I am speaking only of institutionalized dogma or organized religion, which represents how the great majority of people are connected to religion. **There are individuals and organizations that flourish outside of this generality** and it is highly likely that you count yourself and your associations to be among them.

Is it not a simple fact that other people are usually the ones who don't get it, and that the phrase "great majority of people" usually does not include you? Do you not find it logically intriguing that the great majority of people feel rather strongly that they cannot be grouped with the great majority of people? We humans are generally as aware of our individuality as we are blind to our conformity – that is our nature. The unquestionable truth of the bold sentence above should give other people a logical loophole big enough to squeeze through in order to get back into their personal comfort zone.

There are those few who after subtracting organization, socialization, status, tradition, habit, dogma, creed, ritual, and belief from their religion still have something left over that is very significant. For these people, religion is a personal spiritual experience that enables them to evolve the quality of their consciousness as effectively as any other spiritual path. That they choose to integrate this honest spiritual experience within some traditional religious setting merely represents the individual path they have chosen – there is no **intrinsic** benefit or penalty in doing so. All paths have benefits and challenges.

Contrary to popular belief, I do **not** condemn belief and dogma as useless and harmful merely because they are illogical and unnecessary. Much of what we do every day – particularly our habitual activities – is illogical and unnecessary. Inefficiency is not a crime; if it were, we would all be in jail. Condemnation typically flows from arrogance and is not likely to be part of a helpful process nor is it likely to be a good technique for fostering understanding or improving communication. This trilogy is about being helpful, improving understanding, and reducing ego and arrogance.

Be careful not to jump to conclusions. I welcome you to walk your dogma in my neighborhood as long as you clean up after it and keep it under control. Don't let it bite, harass, or intimidate anyone. Make sure it does not dig in our gardens, kill our flowers, bushes, or children, or leave piles of poop in our yards. Finally, do not allow it to terrorize or bully the many vulnerable critters and beings that peacefully live and play in the surrounding environment. If you are a responsible owner of a friendly dogma, you and your dogma are welcome in my neighborhood anytime.

It is possible, though exceedingly unusual, for an individual to lose ego and gain consciousness quality in pursuit of a favorite dogma. For most of us, dogma erects barriers on our path to personal growth, distracts us from what is truly important, confuses our sense of what is right and wrong, arbitrarily limits our reality by snagging us in belief traps, and tends to make us more egocentric, arrogant, and self-righteous. We readily embrace dogma because it soothes our fearful ignorance with a comforting salve of easy to obtain pseudo-knowledge, and because its downside always falls outside our awareness. However, there are a few who outwardly appear to be in pursuit of dogma because of their habits of ritual and association, yet inwardly they have grown beyond its limitations. For these individuals, the dogma (along with any associated ritual) becomes a familiar pattern of doing that is similar in function to a meditation mantra.

▶ Offering either science or religion to one in dire need (as is everyone) of internal substance is like giving a starving person a rubber chicken. It looks good and he immediately feels better. Now filled with hope and confidence, he chews and chews and chews but continues to get thinner and thinner all the same. If his preoccupation with, and his belief in, the nutritional value of the rubber chicken prevents him from procuring real food, the situation becomes worse.

That some real food may be securely hidden within the rubber chicken only makes the situation more pathetic (he can smell it, but doesn't know how to get access to it). The hungrier the man gets, the more he becomes fixated on the rubber chicken, and the less capable he is of eventually figuring out the puzzle. He eventually dies of starvation, forever grateful to the Great Benevolence that provided him the precious gift of hope in the form of a wonderful rubber chicken. ◀

We are, it seems, like the citizens of Flatland (two-dimensional imaginary beings) who can not understand the connection between solid geometry and their stomachs. They had to go inside (through) themselves to begin, what was for them, a mystical and metaphysical journey toward an understanding of the third dimension. We need to make a similar journey to understand the larger reality. They had to transcend their beliefs which were born out of their objective experience within their local reality and limited causal system. We need to do the same. They found the reality of the third dimension through subjective experience combined with careful scientific reasoning – not by dedication to dogma (old or new, religious, cultural, scientific, or personal). We need to do the same.

Some things cannot be comprehended from, or conversely, translated to, the perspective with which we beings, seemingly trapped in this Physical Matter Reality, have to work. If this journey to understand reality appears mystical and metaphysical to us, that is an artifact of our perceptual limitations and small space-time perspective, not a condemnation of the realness of our vision. Solid geometry and the third dimension are real even though they exist beyond the comprehension of belief-limited Flatlanders stuck in their local objective causality.

Our ignorance does not impose limits on the larger reality – only upon our understanding of it.

22

The Right Attitude

Significant personal benefit can be gained simply by developing an explorer's attitude. You must be courageous and open minded enough to contemplate the unknown and then step into it (experience it) to find out for yourself. There is no other way. Your experience, your time, your effort, and your mind compose your only doorway to an understanding that is not belief-based. A belief-based understanding is only slightly better than no understanding at all if, and only if, what you believe turns out serendipitously to be true. Do you think the correct belief system can get you to the finish line without running the race? Unfortunately, it cannot – even if your belief turns out to be true.

Some people believe that they do not have the time, energy, or ability, to gain consciousness quality on their own. They think that if they find the right religion, organization, book, teacher, guru, or advisor, they can minimize the effort required to develop their personal experience of Big Truth because the teacher will explain what is true and they will simply believe it. Do you think this strategy will work? No, it cannot! You cannot believe your way into consciousness quality any more than you can believe your way into being a master violinist, sumo wrestler, or the president of your country. There is yet another problem. You obviously must choose whom to believe very wisely. How can you do that without great wisdom of your own? Though knowledge can be passed from person to person, wisdom is derived only through your personal experience and is non-transferable from others.

You need to **be wise** to choose the belief system that can make you **appear to be wise** so that you do not have to earn wisdom through experience and actually **become** wise. There are no shortcuts. You must develop the quality of your being through your personal experience. Attaining wisdom, choosing paths to spiritual growth, improving the quality of consciousness, discerning pseudo-knowledge from actual knowledge and discriminating good teachers from bad teachers will all be discussed in more depth in Chapters 13 and 14 of Book 2.

Your beliefs (cultural, religious, personal, or scientific) are for the most part not relevant to the quality of your consciousness, except that they may retard it by limiting what your mind can think. Evolution is not a matter of passing an exam. It is a matter of how you are, the quality of your being, not what you believe. Beliefs don't often, if ever, translate into quality of being; they are only about using pseudo-knowledge to fill in for unavailable (or difficult to obtain) real knowledge. You can talk **about it**, know **about it**, and believe anything you want to **about it** for free, but you can't **be it** without **paying** the price (extensive diligent experience generated from rigorous dedicated effort). That is true of a pro football player, a brain surgeon, a nuclear physicist, a master carpenter, a sumo wrestler, or a concert violinist – as well as a spiritually evolved being. No pain, no gain.

There is no free lunch. You either pay the price or forgo the benefits. Because the benefit is the growth and evolution of your consciousness, forgoing it would not be a wise choice. Why? Who cares? What is the cost of an opportunity lost? We will discuss that later. Let me say for now that the costs are severe and once incurred cannot be sidestepped – but its effects **are** reversible. The costs should not be construed as a punishment; they are merely the logical result of not evolving.

For those who are wondering what evolution, belief traps, and consciousness quality could possibly have to do with deriving a more comprehensive physics, be patient and the connections will eventually become clear. First we must develop the conceptual landscape more broadly and in more detail before PMR physics can logically be birthed from a more general level of causality.

I do not want to leave anyone with the impression that spiritual growth (improving the quality and thus decreasing the entropy of your consciousness) is like working in a salt mine. Besides being useful, spiritual growth is also thrilling, interesting, rewarding, fun, and joyful. Once begun, it is so exciting an adventure that you will gladly want to put more of your time and energy toward it. It is also practical: Increasing the quality of your consciousness immediately increases the quality of your life.

23

Who Ya Gonna Call?

True enough, in matters of evolution there is no free lunch. Nevertheless, contemplating and evaluating the ideas of others can be an immensely helpful **aid** to your progress, and to your effort to grow the quality of your consciousness. You do not need to figure everything out for yourself. The advice of others can be like having a map to guide your explorations. An incorrect map can send you off on a wild goose chase. You must evaluate the correctness of the map **as you go** – because, **before** you go, you can only guess and assume your way through a shallow evaluation of any map. A useful map must necessarily be somewhat general, whereas each journey must be individual and personal.

Before going on to the wholly new concepts of the next chapter, let's first pull together what we have learned about the origins and consequences of belief and the requirements of personal growth so that those who are so inclined can get started on developing the experience base you will need to construct your personal Big TOE or, at least, evaluate this one.

In the preceding chapter we determined that you must do your own exploring and grow your own wisdom. You cannot progress by letting others do the work. To believe what someone else (including me) tells you (to become a believer) is lazy, risky, and amounts to accepting **someone else's** belief or knowledge in place of **your** knowledge. Copying the behavior or beliefs of others, or reciting or memorizing their knowledge, cannot produce **significant** spiritual or personal growth for **you**. Although some guidance by a fellow explorer may help you better understand your challenges and choices, discovering Big Truth and increasing the quality of your consciousness is fundamentally an independent individual effort. Talking about it all day and all night with the greatest of gurus won't produce one iota of real progress. Your lasting progress must be the result of your personal effort.

Personal growth is most efficiently and effectively the product of good science. This is subjective science or personal science, not to be confused with either organized or personal religion or objective science. Subjective science is the mother of objective science. Real personal science requires real, verifiable, measurable, **objective results**. Here, the word "results," at the most basic level, refers to significant, continuing verifiable progress toward the improvement of the quality of your conscious being, the evolution of mind, the growing-up and maturing of spirit. Why? Because that is the nature of the reality we live in. You will see that the physical nature as well as the spiritual nature of our reality is straightforwardly derived from the natural process of consciousness evolution. By the end of the next two sections, science will have logically derived the origins, nature, purpose, and mechanics of both spirituality (increasing consciousness quality through evolution) and your physical world.

You will eventually discover that our reality is fundamentally nonphysical (from a PMR perspective) and is animated and driven by profitability toward states of lower entropy. If your efforts do not produce measurable, significant growth, your personal science is only illusory. The knowledge gained through personal science continually and dramatically modifies itself as it **grows and changes**. On the other hand, cultural, personal, religious, or scientific belief systems require only a sincere **belief** in the assumed truth of their associated dogma, doctrine, and creed.

A belief system requires faith in the correctness of its beliefs. Because correctness is simply assumed, actual results are not required (correctness cannot be objectively demonstrated – that is the nature of belief). Mature and stable belief systems, including those generated by cultural, scientific and religious belief, once in place, do not tend to change. There is a logical disincentive to modify significantly what is, **by definition**, assumed to be complete and perfect. In contrast, the knowledge gained from mature personal scientific experience is always in continual flux. Open minded skepticism and continual scientific exploration for new data make sure of that. The search for truth is, by its nature, in a constant state of discovery, refinement, assessment, and reassessment because new data continue to pour in as long as the individual is aware and interested in growth.

Honest truth seekers never become know-it-alls – there is always room to improve your self as well as your knowledge. When you know it all, when you believe that you have all the answers, you have, in fact, lost it all – nothing remains but a hollow shell.

You do not need any particular belief, disbelief, or faith to motivate you to start on this journey. You need only to grasp the **possibility** of a greater reality of some sort. After that, the desire to discover the truth should be motivation enough. Additionally, if this just-perhaps-possible larger reality is also **potentially** very important and significant to your life and being, nothing should hold you back from expending the necessary energy to explore the truth of the matter for yourself.

You can and should learn from others to the greatest extent possible, but you must grow yourself. Learning from those who have gone before can speed your progress; however, choosing those that you think you can best learn from is an iterative process that must constantly be reevaluated in light of your experience and your results. Those who can be most helpful, at any given time of your life, will change as you and your situation changes.

Do not get stuck in patterns, habits, or rituals. Do not look to groups or organizations to tell you what to do. Do not fall into belief traps. Have confidence in yourself. You not only **can** do it yourself, but you **must** do it yourself eventually, quickly or slowly, easily or with great struggle. We are all constantly evolving our consciousness. Evolution **forces** choice and change. Remaining the same by choosing the no action option is not possible. Change cannot be avoided. Change can take place as either positive growth or negative deterioration; the individual choices you make ultimately determine the direction (positive or negative) of your growth.

A good teacher provides encouragement, makes the learning experience more intense and more concentrated, and gives the student an **opportunity** to learn more quickly. Unfortunately, the more you need a good teacher, the less likely you are to be able to tell a good one from a bad one.

A good teacher focuses your effort to speed up your progress; a bad one misdirects your efforts and inhibits progress. Always stay skeptical, open minded and belief free, and most of all, taste that pudding – continue to require and evaluate actual measurable results. If six months go by with no **obvious measurable results**, this indicates that you need to buckle down and get serious, or change your approach.

Results, results, results, results. Actual, clear, un-subtle, measurable results – that is how you must evaluate the efficacy of your process. Intellectual knowledge and intellectual results are **not** the results I am referring to. These are no substitute for the real results of a growing, changing being. **Knowing about it** can be interesting and helpful, but it should never be confused with **being it**.

A change in the quality of your being, growth in the quality of your consciousness, evolution of your spirit: these are the results I am talking about – results of the being, not results of the intellect. It is about who you are, not what you know. It is about **why** you do what you do, not what you say, or what you do. When you start intending, doing, and being differently, you will produce measurable results. The tests you must pass are not written ones. Great factual knowledge cannot help you pass a test of the quality of your being. You are who and what you are – **and it shows** – no matter how good you might be at controlling your behavior with your intellect.

Truth is absolute, but how to discover it, and express it within your being, must be personal. Develop your tentative road map by applying open minded skepticism to the experience and conjecture (theory) of others. Then **modify** that map as **you** collect **your** data. This makes good sense, and offers you the **possibility** of leveraging the accumulated knowledge and wisdom of others as you define your unique growth path. Adopting a set of beliefs is a comparatively unproductive and risky approach to the evolution of your being and the quality of your consciousness.

How do you go about increasing the quality of your consciousness? How do you purposely pursue the evolution of your spirit? If dogma, ritual, and intellectual or emotional group-gropes are out, how do you get from here to there on your own?

For the scientists who are wondering what consciousness and all this blather about spirituality has to do with physics, let me assure you that I have not lost my focus and that this discussion is directly on the path to a scientifically legitimate, more general theory of physics. However, we are now, and will be for some time, developing the necessary basic concepts required to construct this Big TOE. Because this is a Big TOE and not a little TOE, a larger perspective supported by several wholly new paradigms must be developed. This process may appear, from time to time, to wander through irrelevant, ridiculous, or far-out ideological territory but if you can maintain open minded skepticism through the end of Section 6, you will eventually understand these unusual connections and their significance to science.

Because this is science and not theology, let me digress in the following aside on the process of getting from here (wherever you happen to be) to there (an increased quality of consciousness). The journey to higher quality consciousness is more simple and straightforward than you might think. I cannot promise easy and quick, but I can promise easy-to-do techniques and exercises that are simple and effective. For some it will be as easy as learning to swim, for others progress may come slowly; nevertheless, all can succeed superbly if the desire to do so and the requisite courage are sufficient.

▶ Because improving the quality of your consciousness (spiritual growth) is not, and cannot be, an intellectual achievement, it makes little difference how you intellectually approach the initiation of such improvements. **How** you start or what you **do** to improve the quality of your consciousness is insignificant compared to the act of starting. Additionally, an improvement in the quality of your being does not **automatically** flow from any external activity or practice. All you need is the will and the insuppressible drive (energy) to grow your being and the path, the process, to do so will appear before you. You are surrounded by opportunity to grow; your optimal path starts from wherever you are. I am talking about changing your being, intent, motivation, and attitude; modifying the quality of your interactions with others – changes in behavior and action (what you do) are secondary (results, not causes) and will follow on their own. Primary changes, when significant, are clear, obvious, and measurable to you and to others.

The evolution of consciousness is an extremely difficult concept for the Western mind to grasp because we are exclusively focused on the materially productive fact that right results are the products of right action. Westerners want to know what action they should take to get the results they want. Because they deal almost exclusively with external actions designed to produce external results they do not appreciate that internal results follow a different logic. What you are presently doing, how you live your life from day to day, is probably good enough as it is – what you need to change or improve is **why** you are doing it. When the "why" – the motivation and intent of what you do – is right, the "what" will take care of itself. Improving the "why" can start anywhere any time because it requires modifying internal variables, not external variables; nothing must change but you.

You can hope and pray for someone else to provide you with enlightenment (trust me, that won't happen), or you can take the steps to develop and grow it. Do not expect to find shortcuts through the flypaper realms of religious, scientific, or personal dogma, or along the midway of a New Age carnival. You must keep your mind free to change and grow. The right question is: How has the fundamental quality of your being changed. The answer to that question defines the metric of your progress. Self-proclaimed success means nothing; progress must be demonstrated by clear and obvious results.

The answer to how the fundamental quality of your being has changed is either totally obvious to everyone (including yourself), or not much progress has been accumulated. Genuine results are not subtle. You and most other people, given enough time with an individual, have the capability to tell the difference between a wise and loving being and one that is only trying to appear that way. This is not rocket science; it is not difficult to determine if you are making real progress. A significant change in your capacity to love is as subtle as the healing of a badly broken leg – nobody, including you, could miss noticing the change.

Are you like a deer caught in the headlights of an oncoming car – frozen, unable to take the first step? Because of our cultural belief that we must **do** something in PMR in order to affect change (even if that change is within our consciousness), most people are effectively paralyzed and cannot take that first step. "What should I **do**? Where should I start?" they ask, looking for a prescription or set of clearly directed "how to" steps. Improving the quality of your consciousness, energizing spiritual growth, and gaining a Big Picture perspective are not accomplished by changing what you **do**, but by changing what you are. Reread the previous sentence at least twice and think about your need for a physical process to develop your consciousness. You are a product of your culture – you cannot help that.

Spiritual growth, improving the quality of your consciousness, is about changing your attitude, expanding your awareness, outgrowing your fears, reducing your ego, and improving your capacity to love. To succeed, you must change your intent, and modify your motivation. The problem (and the solution) is one of being, not one of doing. You can **do** everything by the book, meditate regularly, be conscientious, try very hard, go through the proper prescribed motions and still make little progress. Going through the motions does nothing if the mind is not open to, and in pursuit of, fundamental **internal** change.

The prospect of fundamental internal change can be very frightening. When change begins to occur, many people run away because they are terrified of the unknown. They are afraid of where the changes may lead (which is often directly into the face of their fear) and of not being able to intellectually control the process. They find that shaking the foundation of their being at its deepest level is too unsettling an activity. What if the entire I-structure comes tumbling down into ruins? The ego begins to fear its own dissolution and death.

Fear and belief cause many well-meaning people to reject fundamental internal change, particularly if their beliefs are incompatible with the required changes. Instead of embracing change and facing fears, many would-be spiritual seekers focus on the external rituals associated with some type of mental or spiritual discipline: They go to church or learn to meditate. Many meditators and a few church goers hope to produce measurable **external** changes and to have cool internal metaphysical experiences.

In the West, meditation is acultural and an individual, rather than a social, activity. Most church goers continue their attendance out of social convenience, habit, duty, or cultural expectation – whereas most meditators eventually decide that meditation does not **do** anything for them, or at least not enough to be worth the effort and time required for a long term commitment. A few of each group pretend their effort has made them superior. The more honest and objective of the failed meditators give up in frustration or due to a simple lack of interest and soon forget about it. "I tried spiritual exercises, and they didn't work for me."

Practicing some form of meditation to effect external change, gain paranormal abilities, placate the guilt of doing nothing, or simply because you think you should, is analogous to a carpenter trying to build cabinets while holding the screwdriver and hammer by the wrong ends. All the pieces are there, but the execution is flawed. Make the required internal changes and the measurable external changes will occur on their own. You have to grab the screwdriver and hammer by the wooden end or you will come to the erroneous conclusion that they are useless tools that only someone else can effectively use. Or, more arrogantly, that nobody could use such stupid tools, that cabinets are a logical impossibility, and that all carpenters are delusional frauds and fools.

You must realize that you cannot modify **being** merely by taking physical action within the local physical reality. Westerners have a particularly difficult time understanding this fact and often feel helpless without a way to compel results from the outside. The opportunity to bolt to personal success and freedom by employing a more complete knowledge is lost in a culturally conditioned false commitment to the little picture. Belief traps are bigger problems than most of us think they are.

I know, after all that, you still want to know what you should **do**, how you can best modify your being, and what the most effective techniques are. Let me guess, you feel that you could use a hint – a little help, a little direction to get started. All right, all right, I give up! To help you get started here are some things you can **do** that **may** lead to opportunities to grow your being; however, it is entirely up to **you** to recognize, seize, and develop the opportunities that come your way. You already have plenty of opportunities, but let's pretend that by doing what I am going to tell you, more obvious and easier opportunities will appear before you. That will get us started with a hopeful, positive attitude.

What is more likely to happen is that by conscientiously working at the following exercises, your perspective will change, enabling you to see opportunities that are now as invisible to you as water is to a fish that lives two miles down in the middle of a four mile deep ocean. With no light and only a dim awareness, the fish knows nothing of water. Water just is, has always been, and is taken for granted. The fish does not ponder the nature of water, it swims in it. We swim in an ocean of consciousness. We are not aware of the ocean, but only of our local interactions with it.

The first and most necessary ingredient is a sincere desire to grow the quality of your consciousness – to evolve your being – to permanently change yourself at a deeply personal level. The second most necessary ingredient is to have the courage to change – the courage to face your fears – to face death and personal destruction, for that is the story your ego will tell (and try to get you to believe) when it comes whining to you with its tail between its legs hoping to dissuade you from increasing the quality of your consciousness.

Why would your sweet little ego do a mean thing like that? Because the ego's main job is to keep you feeling good by managing various systems of belief that are designed to keep your fears beyond the reach of your intellectual awareness. Increasing the quality of your consciousness requires you to face your fears, overcome them, and dissolve your ego. You should expect the ego to struggle mightily. ◀

▶▶ Ego does not necessarily imply arrogant self-centeredness. Ego comes in an infinite array of expressions – arrogance is only one. Being timid, unsure, or a worrier are also manifestations of ego. Insecurity and anxiety about that insecurity are common. How each personality expresses that insecurity and anxiety reflects individual quality and style. The strategies that are used to deal with fear, though common at the top level, are uniquely applied to each individual. Great ego reflects great fear; it does not necessarily reflect great arrogance or great pride, though it may reflect both. Self-centered, self-focused, and self-absorbed are three of the many possible aspects of ego – each of these three can be directed either inwardly (producing timidity) or outwardly (producing arrogance) to create personality traits that appear to be opposite.

Courage and determination will grow sufficiently to overcome fear if the intent to succeed is sufficiently strong, steady, and clear.

I will more carefully define ego and explain its functions (how it works and achieves its goals) in an aside in Chapter 8, Book 2. Go there now if you are seriously confused. ◀◀

▶ The most obvious pathway to the exploration of consciousness is through the exploration of your personal consciousness – a scientific investigation of your subjective experience. Studying consciousness from the outside (objectively) is like studying biology by looking at pictures of zoo animals. Consciousness is fundamentally individual and personal. Our objective sense of consciousness is derived from the reflection of our personal consciousness from the uniquely curvy surface of a mirror that we call "another."

Our objective experience of other consciousness is the result of an interaction of our personal consciousness (representing one set of possible choices or ways of being) with another, which suggests to us new configurations, interactions, and possibilities for **our** being. We project our awareness of consciousness into "other," define the nature of "other" in terms of ourselves, and thus see only a reflection of ourselves in the mirror of interaction with "other."

To preserve the symmetry of interaction, we also serve as a uniquely shaped mirror in which others can see themselves reflected in challenging new ways. Within this funhouse hall of interactive mirrors, your consciousness is a singular actor. Opportunities for change arise, choices are made, reality is actualized, and progress or regression in terms of personal growth is achieved. Your conscious awareness defines your personal reality. There are as many different shades and levels of personal reality as there are of personal awareness. "Other" provides opportunity for the improvement of the quality of your consciousness by accurately reflecting the truth of you.

If improved consciousness quality along with personal effectiveness, growth, and power are your goals, approaching consciousness from the inside, from the scientific exploration of inner space, is the only logical approach that delivers results. An approach from the outside will limit you to collecting the facts about the shadow that consciousness projects upon the wall of PMR.

We project our personal consciousness onto the field of action of a multi-player interactive reality game whose point is our individual growth and learning. The experience of consciousness, as well as the evolution of consciousness through choice, is entirely personal. However, an awareness of a larger (source) consciousness and an understanding of its properties are accessible through scientifically probing and objectively assessing the value and operational characteristics of the subjective experience of personal consciousness.

One method of accomplishing an assessment of subjective inner space is through meditation. Learning to meditate is like learning to play a musical instrument: It takes a serious steady effort before you should expect to make music instead of screeching noises. It takes dedication over a much longer time before you can master the basics of the instrument and play it well. Unfortunately, most people who pick up an instrument and give it a try give up before they ever learn to play it well. So it is with meditation.

As mentioned previously, going through the motions, or in this analogy, **pretending** to play an instrument, regardless of how perfect or impressive the visual (external) display, produces no significant results.

There are many effective paths to personal growth – meditation is only one. Within the wide range of practices that circumscribe what we have loosely defined as meditation, there are many different types, approaches, and methods. Because it is the easiest, most effective, and universally applicable, a simple mental-awareness meditation is the path of choice for most teachers and students who have no dogma to propagate. Within this subset of meditation, there are many differing techniques. The technique you choose is not as important as the application of steady effort – so choose a technique that suits you. Within this genre of meditation, you do not actually have to learn how to meditate; you need only to learn how to stop blocking the meditation state from occurring naturally.

Though we are pursuing the dubious subject of what you can **do** in order to undo what you have inadvertently done, I will help you out here because I know your cultural beliefs force you to begin with a physical process. It will be helpful to your doing and undoing if you understand meditation – its purpose and how it works. With this understanding, you can custom design your own personal spiritual growth **doing** thing – a physical and mental process that may lead you toward a higher quality of being. The doing process cannot get you there by itself, but it **can** serve as the on-ramp.

The meditation state that I encourage you to achieve represents a condition of inner attentiveness wherein you become aware of your personal consciousness. This, in time, leads to the awareness that you are a unit of consciousness among many such units. Eventually, you will regain your fundamental identity as a spiritual (nonphysical) entity – as well as understand your relationship, your oneness, with all consciousness. Personal growth is a natural result of meditation.

Becoming aware of your consciousness is analogous to that fish becoming aware of water. The fish is aware only of its interaction with water. It experiences water through doing, through action, through its objective causal interactions with water. Yet water has existence and significance in its own right beyond the interactions of that and other fish. To become aware of water, one must differentiate between water and a **subset** of the properties of water. The fish is aware only of the latter.

The fish experiences water only in terms of its limited interactions (experience). It experiences variations in current, temperature, salinity, viscosity, and dynamic limitations, but does it actually experience water in a fundamental or broad sense? Is the fish right? Is water nothing more than the sensed **variations** in its properties? Does water with no variations in its properties cease to exist as water, or does it simply become an invisible background to the fish because the fish can no longer perceive it? To appreciate your and the fish's limitations, imagine the perfect sensory deprivation tank where your local environment disappears because of zero input to your senses. Granted, this is not a perfect analogy, but you get the idea. When you are totally immersed in something, such as cultural belief systems for example, that something often becomes invisible because you cannot differentiate it from the background of your local reality – there is no contrast to bring it to the attention of your senses. Consciousness is like that.

Like the fish, we define our consciousness in terms of our doing – in terms of the physical actions it allows us to take. The major attribute of consciousness can be summed up as awareness, yet we and our fish brethren are aware only of what we can physically do with it, how we interact with a **subset** of its properties. Moreover, we can only interact with that subset of properties that are contrasted enough against the invisible background of primal consciousness for us to notice. We create a foreground of contrasts, relationships, and variations in the fabric of absolute consciousness that we define as representing ourselves. "See that cute little wad of wrinkles in the fabric of consciousness? That's me!" But you are more than the wrinkles; you are also consciousness, a piece of the whole. Meditation lets us experience the invisible background of consciousness. It lets us notice the water itself, not just variations and contrasts in its local properties relative to an invariant constant.

The point of meditation is to enable you to become aware of your consciousness and thereby introduce you to your larger self. Becoming aware of your consciousness at a fundamental level will eventually lead you to see the real you, the complete you, the whole you, the sacred and the soiled – fears and all. Without the ego to hide the scary parts by inventing an attention-getting "I vs. other" delusional contrast, it is not always a pretty sight.

How does meditation lead you to experience your consciousness? By turning down the contrast, noise, and other activity that makes up the busy foreground – by turning down, and eventually turning off, the cacophony of mental interactions, judgments, and operational processes. To become aware of your consciousness (as opposed to being aware of the thoughts that inhabit your consciousness) you must eliminate the obsessive preoccupations most of us have with ego based self-definition – the contrasts that you use to define yourself against the relatively unchanging, invisible background of your individual consciousness. Meditation is thus an act of **not doing**. It is an exercise in removing enough of the contrasting clutter of your mind to get a glimpse of the real you.

Individual consciousness is a subset of absolute consciousness. You are not **only** the clutter, the wrinkles, the ego, the thoughts – even if that is how you unwittingly define yourself. You are much more than that. Meditation allows you to discover that fact in a uniquely personal way. That is its purpose – self-discovery – a glimpse of the fundamental reality of which you are an integral part.

This discovery is possible for humans because, at least theoretically, our memory capacity and processing capability is somewhat greater (and contains less entropy) than that of the average fish. The fish will never directly experience or contemplate unvarying water (the fish equivalent to total sensory deprivation), but you can experience the fundamental nature of your consciousness if you truly want to. If your desire to know yourself and to know the truth at the deepest level of your existence is not strong enough to provide the necessary focus, energy, and persistence required to succeed, you are not yet ready to begin that journey. There is no rush and no penalty for not being ready. It is much better to wait until you are ready than to push yourself into a state of self-limiting frustration.

Do you see why meditation is almost universally prescribed as the first step – the doorway to understanding and exploring consciousness, as well as to the attainment of spiritual growth? It makes sense that a program to develop your consciousness should naturally start with finding and becoming acquainted with that consciousness. There are other methods, but they apply less universally, are more difficult to learn, and are much more difficult to teach. Meditation will work wonderfully when you are ready. You may first need to work on getting ready by developing an honest desire to grow spiritually and the courage to pursue Big Truth to its conclusion. You may need to first overcome some of the fear and cultural beliefs to which you have become attached.

How does meditation clear out the clutter and reduce the noise level of a mind caught in a self-referential endless loop of obfuscating circular logic? The technique is simple and straightforward – the trappings of ritual, dogma, belief, and physical process are mostly irrelevant. You simply stop the incessant operational, self-referential, contrast producing chatter of the mind by filling the mind up with something less distracting, less self-focused and less obsessively driven. While the mind is preoccupied with non-operative busy-work, you can experience the still center of your being. Eventually, after much practice, you can let go of the mental busy-work and explore the larger reality of consciousness from an imperturbable, still, and quiet place that will slowly develop and grow larger at the center of your being.

Some traditions call this mental busy-work assignment a "mantra." Traditionally this is a sound of some sort, but in this Big TOE we are bound only by science, not tradition. We quickly move to toss belief, dogma, and ritual out of the window and focus, by experimental result, only on the active ingredients of mantra. Science allows the concept of mantra to be generalized to accommodate the various ways we take in and process information through our five senses. Typically, people tend to take in most of their experiential input data through their ears (auditory), eyes (visual) or sense of touch (kinesthetic). Many people absorb information more effectively through one of these avenues of data input than they do through the others. Over the previous decade or so, the popular literature is full of assessments of personality type and characteristics by data input preference. It makes no sense to force everyone down the traditional auditory path – some people simply do not get it that way.

If you are not now successfully meditating, and have no idea where or how to find a suitable technique to do so, I will provide to you, free of charge – for this one time only – a mentally calming busy work mantra custom made for your personal mind that is based upon each of the dominant perception types. Simply use the one or combination that seems to work the best for you. For those more heavily into smell and taste than the average humanoid form, I am sure that you can follow the three examples given to custom fit a smelly or yummy mantra to suit your individual preferences.

After explaining each mantra, I will, against my better judgment, tell you what you can **do** with them. Oh, no, not like that – I wouldn't be that rude! I understand that your Western mind-set needs to begin everything with physical process whether it makes sense or not.

Those who seriously want to get started on their spiritual journey, but find themselves caught in the headlights of physical action-reaction causality, will now have something to **do**. It may or may not help you improve the quality of your consciousness – that depends on you – but it will give the committed doers a place to start. Often that is what is needed – a place to start – a **do**able approach to the problem of how to modify the quality of your being. This could be the step you need to break free from the mesmerizing glare of those cultural beliefs that reduce, rather than extend, your vision. Try it: You may surprise yourself with some dramatic results.

For the audio types, we need a sound that means nothing, is two syllables, and ends in a soothing or vibratory sound. Here are a few examples of proven quality – take your pick or make up one of your own: "sehr-ring", "da-room", "ra-zing", "ca-ouhn", "sah-roon", and "sher-loom." For a simple multi-syllable repetitive string (chant), try: "ah-lum-bar-dee-dum – ah-lum-baa-dee-dum." When the "bar" and "baa" regularly inter-change themselves effortlessly, you will be well on your way. These are sounds, not words – it is important that they carry no intellectual meaning. The point of this exer-cise is to quiet your operative intellect so that you can experience consciousness directly by reducing the variations, comparisons, and contrasts that your ego-intellect imposes upon consciousness.

Feel free to mix and match – put any of the first syllables in front of any of the sec-ond syllables to produce no fewer than thirty-six unique mantras. For most people, it won't make much difference which sound is used, but if one sound feels more natural than the others, use it. Obsessive-compulsive types should take care not to get wrapped around the axle trying to find the best one – any will do.

Lighten up; do not be intense and serious. **Have no expectations.** Sit in a com-fortable quiet place where you will not be disturbed, close your eyes, and fill your mind with the sound of your chosen mantra – no need to make an actual sound. Focus your attention on the sound. Let the sound fill your mind – think of nothing else. Use what-ever devices you need to stay focused on the sound – merely **listen** to it repeat itself. The repetition may be simple and straightforward or occur in interesting ways – per-haps with complex variations.

Eventually, let the sound of the mantra slow to a rhythmic, bland repetition and then slow and smear further into a continuous background sound. If thoughts creep in, gen-tly put them aside and refill your mind with the sound. If intruding thoughts constantly stream into your awareness, give the mantra a more active form. As thoughts disap-pear, leaving your mind empty, simplify and soften the sound of the mantra. Continue the meditation process uninterrupted for at least twenty minutes, twice a day for three months before evaluating the results. If the sound slips away, but no extraneous thoughts appear, let it go and drift in the quiet blankness of your consciousness – you will love it.

Visual types need a non-personal visualization that begins with complexity (but not detail) and ends with simplicity. You may start with a black and white soccer ball – then let the colors change to red and blue, let the ball begin to rotate slowly, let the colors change. Your image should be as clear as a watercolor painting, not as precise as a high-resolution photograph. Switch to a series of simple geometric shapes such as spheres, cubes, circles, triangles, cylinders, rectangles, and lines. Let them rotate slowly. Slowly change their size and colors. Choose one shape and let it change very slowly. Watch your images intently – think of nothing else.

Gradually progress your images toward greater simplicity and slower motion. Do not force the images; let them do what they want to as long as they do not disturb your tran-quility. Look at your images uncritically and dispassionately, as if you were watching a plotless movie. If thoughts creep in, gently put them aside and refill your mind with more active images. Continue the meditation process uninterrupted for at least twenty minutes, twice a day for three months before evaluating the results. If the images slip away, but no extraneous thoughts appear, let them go and drift in the still oneness of your consciousness.

If you enjoy natural places, you might start with a scene – perhaps a generic beach. Hear the waves, feel the sand, smell the salt spray, listen to the sea gulls. Be there with all of your senses. Slowly simplify your image and focus on a few items at a time. Eventually you may narrow your focus to a single grain of sand. Go in close to inspect the tiny crystal from every angle. Choose the viewing angle you prefer and see how the light plays off the surface of the crystal. Back away until you can barely see its surface features. Hold that view as only you and the grain of sand quietly coexist within the void.

Choose images that particularly suit you. Be careful not to try too hard, and do not struggle with high resolution, image quality, or anything else. Images may be felt as well as seen. Struggling to make your meditation be how you think it should be is always counterproductive. No expectations. No struggle. No demands. The point is not to force your will on the process, but to let the process unfold naturally as it captivates your attention.

Remember that what you are trying to do without trying is to not do. Read that sentence again – don't you just love it? If it makes sense to you, you are on your way. If it sounds like idiotic gibberish you should go back to the beginning of this aside and start over – but don't get stuck in an endless loop – twice is enough.

For the kinesthetic types, we need textures that are non-personal, interesting and pleasant. For example, feel a rich velvet or fur coat as you mentally rub your hands slowly over it. Dig into it with your fingers, feel it rub across your arms and face. Explore the buttons or zipper, the seams, sleeves, and collar. Become tiny (or create a giant coat) and roll around on it, crawl into a pocket. Slowly let your sensing of the coat become simple and rhythmic. You might do the same thing with walking barefoot in squishy mud, or walking in the rain, or swimming in a pool filled with grape jelly. Start with complexity and progress to more and more simple rhythmic sensory stimulations. If thoughts creep in, gently put them aside and refill your mind with the sensations. Continue the meditation process uninterrupted for at least twenty minutes, twice a day for three months before evaluating the results. If the sensations slip away, but no extraneous thoughts appear, let the sensations go and drift aimlessly in the boundless depths of your consciousness.

Smell and taste mantras would work similarly to the kinesthetic mantra above. Use your imagination. Do not be afraid to mix and match the senses; combine them in ways that work for you. Have no intellectual or emotional connection to your mantra. Maintain only enough complexity to keep extraneous thoughts away – nothing should be in your mind except the sound, sight, feel, taste, or smell of the mantra. As intruding thoughts become less of a problem, simplify your mantra. When you no longer need it to maintain a state of blank thoughtless existence, let it go. ◀

▶▶ Speaking of experiencing a state of thoughtless existence through meditation – let's do another ego-tweak – a real blatant one this time – and have some fun.

Hey ladies, why do you think most spiritual gurus are men? Think about it. Do you give up? Because, men are born thoughtless and remain that way the rest of their lives! Why else?

Oooh…what a low blow!

Uh oh, easy fellows, I was only kidding – just a little double-entendre word play. Come on now…what's the matter guys? Remember the rules: peace and light – no violence until after I leave.

Oh well, at least the ladies thought it was funny – they get it. ◀◀

▶ The point here is to learn to control your thoughts and your operative mind so that you can experience your consciousness. This is a first and necessary step. Later you can learn how to direct that consciousness once you have freed it from a noisy, frantic, ego serving, perpetual tail chase. Do not try to direct it too soon – that will only delay your progress – get in touch with, and follow, the source of your intuition. Do not pursue or chase after specific or general results. All results must come to you. If you go after them, it will only delay your progress.

Continue to experiment and to taste the pudding periodically. Natural, easy, patient, and gentle are the hallmarks of a successful process. Result driven, ego driven, success driven, frustrated, forced, fearful, and having preconceived notions and expectations are the hallmarks of a wrong-headed flawed execution of the meditation process.

Experiment to find what works best and what feels most natural to you. After you find it, stick with it for a while. If thoughts intrude, as soon as you realize that your mind is no longer exclusively working with the mantra, put them gently aside. If thoughts continue to come, increase the complexity of your mantra a little. As thoughts disappear and do not return, decrease the complexity. Never try too hard. If you ever become frustrated, you are trying too hard. This is most important: Have absolutely no expectations and no specific goals.

This is also important: Do not **begin** to judge how well or poorly your meditation is working until you have found and implemented a productive meditation process twice daily for at least three to six months – **then** taste the pudding.

Do not analyze or compare, just experience – this is not an intellectual exercise and your analyzing justifying intellect will only get in the way. Never force the mantra – go with it, flow with it, and let whatever happens happen – this is a gentle activity with no preconceived notions of what the outcome should be or feel like. There will be plenty of time for evaluation and pudding tasting after you gain some basic competence. There must be a time to be critical, but not now – you do not know enough to be productively critical yet.

Let every meditation be an entirely new and unique experience. Do not force every meditation experience to be like a previous experience that was judged to be a good one. Continue tasting the pudding at three month intervals. Look for the existence of measurable results in the form of objective changes in your being. After six months, ask people who are close to you if they notice a change in your approach to life. Be aware of your mental state, and how that state changes as the meditation progresses. Customize your meditation to suit yourself. Your meditation should become easier, more effective, and more efficient over time. Be patient, do not rush the process – trying to speed-up or push the process will only delay your progress.

Pay careful attention to the choices you make throughout your day. Examine your motivations and intent relative to those choices. By an act of your will, modify your intents to be more giving, caring, loving, and to be less self-serving. Shift the focus from you, from what you want, need and desire, to what you can give to, and do for, others. In the same manner, change where and how you invest the energy that follows your intent in your relationships and interactions with other people.

Examine your motivations and intent as described above immediately before and after, but not during, each meditation. You must be consistent – that is most important. Once you get used to the exercise, thirty minutes twice a day is enough to accomplish both the meditation and the examination of your choices – take more if you wish, but much more is not necessary.

If you constantly end up in a state of frustration instead of a state of expanded awareness, let go, back off, and take a break until you can find a different perspective, a different attitude, or a different intent. Try a different mantra. Perhaps you are trying too hard. Perhaps you are limited by your belief and fear, or lack the necessary courage and drive. Perhaps you need to read and follow the instructions more carefully. Perhaps you are using a meditation technique that does not suit you. Perhaps you are not ready at this time. Don't worry: Everything works out in its own time. There is no blame, no reason to feel badly, and no failure on your part. Continue to apply the meditation process gently and consistently and one day, when you relax, success will take you by surprise.

Everyone grows in their own way and in their own time. No one faults children for not being adults, though most children wish they were adults. There is no practical technique that allows you to skip steps. You are who and what you are – accept that gracefully. Work on getting ready by continuing to practice the given exercises gently and with no expectations. There is no faster process or better way to get ready than that.

Thus, we see that getting prepared and ready to grow, as well as actively progressing along a growth path, as well as optimizing the growth path that you are on, all follow the same prescription. It matters not what your initial conditions are or where your starting point is, the same set of meditation exercises are optimal and appropriate for all. That is why virtually everyone who wishes to follow the Path of Knowledge toward spiritual growth, toward improving the quality of their consciousness, is instructed to begin with daily meditation. Each individual will naturally extract from their meditation what they need for their next step. This personalization of the growth process takes place naturally because each individual is essentially engaged in a "bootstrapping" (pulling themselves up by their bootstraps) operation with his or her own consciousness. The meditation experience is as individual and personal as is your consciousness.

This is a life's work; it takes significant time to take root, blossom and bear fruit. Results will accrue in proportion to the energy that is invested productively. For example, with moderate effort, significant results should become obvious within six months to a year. Continue to apply the meditation process with gentle resolve; there is no rush, no test, and no diploma. You have all the time you need to get it right. Some will get it right away; others may take a long time. Gracefully accept however it comes to you – you have no choice. A teacher can only encourage and facilitate the evolution of your consciousness by helping you find opportunities to exploit on your own – spiritual growth, as any growth, is an internal process and cannot be forced from the outside.

Hopefully, these meditation exercises have addressed your need for a physical process to facilitate positive consciousness development. However, in doing so, I may have created a new problem for you – how to deal with the frustration that is often created by the inadequacy of **doing** to produce dramatic spiritual progress quickly. The Western attention span is notoriously short. To make matters worse, dramatic results are often required to overcome strongly opposing cultural belief systems. The fact is that progress in meditation, like progress in playing a musical instrument, usually accrues slowly and only becomes dramatic after significant time and effort has been invested. Progress accrues by the accumulation of many unnoticeable tiny successes. Take the long view and have patience.

Westerners caught in the glaring headlights of their cultural beliefs desperately need something to **do** before they become spiritual road kill – run-over by mindless conformity and a blind obedience to the cultural norm. Thump! Splat! Oh jeez, what a mess! All the king's horses and all the king's men will have a difficult time getting that one back on the road to spiritual progress again.

Actually, it is unfair of me to pick on Westerners as being particularly limited by needing to **do** something in order to **be** something. Most Easterners are in the same doing-fixated boat. Their do-boat **may** appear to be bigger – not as confining perhaps – but just as limiting. **Doing** within a spiritual-cultural tradition is as problematical and unproductive as **doing** within a material-cultural tradition.

If you are so inclined, you now have something productive to **do** as well as an expanded perspective on the limitations and personal nature of that doing. ◀

You now know what to **do** and how to **do** it, and if you settle in for the long haul with a serious commitment to finding Big Truth, you will succeed beyond your wildest dreams.

24

Two Concepts

The previous chapters should have destroyed the illusion of a quick and easy fix, leaving you with your feet firmly planted in the personal as well as the shared nature of reality. With your attitude, perspective, and focus now properly adjusted, let us get back to the job of developing a credible Big Picture Theory Of Everything (Big TOE). The best process that can be employed when exploring new theoretical ground is to: (1) minimize the number of assumptions required, and (2) simplify all remaining assumptions to the most basic level possible. Albert Einstein put it succinctly when he said: *"The grand aim of all science is to cover the greatest number of empirical facts by logical deduction from the smallest number of hypotheses or axioms."*

I think that Dr. Einstein would be proud of us – we are going to derive a comprehensive Big TOE that explains the empirical facts – mind as well as matter, philosophy as well as physics, the normal as well as the paranormal, consciousness as well as concrete – by logical deduction from just two simple assumptions. And only one of those two assumptions is extraordinary.

Theorists can build a complex speculative structure, but the foundation should be as simple and straightforward as possible. The first assumption, referred to as the Fundamental Process of evolution, is readily understandable and is well within our experience. The second, often called the "Absolute" or the "One Source" by philosophers and theologians, may require our spatially limited worldview and our cultural beliefs to stretch beyond their normal patterns. As it turns out, this "One Source" is simply consciousness – primordial consciousness – the fundamental energy that is the media of reality.

If the concept of primordial consciousness cast into the form of a finite, but practically infinite, monolithic undifferentiated form of potential energy makes you feel uneasy, that is as it should be. You should remain skeptical of any premise and doubly skeptical of any mystical premise – even if logic demands that at least one mystical (beyond objective knowing from the PMR point of view) premise must be at the base of any successful Big TOE.

Things beyond **objective** knowing, from the PMR point of view, are by definition things that we cannot hold with a firm intellectual grip. If this concept fell within your objective experience, if you could be intellectually and rationally comfortable with it, it would no longer qualify as the mystical or metaphysical foundation upon which we could build a Big TOE capable of logically accounting for our beginnings, for mind as well as matter, for the paranormal as well as the normal.

The Fundamental Process of evolution along with primordial consciousness as a fundamental source of structurable energy are the two basic assumptions on which *MY Big TOE* is based. Everything that follows will be logically derived and explained from these two fundamental assumptions.

I am **not** asking you to **believe** in the truth of these assumptions, nor to have **faith** in their correctness. I am not trying to start a religion here. These are the logical underpinnings of this Big TOE. They are the assumptions, assertions, logical premises upon which the structure of *My Big TOE* is built. *My Big TOE* is a model. **Its usefulness**, and the value of these assumptions, **is based exclusively on its ability to explain the data – period!** Please reread the previous two sentences enough times to commit them to memory. By the end of Section 6 you will have a much better idea about this reality model's usefulness, and the potential correctness of these assumptions.

The data, or "empirical facts" in Einstein's words, are any and all of the carefully evaluated experience or truth that you and others have accumulated about life and the nature of reality. These data come in two types – **personal data** that are unique to your subjective experience and **shared data** that represent the objective physical experience of PMR (the realm of PMR science). If your personal data have been objectively evaluated and are un-warped by ego, attachment, belief and fear, they can be used to either corroborate or invalidate this model. For these types of data you are the sole judge, the only possible judge. Because of the personal nature of subjective experience, you can only be the judge for yourself.

Shared data are also important. Physical reality and PMR science must be an integral part of any Big TOE. We, after all, are at this moment interacting in what appears quite convincingly as a physical reality. No one can reasonably deny the importance, or the necessity, of physical experience, even if consciousness is at the core. Physical reality and its science must be a necessary, rational, and derivable part of the Big Picture. Furthermore, it is the interactions that take place in PMR (as defined by our physical experience) that enables one to test and measure the **objective** results of an increased quality (decreased entropy) of consciousness.

▶ This is where the metaphysical rubber first meets the road. What I am offering in this chapter is **not** what I **believe** to be true. This is not about what I believe about reality. This is about a **model of reality** based upon my experience and research. If the difference between the two is not crystal clear, I have not communicated as clearly as I need to.

Some may **believe** there can **never** be a significant difference between the two – that belief and subjective knowledge are the same. Not so. Results, objectively measurable results **can** differentiate between the two. **If there are no objective measurable results, there can be no solid or scientific conclusions.** My Big TOE represents a serious attempt to describe and model the larger reality in which you exist as a digital consciousness. If what you have read thus far seems to be far removed from hard science, be patient. The merger of physics and metaphysics, which is a logical requirement of any correct **Big** TOE, requires substantial background development.

From the little picture perspective of our local objective causality, all one needs to do to make a strong scientific argument is write down the appropriate equations. Math is merely symbolic logic. The limited local logic of the little picture is clearly expressed by little picture mathematics. Within the PMR causality system, if the assumptions are correct and the math is correct, the results will be correct – that is how little picture physics works. The Big Picture, responding to a more general causality, cannot be adequately described in terms of little picture logic. I know that this is a difficult paradigm for many (particularly scientists) to transcend, but it is logical that the Big Picture with its more general causality cannot be fully described from a little picture perspective. In other words, the larger reality (NPMR – consciousness) cannot be fully specified by a limited local logic and knowledge that belongs to a small subset (PMR) of that larger reality. If I could describe My Big TOE in terms of little picture (PMR) mathematics (logic), it could not possibly be more than a little TOE. That is one of the invisible walls that Einstein ran into with his failed Unified Field Theory – he tried to describe the Big Picture exclusively in terms of little picture logic. At least he knew there was a Big Picture even if he did not know it constituted a superset of the little picture.

The traditional belief-blinded little picture perspective will maintain old paradigms and preserve cultural and scientific dogma by simply denying the existence of a larger reality. To be consistent, it must also deny, or concoct excuses for, any scientifically validated data and experience that directly conflict with its beliefs. That is the old tried and true head in the sand, butt in the air trick. I can assure you from first hand experience that attempting to engage these elevated butts in intelligent conversation is often not productive – low IQ, bad breath, no vision. Fortunately, minds can sometimes be pried open and perspectives can sometimes change with additional experience, knowledge, and understanding.

If the above ideas are fuzzy, hold on – understanding will improve and become clear as you continue. This model, as any model, is constructed mostly of knowledge and experience with a little conjecture or theorizing to bind (integrate) the various discrete data together into a coherent and consistent whole. I approach this model with open minded skepticism as you should. If I believed in it, it would limit my ability to grow the model in new directions as new data accumulates. If it makes you feel better, I don't **believe** any of this stuff either.

I either know it as fact (knowledge), or regard it as the most likely possibility or best hypothesis thus far (based on the scientific data available to me as of this writing). In other words, this trilogy represents the **tentative** results and conclusions of thirty years of my personal, serious, careful, scientific exploration of the physical and the nonphysical. I have been strongly encouraged to share the results and conclusions of my experience with you. These books are it. What you do with it, get out of it, or take from it is entirely up to you.

Models should always remain tentative to preclude shutting themselves off from the possibility of further evolution. For the sake of argument and to give proper credit to those who **believe** that belief and knowledge can never be entirely separated, let's take the opposite view. Even if this trilogy represents my belief, and is an effort to convince you to believe what I believe, the potential it holds for you is undiminished as long as you approach it with open minded skepticism and resist the compulsion to either believe it or disbelieve it. There is no reasonable, rational, or logical alternative to open minded skepticism.

My Big TOE, among other things represents a personal map of the reality I have explored and the explanations I have created to make coherent sense out of my individual experiences. Because of the personal nature of experience, your experiences will be somewhat different from mine. However, If your experience is interpreted and gathered scientifically and not created out of belief or fear, then the underlying truth from which both of our experiences spring will be perceived as the same. The underlying truth is absolute (the same for everyone) and is not a function of our experience or our existence (or anyone else's). That is why my map, though it reflects my individuality, can serve as a valuable **guide** for you. Though the destination (Big Truth) is the same for everyone, you must take your own journey and find your own way.

A word about truth. Many people think of truth in terms of local and universal truth. Local truth may be relative. It may be in the eye of the beholder. It is sometimes dependent upon the perspective and beliefs of the individual. This is **not** the truth I am referring to. Universal or absolute truth is the same for everyone – it is timeless and unchangeable. The paths to absolute truth (Big Truth) and the individuals who walk those paths can be so different that the description of the same absolute truth may appear to be very different – particularly to those of less understanding. Individual inter-pretations are, as they should be, a reflection of that Big Truth within the mind and experience of that individual.

A group of similar (by depth of understanding) but different (by path, culture and personality) truly wise and knowledgeable individuals would view the differences in each other's descriptions of the same absolute truth as insignificant and trivial. Unfortunately, in their absence, their less knowledgeable followers may actually kill each other over the **apparent** differences as they vie for relative power and superior correctness within their own and competing organizations.

The actual differences between descriptions of the same absolute truth are – after differing language, cultural, and religious modes of expression are removed – much smaller than you would likely imagine. This is because all spiritual paths converge on the same absolute truths by means of reducing ego and fear, which are the primary generators of confusion and divisiveness.

Models can be a practical representation of an underlying truth or process. The shell model of the atom is not based on a theory of why atoms, like mollusks, should have shells. The shells are simply assumed; the model is useful because it explains some of the data better than any other viewpoint. **Believing** in the shells is intellectually limit-ing silliness. What are atomic shells made of and where do they come from are not rea-sonable questions – atomic shells are only conceptual tools – they are a metaphorical structure describing (modeling) an underlying reality.

My Big TOE is also conceptual. We know that from our limited 3D perspective and local objective causality, a Big TOE that reaches beyond PMR absolutely **must** have at least one mystical leg to stand on. That mystical leg must be beyond the reach of our objective PMR based logic. As you recall, that same logical requirement was placed upon the understanding our local reality's beginnings (see Chapter 18 of this book). Causality and rationality require that we enter the metaphysical or mystical realm (from the PMR point of view) whenever we go beyond PMR. The existence of an appar-ently infinite absolute something seems both mystical and vague from our PMR per-spective, nevertheless, that is not a weakness of this model. Quite the contrary, it is a requirement.

A **Big** TOE that contains no mystical (from PMR view) assumptions must necessarily be incorrect or incomplete and can logically never amount to more than a little TOE focused solely upon PMR. A little TOE restricted to PMR objective causality can never, even theoretically, grow up to be a Big TOE because it has, by definition, shut itself off from the solution space required to span the data. As we have shown, little TOEs can have nothing logical to say about our beginnings or our relationship to the circumstances of those beginnings.

We shall see that we are inextricably bound up with, and an extension of, our beginnings. A higher-level objective causality (of which PMR's objective causality and physics is a constrained subset) demands that we be solidly connected to what came before us. As a very young child is connected to, dependent upon, and extrapolated from its parents, we are connected to, dependent upon, and extrapolated from our beginnings. The inclusion of an assumption that is beyond the objective causal logic of PMR is an essential and necessary ingredient of a successful Big TOE.

With believers of all sorts dismissing every datum that conflicts with their dogma, self-limiting, self-inflicted belief-based blindness becomes a common social disease. So common, in fact, that it defines the normal and therefore the rational view within any given culture. The point is: One should not necessarily expect the normal or traditionally rational view to shed light on new paradigms. When it comes to evaluating new scientific paradigms, one must look forward for answers and only glance backward long enough to make sure the new properly contains the old as a special case.

The only issues are whether or not this apparently infinite absolute something that I have chosen as my one mystical (from the PMR point of view only) assumption produces the desired results, and whether or not it is the simplest, most basic and fundamental place to begin our beginning. We will more precisely develop its characteristics and properties as we proceed.

The most important question is: can these two assumptions (the existence of consciousness and the process of evolution) deliver the goods? Can they provide a logical foundation broad enough and solid enough to support a comprehensive model of reality? Can a comprehensive, honest, and straightforward Big TOE, reflecting the elegant simplicity of our reality, be built upon them? Is the model based upon these assumptions both general and accurate? Does it make sense and fit **all** the data? Is it useful, practical and predictive? Does it produce objective measurable results? These are the proper criteria for judging the correctness and usefulness of the two given assumptions. As these two concepts are more fully developed throughout the next three sections, you will understand them and their implications more clearly and precisely. After you have completed Section 6, you will be in a much better position to judge the efficacy and value of the *My Big Toe* reality model.

This model, as all models, is results oriented. An important question is how well does it fit the present knowledge-base including physics (all science). An equally important question is how well does it fit **your** personal data and the personal data of others? Consciousness has both public and personal components; consequently, both questions must be answered fully. However, though you may not see it this way now, you will probably come to the conclusion that it is the personal side that contains the most value and significance to you as an individual – even if you are a scientist. Make out of it (interpret it) and get from it (use it) whatever you can. The *My Big Toe* reality model will help you understand your life, your purpose, all of the reality you experience, how that reality works, and how you might interact most profitably with it.

Each reader brings to the table his or her personal data – their carefully evaluated experience. Most people will approach this model from one of four initial conditions. (1) They have no data to either support or contradict the model. (2) Their data supports the model. (3) Their data contradicts the model. And (4) their data supports and contradicts the model.

Let me address each initial condition separately: (1) If you do not have scientific or trustworthy personal or public data with which to assess the model, you should nevertheless find its exploration a thought provoking journey through a hypothetical landscape of very unusual yet coherent and reasonable conjecture. With no trustworthy data of your own, everything necessarily **appears** to be conjecture; however, this Big TOE offers a set of **potentially** useful maps that may help guide you toward the further evolution of your being and a better understanding of the world around you. Perhaps an intellectual or logical appreciation of the model will help you effectively evaluate and understand future data that you will no doubt discover now that your mind is open to the possibilities.

(2) If this model fits your data, it will provide a rational structure for your experience; a context wherein the whole of your experience makes good sense. You can either enhance your pre-existing Big TOE, or grow a new Big TOE. Either choice may potentially redirect and refocus your path of growth, development, and evolution.

(3) If your data clearly and directly conflict with this model, you should continue on in order to understand your own conceptual model more clearly and so you will be better able to protect yourself from the confusion of some of the delusional fools you must share this planet with.

(4) If you find that some of your data support the model, yet some of your data contradict the model, you are most likely going to be confused. In this case, you need to pay close attention to understanding the limitations of your beliefs, reevaluate the data in conflict, make plans to collect additional data, and above all, stick to your guns until you have developed clear evidence and experience to the contrary. No one else's data or experience can be profitably substituted for yours.

The following advice is to all readers, irrespective of what their initial conditions are. (1) Always keep your mind wide open and remain skeptical – two traits common to all great scientists and explorers. (2) Do not leap to conclusions that are familiar, convenient, or easy because of belief or faith; instead, rely only on your personal experience data. (3) While contemplating **your** Big TOE, develop some ideas about what additional data you might need to collect and how you might go about collecting them. (4) Begin a program to collect the data you need to develop the knowledge and understanding you want to have.

You can always change your mind no matter which of the above four initial conditions you start with. Whether the *My Big TOE* trilogy **appears** to you as belief, knowledge, conjecture, or fact, or however you perceive the relative proportions of each, is entirely and only a function of **your** perspective – your belief, your knowledge, your experience. If you are "normal," you strongly believe (consciously or subconsciously) that your perspective and judgment is nearly flawless. Take care not to limit yourself. Maintaining an attitude of open minded skepticism will maximize the probability that you will not inadvertently or purposefully cut yourself off from the solution-set that contains the truth. ◀

Now that you have been properly initialized and calibrated, let us get back to work. Let's start with the most difficult concept first, the one that appears mystical from the PMR point of view. This concept assumes the existence of an apparently (not necessarily actually) infinite absolute something: A Oneness that is uniform, plain, and without differentiation. This **apparently** infinite source of our larger reality has no **discernable** boundaries, edges, or limits (as a perfectly calm ocean would appear to you if you were floating in the middle of it). This undifferentiated something would seem to be, and has often been called "All That Is," "The One," "The Void," "The Primordial Big Dude," and other similar philosophical descriptions. It represents the fundamental core of existence. It is a familiar concept to various religious and spiritual conceptualizations. An absolute no-thing, pervasive, yet exists beyond our space and time. It is simultaneously everything (in potential) and nothing (no-thing, no differentiation or boundaries).

Unfortunately, this is how we 3D creatures must express this concept. It is not an especially satisfying concept in light of our need to seem objective. It sounds mystical like curved space-time sounds mystical to those uninitiated in the mathematical basis of the general theory of relativity. From the larger perspective of a wider (beyond PMR) experience, it is as real as moon rocks. "Mystical" in this context means beyond our personal and collective ability to make an explanation within the context of PMR. Thus, to explain something (such as reality) that is a **superset** of PMR, one must not be afraid to explore the metaphysical, nor to offer serious scientific consideration to the seemingly mystical. That is the only doorway to a larger perspective, to peeking over the cultural-scientific-causality blindfold.

If exploring the conceptual mountains and swamps of metaphysical and mystical thought is at this point still discomfortingly unfamiliar or **believed** to be unproductive or just plain dumb, continue reading. Later in Section 3 (Chapters 13 and 14 of Book 2) and Section 5 (Chapter 2, Book 3) we will discuss a few issues of science and philosophy that may enlarge your perspective to the point that you feel more intellectually comfortable with being part of a bigger picture. Unfortunately, there are many who reflexively shake their heads and roll their eyes upon hearing the words mysticism and metaphysics: those individuals should reconsider the limitations of their basic assumptions and beliefs.

Each of us needs to continually make an effort to maintain an open mind, suspend our limiting beliefs, and raise our intellectual courage to the point that we can honestly explore new and uncertain territory: Vigilance and unending effort is the nonnegotiable price of intellectual freedom. A mind that is not free is simply a self-referential belief machine that continuously spins off useless and unprofitable thought energy. Belief and fear are the only ties that can bind a mind, while unconditional love and open minded skepticism set it free. A body may be enslaved by others, while a mind can only be enslaved by itself.

Open yourself to the possibilities and remain skeptical. Even if this journey takes you right back to the point at which you started, your time will have been well spent. Big Picture thinking will have taken place, concepts defined, possibilities raised, new perspectives viewed, old conclusions re-evaluated, and goofy ideas debunked.

Like Flatlanders, you must step through your mind, with a careful scientific evaluation of your subjective experience to understand what is beyond PMR. This simultaneously ancient and modern metaphysical concept of the infinite absolute unbounded oneness is a very useful idea, even if it is disconcertingly fuzzy. It is naturally impossible to get a firm intellectual grip on this idea because our PMR perspective is necessarily limited. It is a big concept, one that appears to fly in the face of two of our most sacred cultural dogmas, causality and objectivity. There is no point in struggling. Even if you were brilliant, (actually, I am sure you are – it is all the others I am referring to) it would still be a fuzzy concept. Do not despair; it is our nature as 3D beings in space-time to be removed from an **objective** sense of infinite absolute oneness.

I did not say that this absolute oneness exists everywhere. Space in this concept doesn't exist yet. Location, even relative location is not yet defined

– everywhere, in this context, has no meaning. I also did not say that this primordial consciousness was all knowing, omniscient, self-aware, or even vaguely intelligent – it is not. At this point, this rudimentary form of consciousness is not capable of forming or holding a single coherent thought. Imagine an immense unstructured, but structurable form of digital potential (the potential to be more profitably organized) energy.

You will soon discover that this seemingly infinite Absolute Unbounded Oneness (AUO) is not infinite. Nor is it absolute, unbounded, or a oneness – but only appears to be an infinite absolute unbounded oneness from a limited point of view within PMR. Although the name Absolute Unbounded Oneness is a descriptive misnomer, I use it because many readers will find the concept to be comfortably familiar. It would appear to be a better communications strategy to begin with a familiar concept and expand the basis upon which it rests, rather than the alternative (begin with an unfamiliar concept and then attempt to explain it in more common terms).

▶ The third logical possibility, to begin with an unfamiliar concept and explain it in terms of other even more unfamiliar concepts, is reserved for sophisticated university professors, physicians, and other specialists who are trying to set themselves apart, emphasize their superior knowledge, and mightily impress lesser beings such as you and me.

This trilogy is not sophisticated – you have probably noticed that by now – the only big word I know is "bifurcate" (to split in two) and I have used that one already in Chapter 17 of this book. So, I'm done – that's as impressive as I get. Sorry mom.

Because we are using humor to delineate a few common communication styles, I would be remiss if I did not also mention lawyers and politicians who explain simple and familiar ideas in the most complex and convoluted terms possible in order to create the illusion that they have special knowledge that is critically important.

The point is: There are many communication strategies, each designed to meet specific personal needs and purposes, and that these strategies determine not only what you say and how you say it, but also what you hear and understand.

Your purpose and needs dictate your communication strategy whether you are transmitting or receiving. Think about that. Does your personal communication strategy open you up, or close you down with regard to receiving and understanding a concept like AUO?

It always takes at least two to communicate – each through selective send and receive filters of their own making. Receivers (listeners, watchers, or readers) appear to be in a solely passive role, but that is not so. They, knowingly or not, actively put a spin on every datum that they receive in order to make the interpretation of that experience-datum fit satisfactorily within their current worldview. No doubt about it, the internal spin doctor is there to make you feel confident and secure in your knowledge and beliefs about how the world and the people in it work.

This subject will be taken up again from an entirely different perspective in a discussion of ego in Chapter 8, Book 2. I encourage you to make an effort to become aware of the particular implementation of interpretive listening that necessarily colors and filters **your** end of any attempted communication.

I will eventually paint a detailed high resolution Big Picture for your consideration, but if your beliefs distort it or filter it out, your awareness will never get the opportunity to evaluate its general significance or assess its personal value.

You will have to rely on open minded skepticism to deal with transmission spin that you suspect might be placed on the signal you receive. ◀

The word "infinite," used as a **practical** descriptor of this absolute oneness, does not refer to size in space. It refers to something we 3D humans don't experience directly – perhaps the concept of an apparently infinite potential merged with the concept of a totally blank mind will get you as close as you are going to get. Neither space nor time has been invented yet. I will get to those clever and necessary inventions later, but first this seemingly boundless something must evolve.

The concept of an **apparently** infinite Absolute Unbounded Oneness (AUO) is only half the ingredients we need to grow a new Big TOE. The remaining ingredient is what I call the "Fundamental Process." The Fundamental Process is the basic process of evolution. It is the repetitive pattern of trial and error, of spontaneous change and choice, of random events and encouraged behavior that enables evolution to result in progress. Progress is defined as change within an entity or group of entities that is in some way immediately beneficial or profitable to that entity. Profitable change leaves the entity or its group, or both, in a comparatively better, stronger, more functional, capable, and successful position relative to its internal and external environments.

An entity is a well defined, self-contained (bounded) interactive system. It can be an atom, molecule, rock, technology, computer, worm, monkey, human, organization, city, nation, planet, or an aware individual non-physical consciousness. The interaction of an entity with its internal and external environments is constrained by what those environments will support, encourage, or discourage. Thus, constraints that reflect the demands of the internal and external environments define the criteria for profitability and are the source of evolutionary pressure that pushes every evolving entity forward. When I describe evolution as an imperative, as a force that moves an entity along its evolutionary path, as a pressure, or a driver of change, remember that I am talking about a self-initiating natural process that represents how a self-modifying system or entity interacts with its internal and external environments. We will go over these concepts again in more detail.

The Fundamental Process, as it is applied to a complex entity, moves that entity toward those internal and external states of being that are the most immediately profitable. This motion is the result of external and internal pressures. Changes (evolutionary motion) that result from external pressures can be viewed as the cumulative results of the sum total of the dynamic interactions between an individual entity and everything else, which in aggregate constitutes its external (outside) environment. Evolutionary motion that results from internal pressures can be viewed as the cumulative results of the sum total of the choices or selections that an individual entity makes relative to all available internal configurations and potential states of being.

People genetically engineering better people would be one example of evolutionary motion produced by internal pressures. Fear, ego, love, purpose, stress, pleasure, growth, contentment, ambition, self-improvement, satisfaction, confidence, self-esteem, and social interaction are a few of the internal constraints creating evolutionary pressure. Internal physical environments (internal to your body) may also pressure subsystems (internal organs) and specific tissues to modify themselves in order to gain individual or system efficiencies.

Consciousness primarily evolves by responding to internal pressures; simple biological systems primarily evolve by responding to external pressures. Internal and external evolutionary pressures may interact with, and influence, each other.

As individuals strive for maximum profitability, groups of interdependent entities may evolve together interactively to form a larger system or ecosystem. Interrelated systems interact with each other to form larger systems (such as earth's biological ecosystem and the solar system). Nothing stands alone – all are interrelated from the perspective of the largest level of organization. This applies to all evolving systems and systems of systems – animal, vegetable, mineral, technological, or organizational – and to subsets of systems (including your brain, stomach, or a networked computer), and to subsets of subsets of systems (including your blood and bone cells, or a microprocessor), and so on and so forth (cell parts and transistors followed by their supporting molecular and atomic layers).

Everything within a system evolves together, layer upon layer, within one big web of interaction. All systems exist, survive, and thrive by virtue of a local ecology that defines how their various interdependent internal groupings interrelate. Consciousness, the earth and everything that exists on it, governments, and the internet all evolve their own supporting ecologies. To understand the dynamics of these systems, one must first understand each systems **local** ecology. To understand their significance, one must first understand each systems **larger** ecology.

In Section 5, where we discuss evolution as a process fractal, you will find the same basic evolutionary process turns up again and again at every level of reality – physical and nonphysical. You will see it is the Fundamental Process that drives the smallest sub-atomic particle to populate the states available to it and it is the same Fundamental Process that leads to Our System (OS) spinning off multiple probable realities containing multiple universes within nonphysical-matter reality (NPMR).

▶ Another short aside is now necessary to define two important terms that we are going to use repeatedly.

The term "Our System" (OS) is used often in this section as a high-level descriptor of the larger "place" we live in (OS is discussed in more detail in Chapters 7 through 9, Book 3). OS is defined to be PMR (our physical universe) **plus** the subset of $NPMR_N$ that is interactive with PMR. Here, the notation $NPMR_N$ simply represents a specific subset of NPMR.

If this terminology seems confusing, don't be concerned; it will become clear later. In the meantime, all you need to know is that OS is our home-base reality – the reality system in which we primarily interact. OS is composed of interactive elements that are both physical (such as sentient beings, information, energy, physical matter, organizations, PMR physics, all physical forms, and assorted critters) and nonphysical (such as sentient beings, information, energy, nonphysical matter, organizations, NPMR physics, all thought forms, and assorted critters).

The second concept to be discussed is that of entropy. It is my guess that most readers are not particularly brushed up on the meaning and significance of entropy – a word I use throughout this trilogy. Actually, I slipped in the first use of the word "entropy" toward the end of Chapter 21 – I hoped you wouldn't mind a few isolated instances of physics-speak. However, from now on, you are going to hear more about entropy; accordingly, it is time for me to be more helpful. This aside will theoretically save you the trouble of looking up the word "entropy" and give you a good idea what entropy is all about without becoming too precise or technical. ◀

▶▶ I say "theoretically" because almost nobody actually takes the time and trouble to look something up these days. We are always in a hurry despite how much time we have. We have a strong need to press on with or without the necessary information. Fuzzy understanding seems to always be preferred over delay or loss of continuity – detours are **fundamentally** annoying beyond the extra trouble they cause.

Before I get back to the task of defining entropy, let's wander a little farther down this particular rabbit hole and see what we can learn about how we personally relate to information, and how we are affected by a changing Western culture that is in the process of redefining itself through a revolution in electronics and information technology. The cultural metamorphosis accompanying our transition from the industrial age to the information age is as much about who and what we are as it is about what we do and how we do it. As out tools and relationships change, we and our reality change with them.

From radio to TV to video games to computers, the evolution of consumer electronics has modified how humans think and interact. Most of us, like kids watching *Sesame Street,* need constant stimulation and constant input or our attention wanders and boredom quickly sets in. To the electronic generation, thoughtful pauses become superfluous interruptions, and serious reflection becomes nearly impossible. Under a "use it or lose it" evolutionary mandate, depth and quality of thought are quickly becoming unnecessary and obsolete.

In pursuit of short-term goals in our professional lives and continual entertainment and stimulation in our personal lives, our attention spans grow shorter as superficiality dominates our mental processes.

I understand – we are all in the same boat – it is a Western cultural thing. This is how electronic entertainment and communications technology have affected our minds and thus our perception of reality. Our limited reality is slowly getting broader and shallower. The ecology of our minds is changing from a local lake to a global swamp.

To come full circle along the chain of cause and effect, you should note that the quality and significance of what the commercial media and book vendors produce for us to read is generally so unchallenging and superficial that missing a few words here and there does not make a significant difference. Guess and keep going is a time saving strategy that will always appear to work reasonably well because whatever we miss, by definition, is unknown and not worth the effort.

Our experience tells us that what we miss can be easily surmised from the context of what we get. Finding the most productive and efficient ratio of get-to-miss allows us to process the huge amount of largely inconsequential information that continually bombards us. In the information age, skimming instead of reading is a survival tactic. The calculated skipping and missing of random, difficult, or prickly pieces of content eventually becomes a well justified sampling technique that ultimately grows to exclude much more than irrelevant details. ◀◀

▶▶▶ In a practical sense, anything that we define as irrelevant quickly becomes that way. You do not miss what you are unaware of; consequently, all that lies beyond your vision appears to be irrelevant to you. That is why the uneducated care little for education and are unaware of what they are missing. The uneducated do not know or appreciate the deeper significance of being uneducated. A fact of life: The implications and consequences of your self-imposed limitations can only be seen and appreciated by someone else who does not share them.

If you wish to expand the paradigms that make up your worldview, the most salient question becomes: Who ya gonna call? (See Chapter 23 of this book.) Predicating the validation of a broader viewpoint upon the consensus of the people you respect and associate with is a particularly risky business because you like people who are like you – people who are likely to share your basic beliefs and limitations.

Among these people you feel solid, confident and self-assured. They confirm the soundness of your understanding and the correctness of your vision. You do the same for them. They define your community or social set at all levels of social organization.

Let me take a wild guess. As I look into my crystal ball, I see that you and your best friends are aware of almost everything that is **truly important** for you to know. Furthermore, it appears that you and your closest associates have an excellent understanding (probably better than most) of the truth that lies beneath the surface of most events and actions. Did I guess correctly? You are not alone. Almost everyone on every side of every issue (including wackos and fanatics of all sorts) feel exactly the same way.

"Hey, I'm doing well the way I am – what's the big deal over a little minor ignorance? Serious ignorance? Lots of it? Much important truth lies beyond my vision? Bullpucky! That's impossible! You must be talking about someone else. The people I hold in low esteem are like that, but not me, I know what's **really** going on." ◀◀◀

▶▶ Looking up unfamiliar words, concepts, or events is accurately assessed as an impractical exercise by busy people who are focused outwardly on entertainment and practical information. We focus on what we value. Don't blame the media guys; they produce whatever we are willing to pay for. We value what is quick, convenient, entertaining, easy, practical, and feels good or pays well. What else is there? For most of us, that is a difficult question, the honest answer to which is either the null set or an exceedingly short list.

Time management, a concept born in the Industrial Age, goes critical in the Information Age. If we are not sleeping, we are very, very busy and in hot pursuit of whatever is happening next. Most of us only value the present moment as a bridge to the future. Because we live on the run, we have a tendency to confuse life, meaning, and purpose with motion. The fact is, the choices we make (that ultimately define us) all occur in the present.

Talk about detours! This aside containing an aside that contains yet another aside is forcing you to think in multiple layers. I need to quit and get back on track before we both get lost and decide to go watch TV instead. ◀◀

▶ Entropy is a physics term that you learn about when studying thermodynamics – which is why it is probably not on your list of everyday words to use. Nevertheless, because of its dramatic implications, it is reasonably well known in many technical and philosophical circles.

PMR systems naturally dissipate their energy. If no new energy is put into a system, the energy that is available to do work within that system will eventually waste away. Everything, such as a new battery, has a shelf-life. Constrained energy (such as a flashlight battery or full tank of gasoline in your car), which is energy in a form that can do work, is either used up doing that work or eventually dissipates away (as its shelf life is exceeded). In either case, all the original highly organized and structured molecules and atoms making up the gasoline and automobile and the new battery and flashlight have been converted (after doing work or dissipating) to a new, less organized and less structured collection of atoms and molecules (including fumes, vapor, light, heat, worn off brake and tire particles, and metal flakes in the oil) that no longer can do as much work as the original configuration. We say that energy has been used up when actually it has only changed into a less structured, less usable form such as heat that is diffused throughout the system.

Any closed physical system must eventually run out of **useable** gas or batteries and become no longer able to do work because gas evaporates and both chemically degenerate over time even if they are not purposely consumed to produce light or provide transportation. We say that the entropy of the closed system has increased. "Closed" means that nothing is added or taken away – all the same particles and same total energy remain within the system before and after. Though the **total** energy must remain constant, it continuously, spontaneously, and slowly changes form over time (naturally degenerates as it grows older) as well as occasionally changes form (turn on the flashlight or ignite the gasoline) rather quickly. Eventually, one way or another, the available-for-use full potential of a new battery or fresh tank of gasoline becomes a comparatively useless collection of uniformly distributed vapor, radiation, and heat).

The change in entropy is a measure of how much energy is now (as compared to earlier) no longer available to do work. Equivalently, entropy is a measure of the disorder within our hypothetical system (less organization and less structure among the atoms and molecules in our closed system). More entropy means more disorder and less energy that is available to do work. Conversely, less entropy means less disorder (more order and structure within the system) and that more of the system's energy is available to do work.

The second law of thermodynamics states that the **average** entropy of the PMR universe (initially **assumed** to be a closed system) must increase with time. This means that all matter and energy in the universe will eventually move toward a state of inert uniformity – absolutely nothing left of our entire universe but hydrogen ions and elementary particles.

Don't sweat it, you still have time to finish *My Big TOE* and grow one of your own before you decompose. A universe that is as massively chunky as ours takes a long time to disintegrate. Look on the bright side: 1) the physical universe may not be a closed system and 2) the sun will expand and vaporize our entire planet long before the universe decays into a homogeneous soup of simple particles. ◀

You will get more detailed information about these concepts later. For the purposes of this section, you need only to understand that **all** things and systems of things are in an active process of change – animal, vegetable, mineral, technological, and organizational – and that the Fundamental Process is the basis for that change. All things evolve toward greater profitability. Profitability is defined by the degree of immediate success an entity has in dealing with the evolutionary pressures created by the constraints within their internal and external environments. This is true if the entity is an individual or a complex system of interrelated dissimilar individuals.

Non-living and non-growing things (such as uranium atoms, organic molecules, the house you live in, and the rocks in your back yard) generally evolve toward minimum energy states. When non-growing entities make a natural, spontaneous, or evolutionary change of state, the lowest **available** energy state is defined as the most profitable next-state to occupy. Most of the physical matter, on and in our planet, falls into this category. Thus, physical matter gradually follows a path to ever lower energy states, increasing its entropy as it evolves. To inanimate matter, natural spontaneous change due to interaction with its internal and external environments (evolution), disintegration, and increasing entropy are all related and moving together in the same general direction.

Typically, growing things (things that are in a state of becoming) can naturally and spontaneously – for at least some limited period of time – decrease their entropy. In contrast, the entropy of non-growing things always naturally increases. In PMR, the growing things ultimately depend on the non-growing things, thus fulfilling the grim prediction of the second law of thermodynamics. We will discover that in mind-space where AUO exists as dim consciousness, there are no physical things and **everything** has the potential to grow. In mind-space, seeking the lowest energy state is never a goal. Quite the contrary, for a consciousness system the most profitable next-state is one that enables that system to minimize its entropy. In other words, evolutionary change within a consciousness system is profitable for that system if it causes the entropy of the system to decrease.

There is a natural tendency for an entity to make those choices, or to exploit or succumb to those changes that move that entity toward its evolutionary goals. That is, toward a more profitable configuration or mutually beneficial arrangement – toward a lower energy state for physical matter (higher entropy) or a lower entropy state (higher usable energy) for consciousness. The Fundamental Process explores all the opportunities and possibilities for change, then inextricably and statistically moves each entity, each collection of similar entities (such as a species or a field full of rocks), or each collection of collections of diverse entities (community or ecosystem) toward its immediate goals by continuing to evolve the winners. The Fundamental Process of evolution is a recursive process that builds layer upon layer of interdependent organization and structure: a process that repeats and folds back upon itself at many different scales and levels of interaction.

Again, let me caution you to not be confused by the use of verbs in a sentence that has the Fundamental Process as the subject. That particular language construction is simply convenient and more succinctly expressive in describing the dynamics of evolutionary change. The Fundamental Process is a simple natural process – not an active sentient growth manager that can execute action verbs toward the achievement of some preconceived goal.

Each evolving entity moves into all the possibilities open to it that it can afford to occupy. It continues to invest in the winners by succeeding within those possibilities that provide the most value or profitability – not by deliberate **intellectual** choice making – but by trying everything available and allowing whatever works (holds immediate value for the entity) to progress forward while letting whatever does not work (the losers) flounder. This is a natural selection activity from the inside executed by the evolving entity, not an intellectual activity or a directed response from the outside executed by the Fundamental Process. The only **external** forcing function is the external environment in which the entity exists.

From now on, when you read that the Fundamental Process does this or that, or makes this or that happen, or I use any action verb to describe an evolutionary effect, you will know what I mean, right?

This same Fundamental Process, when it is applied to earth-based biological systems, produces the evolution you learned about in school. The Fundamental Process applied to consciousness produces different results, because consciousness and its environments are different, but it is the exact same idea, the exact same process raised to a more general understanding.

For that matter, the Fundamental Process also drives change in organizations and technologies. All sorts of technologies have evolved – from the complex nest building of many insects, birds, and mammals to the transportation, medical, agricultural, communication, networking, and computer technology developed by humans during the preceding century.

The evolution of technology follows a similar Fundamental Process. It expands into the available states (needs, uses, applications) progressing the winners and dropping the losers. The evolutionary pressure, defined by the criteria for profitability, flows from the constraints of usefulness, feasibility, marketing, economics, and business. Here, profitability can be literal as well as figurative. Technological evolution (the evolution of a technical entity) is like the evolution of any entity. As technology evolves, it produces an increased richness and complexity of potential future states that creates more evolutionary opportunities for new or improved technologies. As evolution progresses, the pace of change accelerates.

Technological evolutionary pressure comes from the external economic environments of raw materials, marketing, supply, distribution, demand, and price, as well as the internal environments of feasibility, design, engineering, parts availability, manufacturing, quality, pricing, and finance. Mutations and new technical entities may seem to spring into being quickly and discontinuously, yet all are built upon the knowledge base or genetic pool of earlier technical entities. The Fundamental Process works basically the same way with all types of entities – physical, nonphysical, human, insects, bacteria, molecules, rivers, mountains, rocks, organizations, nations, consciousness, automobiles, or computers. The differences in evolutionary patterns among animals, organizations, consciousness, and technology are not due to differences in the evolutionary process, but rather to the variety of entities and to the variety of environments and constraints that define the criteria for their profitability.

It is the Fundamental Process that encourages life and other types of evolvable systems or entities (including technological, organizational, social, and so on) to flow into any niche or configuration that can profitably sustain them.

For consciousness, living things, organizations, and technology, dynamic repetitive implementation of the Fundamental Process of evolution represents the natural statistical inclination of an entity, organism, species, or a complex interconnected population of entities to grow into and become whatever is most profitable from each organism's point of view. Simpler entities sometimes band together cooperatively to form more complex entities and systems that are more powerful and thus more profitable for all participants.

Groups of entities may develop mutually beneficial relationships and dependencies because they share an interactive synergetic environment. Eventually, after much integration, the view of the whole becomes more significant than the view of each part – they become one complex thing – a system that evolves as its parts evolve. Next comes systems of systems, and so on as complexity, specialization, and higher orders of organization (decreasing entropy) become profitable. Consciousness, alligators, governments, planet earth, and the internet all evolve the same way. Exactly what constitutes living and conscious and how such systems are uniquely defined will be defined later in this section.

In short, the Fundamental Process explores every available opportunity and every possibility on all levels, and invests more heavily in whatever actually returns the best overall profits. In carbon-based biology, the assessment of profit has traditionally been based upon the constraints of survival and reproduction. The earth's biology represents one special case of the application of a much more general evolutionary process. For instance, for non-living and non-growing entities, what is most profitable is usually the lowest available energy state – the easiest and cheapest state to achieve. The **sequence** of these lowest available energy state "choices" made by an inanimate entity defines the path of least resistance, which that entity **naturally** follows if it is not impacted by external energy forcing it to do otherwise. That is why atoms decay, your house continually needs maintenance, and rocks roll downhill.

Even the most basic forms of PMR activity follow the evolutionary pattern of choice and profitability. Thus a radioactive atom decays and the shelf-life of a battery deteriorates according to the Fundamental Process. On the other hand, an atom is pumped up to a higher energy state, sand is turned into sandstone, and mountains are thrust up along fault lines because of the input and absorption of external energy. Even in these circumstances, the entity **plus** the absorbed and retained energy will arrange themselves into the most profitable minimum energy configuration.

The Big Picture Fundamental Process of evolution (or Fundamental Process, for short) is as follows. An entity starts from any point (level) of existence or being, spreads out its potentiality into (explores) all the available possibilities open to its existence, **eventually** populating only the states that are immediately profitable while letting the others go. It then iteratively progresses the successful states to their logical conclusions by probing new opportunities and limitations. As long as there are profitable opportunities, the process continues to iterate and the entity continues to evolve. Additionally, intermediate states can generate (branch to, or be the potential seeds for) new states. States that no longer hold potential for (do not support) profitable growth may persist or be recombined with others with which they are redundant. Potential is generally maintained, in the event that new initial conditions appear.

We will now apply the Fundamental Process to our assumption of an Absolute Unbounded Oneness (AUO). The first step in that process is to expand an entity's potential for existence or being into all the significant possibilities (available states). An apparently (but not actually) infinite, absolute, unbounded, undifferentiated, thing can most obviously find potential new states of existence or possibilities of being by changing its undifferentiated oneness. That is, it can most directly and easily interact with itself. Additionally, because at this point in our story AUO is the only thing we have posited to exist, it is logically necessary that it interact only with itself.

Most biological things are aware of their environment (external awareness of things such as hot/cold, acid/base, and wet/dry). Additionally, they are aware of themselves (internal or self-awareness of things such as hungry/full, hydrated/dehydrated, threatened/safe, peaceful/agitated, hurt/not hurt, pain/pleasure, joy/sadness, and fear/love). All life-forms (biological, consciousness, or otherwise) change themselves. Sometimes the change is in reaction to their environment – they adapt. Sometimes the change is internally generated – they mutate. Evolution typically moves toward more complex, capable, and highly organized lower entropy forms – building upon or enhancing the earlier simpler forms. More advanced products of evolution can sometimes successfully change their environment – like prairie dogs building cool moist underground homes in hot arid places.

▶ Beep. Beep. Beep. Beep. Beep… Uh, oh… that is the number three audio alarm on my new problemometer. Hang on a minute while I find out what's the matter…. All right. …I see…. *No Problema,* the solution is a simple one.

Relax, you are not brain damaged, retarded, or becoming mentally infirm with old age. If you have not been graced with a career that brushes up against government organizations awash in acronym stew, a poor memory for acronyms is normal. If you are not used to using acronyms, they seem, for most people, to have been given a special non-stick coating that causes them to constantly slip from memory. It is a natural brain wiring and symbol association problem that occurs when the name-symbol represents a string of associated words instead of a single common name. The solution? Forget the words; let the acronym be a single name.

For those not used to acronyms, here is how it works. The first time or two you encounter an acronym, think about what the words mean, get a sense, an understanding, of the concept being talked about – then forget about the individual words making up the acronym and use the acronym as a name associated with the meaning and concept the acronym represents. Subsequently "AUO" becomes a name like "Fred" – a name that you associate with a finite, but seemingly infinite, evolving primordial consciousness. It is that simple – AUO becomes the proper name of a particular conceptual entity.

If you do not treat the acronym as a name, you may feel obligated to look up what the constituting words are every time you see it. Dutifully looking up acronyms wastes time and effort and generates little value. The individual words are not important; the concept, the definition, the meaning is important – attach those to the acronym itself and go on.

If you forget the **concept** associated with AUO, look it up in the acronym list at the beginning of each book and follow the page reference to where it was first defined. However, if you have a firm grasp of the meaning and significance of AUO, then the individual words that AUO represents are not important – let them go. Do not struggle with how habitual language use has wired your brain. Rewiring is difficult and provides little value for the effort spent.

Acronyms are handy for condensing long **descriptive** titles into short names. I use them extensively throughout the text because an acronym has the nifty attribute that it carries its own definition within its name. Treat them as words and symbols, the same way you would treat any name of any noun and your memory will not seem so sieve-like. Problem solved. ◀

We now have our two fundamental concepts in place, and as required by our local PMR causal logic, at least one, AUO, appears to be mystical from the view of PMR. These two assumptions provide the necessary and sufficient foundation (called a "footer" in the construction trades) from which to build a new Big TOE. Neither are new ideas.

Darwin ushered in the theory of evolution by natural selection in the late 1850s. The concept of AUO is, and has always been (at least since about 600 B.C.), a fundamental concept in various philosophic, spiritual, metaphysical, and religious traditions. For our purposes, we utilize only the bare basics of this concept, no frills, no dogma, and no extraneous conditions or attributes – just a plain, simple, minimalistic Absolute Unbounded Oneness – a form of potential energy that appears to be non-physical from the limited PMR point of view. AUO is a seemingly infinite primordial consciousness whose beginning depends upon a causal requirement that is so far beyond our local reality that it is outside our rational consideration – as refrigerator light bulbs, sunshine, or stock market dynamics are outside the rational consideration of our intestinal bacteria – nevertheless, the bacteria are **indirectly** and powerfully affected by these things.

The Fundamental Process of evolution is what enables and necessitates growth, learning, and change. Without the Fundamental Process, nothing could become more than it is now, all change would be random, direction-less, and purposeless. We know from our personal experience and the diversity of biological systems that this is not the case; that there is a fundamental imperative for all life-forms to grow and evolve is obvious. Furthermore, it is also obvious that exploring the possibilities and investing in what works is the engine that drives the process. The evolution of bio-logical forms on earth, though a special application of a more general Fundamental Process, demonstrates these facts adequately.

From the foundation of these two assumptions alone, we will construct piece-by-piece, a rational Big TOE based primarily on direct experimen-tal evidence with some reasonable conjecture added to bind it all together. It will be shaped by whatever common data points (accepted facts and truths) we can find. If successful, there will be no known facts or truths that conflict with this Big TOE. The degree of your success in corroborating this reality model with your experience depends on the correctness of My Big TOE and on the correctness of the truths and facts with which you test it.

The sub-foundation has been laid. Next we need to develop the basic logical results and consequences of our two basic assumptions. In the process we will improve and refine our understanding of each assump-tion. If things are not crystal clear at this point, they will become clearer as we proceed. By the end of Section 4, you will be able to pull these con-cepts together into a complete foundation for the reality model of Section 5. Developing basic concepts may be tedious, but this is where the Big Picture must necessarily begin. Getting the basics is usually the least fun part, but also the most crucial. Let's get started.

The adventure begins! Ladies and gentlemen...start your engines!

25
■■■
The Evolution of AUO: Awareness
■■■

The awareness of a single cell, an amoeba, a worm, a bumblebee, a chimpanzee, or a human being are all fundamentally based upon the same process. Awareness differs mainly by degree. Somewhere along the path from simple single process action-reaction (or stimulus-response) to a more complex multi-process interaction-reaction, the capacity to remember (store information) evolved. It is this ability to store or retain information that enables learning. Even the simplest of biological life-forms have the capacity to learn by retaining or storing information in their physical structures (DNA for example). This learned information can be transferred to future generations through reproduction. Learning through the evolutionary process of exploring the possibilities and retaining the results of lessons learned (in your DNA or in the Library of Congress) so that they can be passed on to future generations is a natural self-reinforcing process.

Deoxyribo Nucleic Acid (DNA – a nucleic acid that carries the genetic information in the cell and is capable of self-replication and synthesis of ribonucleic acid), or other forms of bio-memory, are not as difficult to influence or modify as most scientists think. It is commonly thought that it takes thousands of years for evolution to modify biology substantially – that many millennia must pass before complex biological systems (like people or polar bears) evolve new ways of being – new instincts, new firmware. Quite the contrary, biological systems do not necessarily go through a long drawn out and difficult random mutation and selection process to modify bio-memory. In a relatively short time, significant change can be established or disestablished that will be passed from generation to generation if those latter generations reinforce the change because they also find it profitable. Memory, capable of inputting and retrieving data quickly enough to support cognition, is a primary enabler of both species learning and dim awareness.

Shorter data input and data modification times, as well as quick read and write access, are required for **individual** learning and to support a brighter awareness. It should be obvious to you that a brighter, more functional awareness is naturally associated with larger memory, shorter memory input and access times, and better information processing capabilities. What does that remind you of? A biological brain connected to a sensory apparatus – or maybe a computer? It appears as if biological brain consciousness or digital consciousness systems, operating with high bandwidth input-output (I/O) and very short processor cycle times and memory access times, might **theoretically** have an exceptional capacity for individual learning and brightness (evolving their own firmware and software). That theoretical potential for the exceptional brightness of a brain or a digital computer could perhaps become actual brightness if the data input-output systems connecting it to its internal and external data-source environments, along with its purpose-goal-intent-action-result feedback systems, generate a rich enough set of uniquely profitable possibilities to provide adequate evolutionary potential to support the development of a high level of mental function. In other words, if the entity **interacts** (at a minimum receives data and makes choices based on those data) within sufficiently complex environments and develops sufficiently high bandwidth connections to those environments, it will eventually evolve a higher, brighter level of awareness to better utilize that data. If the range of possible choices and the methods of selection between choices are also sufficiently rich and complex, the potential for brightness greatly expands. Hold on to these concepts: They will become more important later on as brains and computers are related to digital consciousness.

Thus, biological systems – living things – evolve, learn, grow, and change purposely. They make progress. Their existence is directed by finding more profitable ways of being and relating. Profitable strategies such as storing food for the winter, and technologies such as nest building, are developed, internalized, and "remembered" (retained by biological modification) and put to good use by later, more successful generations. Over time, a biological or genetic group memory may develop – a sort of hardwired cultural belief system.

Heredity is not the only transfer mechanism. Simple flatworms have been trained to respond to external stimuli. Untrained flatworms that are fed the trained worms seem to gain the knowledge of their consumed brethren. (Kids, don't try this at home. Unless you are a flatworm, eating your parents or teachers will not make you any smarter and could get you into serious trouble).

Most of the more advanced products of evolution eschew chewing on their intelligentsia and find it more efficient to exchange information by energizing each other's sensory inputs and outputs – sight, sound, smell, touch, and taste for example. This communicated information is processed, evaluated, acted on, stored, and retrieved. When a large dog faces you squarely, growls and shows his teeth while the hair stands up on the back of his neck, do you get the intended message? Is there a successful audio-visual information transfer?

Simple life-forms know when things feel better. For instance, they know what, when, and how to eat and reproduce **selectively**. The extent to which learning takes place depends on the extent and efficiency with which experience interacts with memory. The degree of complexity of the life-form allows for variations in the specialization of the organs of awareness. Such specializations define the breadth and depth of the sensory input and the speed and efficiency of storing, retrieving and using information to describe, evaluate and select possible action-reaction sequences. All life-forms react to both their internal and external environments. Every life-form is in the problem solving mode trying to improve its situation and increase its immediate profitability. Problem-solving is the natural response to environmental pressure. Plants move toward the sun, night-crawlers scurry down their holes as they assess minute seismic danger signals, and humans have invented whiskey and nuclear bombs.

Awareness is a characteristic of consciousness. To some extent, all the earth's life-forms are aware and conscious. All store and retrieve information more or less continually and therefore have the capacity to learn, to improve themselves, and to become more than what they presently are – to evolve. Some awareness is more or less efficient, brighter or dimmer, than others. It is a continuum. Jellyfish, raccoons, and people are all aware of some things and unaware of other things. It is more a matter of degree and focus than a fundamental difference in the nature of awareness. Limitations on the richness and complexity of the possible interactions and responses that an entity can have with its external and internal environments are what define each entity's capacity for awareness. The process of developing awareness is the same for all entities, whereas the limitations and the environments of each entity are unique.

By now, it should be clear that developing and evolving awareness is a standard, normal and natural happening among biological entities. Similarly to a one-celled biological entity, AUO (Absolute Unbounded Oneness) develops awareness of itself in relation to itself by mutating or modifying its internal uniformity or structure. I am using the term awareness here relative to AUO in the same way that it is used above. Let's call it dim awareness. Dim awareness is fundamentally the same as any awareness, only very limited in its scope and complexity. At its dimmest, dim awareness is simply the potential for awareness.

Consider the first simple multi-celled creatures floating in our oceans eons ago. This dim cellular awareness figured out (in the evolutionary sense) that if certain cells would specialize in specific functions (eating, digestion, reproduction, locomotion, coordination, control), then more complex and more successful creatures could evolve (improved survivability and procreation). What a discovery!

This and many other pivotal evolutionary discoveries provide strong testimonial for the usefulness and efficacy of dim awareness as motivated by the Fundamental Process. One thing leads to another and, long before time runs out (our sun expands to incinerate the earth), evolution progresses earth biology from simple groups of dimly aware cells to a diversity of relatively clever fish and reptiles (complex biology that is more aware of, and interactive with, its environment). Eventually, this brain train moves on to a quirky species of naked apes capable of genetically engineering themselves. Awareness grows and evolves similarly to how physical bodies have grown and evolved. That is an important concept to understand.

How does this Absolute Unbounded Oneness indescribable something acquire dim awareness? The same way one celled things did, and simple multi-celled things did, and so on up the ladder of evolution: by interacting with whatever constitutes the external and internal environments. AUO is real and therefore not actually infinite and thus may have an external environment as well as an internal environment. Nevertheless, because this external environment and its description are beyond our comprehension, we will not use it to develop our TOE.

An external environment may or may not have contributed to AUO's initial dim awareness, but we have no logical need to include it. It is adequate for our purposes to assume that AUO interacts only with itself (mutation) to gain dim awareness. Developing awareness is the natural result of a self-modifying entity applying the Fundamental Process to challenging environments (internal or external) that contain large numbers of multiple possibilities.

Awareness at the cellular (dim) level evolves naturally from the existence of a rich and varied array of available potential states. These states are generated by direct choice, random events, and dumb luck – being at the right place at the right time with the right stuff. The entity explores all the potential states it can successfully populate. The more successful or profitable configurations continue to evolve while the less profitable ones either remain in their niche or die off. Over time, hardware (body), firmware (instincts) and software (mind – processing capability) are slowly improved.

Applying the Fundamental Process is natural and intuitively obvious to even extremely dim awareness. Try everything that is accessible and affordable, and go with what works. Is AUO alive? Certainly not by our 3D earth related (biological) standards and perspective, but then our standards are only relevant to PMR. I will show that AUO meets the requirements for developing awareness and eventually intelligence.

All that is required for AUO to evolve some type of limited awareness is that it exist interactively within the context of a challenging environment (external or self-generated) that contains a large number of multiple possibilities, and that there is available to it a rich and varied array of potential choices or states of being with variable profitability it can explore. Remember, we are conceptualizing and postulating something that by definition lies beyond our 3D comprehension. In our effort to understand AUO and NPMR, we are like Flatlanders struggling to visualize a tetrahedron slowly tumbling within a rotating hollow cube that is spiraling down the inner surface of an elliptical funnel. Go explain that to your two-dimensional buddies over flat beer.

Because the existence of AUO is the one mystical or metaphysical (from a PMR perspective) assumption that enables this Big TOE to discuss our beginnings logically, we need to understand this AUO-thing. In some ways, AUO can be thought of as roughly analogous to the first biological cells from which many of our planet's living things evolved. AUO was dimly aware of itself in the same way that primordial biological cells were dimly aware of (could interact with) themselves and their environment. Where did AUO come from? Our relentless and illogical sense of a universal causality forces this question. There is no good answer. The best bad answer: AUO came into existence the same way those first biological cells did. Good luck eventually ran into the right ingredients at the right time with a supporting environment and perhaps a spark of some sort of mental energy thrown in for good measure – I truly do not know. AUO's origins lie beyond the logical reach of our understanding. Our PMR causality can offer no rational input on its own beginnings, much less AUO's beginnings. The only logical failure is in the asking of the question.

Where did the ingredients, the environment, and the spark come from? Leave me alone – go ask your mother! It is not an appropriate question. Demanding answers to questions such as these is analogous to demanding that a Linelander (a one-dimensional being) describe a sphere to his two pointy-headed friends. He cannot do it. He does not have the capacity to comprehend spheres because of the fundamental limitations of his existence and his reality. The question is simply not relevant to his reality or to his existence. Likewise, intestinal bacteria cannot understand the stock market or the properties and value of sunshine – these are beyond rational consideration for intestinal bacteria. We humans are in the same position relative to the origins of AUO. There are some things, which may affect us indirectly, that we do not have the practical or theoretical ability to perceive or understand. Denial of that fact (or at least that possibility) may change our perception of reality and support our needs, but it cannot change the nature of reality.

You should continually work on developing scientific data about what you can understand while avoiding making assumptions and creating beliefs about what you cannot understand. Appreciating your limitations is the first step toward both knowledge and wisdom.

From some limited perspectives (like the perspective of our space-time PMR universe) the answers to some questions cannot be comprehended or conceived. You have to live with that fact. Metaphysics, mind, and a careful exploration of the subjective offer a less limited perspective that goes a step or two beyond our current objective science, but go too far beyond that, and truth dissolves into speculation while speculation degenerates into fantasy. To be sure, conjecture can quickly wander into fantasyland if it does not remain connected to a rational foundation of objective, measurable truth-data. How well the model performs is what lends credibility to the assumptions made at the beginning. Save your judgments until later.

You will discover by the end of Section 5 that everything we do in this reality seems to **follow** (is in the image of, one might say) AUO's pattern of being. It will become clear that our existence, being, and evolution are an expression of, and the result of, the existence, being, and evolvement of AUO. Our individual consciousness reflects the pattern of AUO as a piece of a hologram, or each individual element of a large fractal design, contains the pattern that defines the whole. If the evolution of our consciousness and our physical reality is a reflection of AUO's evolution, it would seem reasonable (as one can be addressing this issue) that AUO's evolution should exhibit similar processes to our own. The actual reasonableness of that statement depends on how closely we followed AUO's original pattern. AUO is primary consciousness, we are derivative consciousness. It is not unusual that a child might resemble its parent.

26
■■■

The Evolution of AUO:
Who Is That Masked Consciousness
Thing, and What Can It Do?

■■■

At this point in our exposition, AUO is apparently the only thing that exists (no space, no time), and its dim awareness interacts primarily with itself, in relation to itself. To be more accurate, AUO is apparently the only thing that exists that is interactive with, or relevant to, our reality or us. What may or may not exist beyond AUO is also beyond relevance to us. Thus, for now, we can ignore any hypothetical external supporting environment, or conceptualize it as a non-interactive void – whether it is or not.

What else do we know that can exist outside the bounds of space and time? If you think about it for a moment, you will immediately become dimly aware that thought, mind, consciousness or spirit are the only things known to us that are not bounded by our time and space. AUO is primordial consciousness. Could our individual consciousness as well as the physical universe be related to, or derived from, AUO? Absolutely!

▶ A quick glance forward may provide a more solid basis for you to properly structure the concepts that are now popping up in front of you. Sometimes it is easier to make sense out of what you are doing if you can see where it is leading. As this Big TOE slowly comes into focus over the next three sections, you will eventually come to realize that consciousness is the basic media from which reality is formed – the fundamental non-material material of existence. It will also become apparent that a more structured form of this fundamental primordial consciousness energy can reasonably evolve into an ultra-low entropy consciousness that can generate the operative digital mind required to animate and define the content of our larger reality.

Consciousness provides the basic organizational energy from which all individuated existence is derived. It provides the self-modifiable form, function, and potential energy the Fundamental Process of evolution optimizes. Eventually, something analogous to cell specialization evolves within AUO to create internal dimensions that support various realities populated by individuated units of consciousness. The Fundamental Process drives change at all levels including the growth opportunities that eventually define individuated consciousness content such as yourself. By the end of Section 5, you should understand how our physical reality, including you, is created, the process by which it operates, and what purpose it serves. You will also better understand the nonphysical dynamics underlying your physical existence as well as the nature of both personal and public reality. I do not want to get too far ahead of my story lest it tempt you to jump to conclusions that are wrong-headed and in error even though they might seem obvious at this point in the unraveling. ◀

Let's be careful not to fall into an anthropomorphic trap. I am not implying that AUO is (or ever becomes) conscious or sentient in the same way that a human being is conscious or sentient. I am implying that AUO is (or represents) primordial consciousness – an energy form that, like earth's early carbon based bio-forms, has the potential to evolve awareness. AUO represents the primordial substance of consciousness itself, not the attribute of being conscious.

Consciousness is the result of evolution offering profitability to a self-organizing complex system of relational digital content. Another way of conceptualizing AUO is as an apparently infinite potential energy. The potential energy of digital consciousness is the potential to self-organize, which is derived from the potential of a digital system to reduce its average entropy through evolution. A system able to lower its entropy through self organization will eventually host some level of consciousness. Over the next several chapters we will see how a digital model of highly aware consciousness can be derived from a single monolithic consciousness system that is driven to ever lower values of average entropy (higher values of usable energy) by the requirements of evolutionary profitability.

What can AUO do with itself to create the stimulating environment that drives evolution and how did it figure out how to do this? It figured out how in the same way those biological cells did. It may take an extremely long time (dim awareness can be very slow), but under the steady pressure of a relentless evolution constantly nudging all systems toward greater profitability, progress is eventually made as new possibilities are explored.

What could AUO do that was interesting and challenging and stimulating?

It can first create a duality within itself. This vs. not this. It can alter its uniformity to create a local disturbance or distortion. Then there exists, distorted relative to non-distorted. A duality has been created. It is as if that calm, still ocean you were floating in a few chapters ago to gain an intuitive sense of apparently infinite absolute unbounded oneness now has evolved to the point of making a tiny ripple. With lots of practice and some good luck, ripples eventually become waves and whirlpools. Distortion or any other non-uniformity exists only in relation to uniformity. How many different kinds or types of disturbance can AUO create relative to its uniformity? Who knows? For our purposes, we need only one.

A single localized modification of the uniform state is all that is required to derive ourselves, our physics, and all the rest of our reality (physical and nonphysical). This way (uniform) relative to that way (locally non-uniform) is sufficient. Given that AUO somehow discovers a disturbance or non-uniformity relative to itself, it can return to uniform, then intentionally reestablish the locally disturbed state, then return back to uniform and so on. We now have the possibility of a regularly recurring event that will eventually evolve into a precisely recurring event. Figures 2-1, 2-2, and 2-3 show three examples of a regularly occurring continuous change between non-uniform and uniform states. A precisely occurring event might eventually be used to invent time (the first tick-tock, tick-tock, tick-tock as it were). But before we could reasonably expect something as advanced as uniform vibration or oscillation, AUO has a lot more evolving yet to accomplish.

Considering biological evolution on earth, one would say that one-celled critters discovered multi-celled configurations were more effective, and later discovered that cell specialization provided a more efficient multi-celled organism. Here, I am using the word "discovered" in the evolutionary sense. Such discoveries are not necessarily well defined events. They are more typically diffused happenings that occur over long periods of time and after huge numbers of more or less random internal experiments have been evaluated for profitability (improved survivability for bio-organisms or lower entropy for consciousness organisms).

The continuing evolution of AUO requires more and more complexity in the ways that AUO might express differentiation of one part of itself relative to another. What are its opportunities (the possibilities) for dualizing? There are many ways AUO could change state and then change back. Here are a few of the simplest ways. AUO could, for example, discover dualization in a bipolar as well as unipolar mode. The unipolar mode (uniform, positive-disturbance, uniform, positive-disturbance, uniform, and so on), could be in the form of $|\sin(\omega t)|$ (shown in Fig. 2-1),

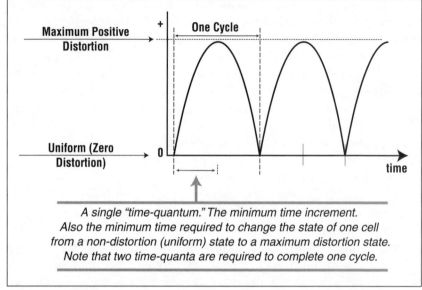

Figure 2.1: Unipolar oscillation in the form of $|\sin(\omega t)|$

or perhaps $[\sin(\omega t) +1]/2$, or $\sin^2(\omega t)$. It could also be in the form of a linear sawtooth (Fig. 2-2), or any number of other useful forms.

AUO could also oscillate between positive and negative disturbance states (uniform, positive-disturbance, uniform, negative-disturbance, uniform,

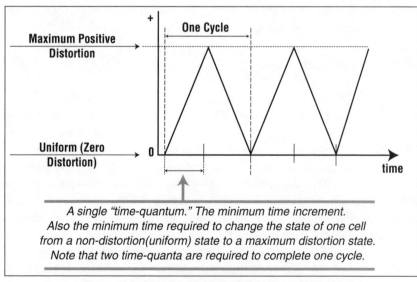

Figure 2.2: Linear unipolar oscillation (sawtooth)

positive-disturbance, uniform, negative-disturbance, uniform, and so on). This type of oscillation is called "bipolar" and could, for example, be in the form of sin(ωt) (as shown in Fig. 2-3). Here, the words "positive" and "negative" represent opposite disturbances such as good/bad, hot/cold, more/less, sharp/dull, bright/dim, acid/base, hungry/full, thought/no-thought, or whatever suits AUO's nature and newly found sensibilities. Notice that I avoided using spatial opposites (such as here/there, up/down and in/out) because space is not a native construct of AUO and has not yet been discovered by AUO.

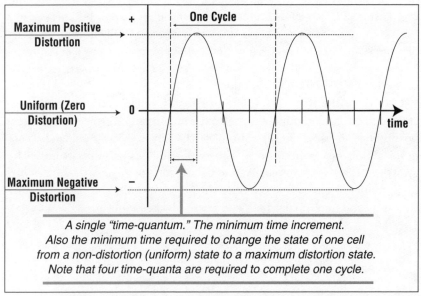

A single "time-quantum." The minimum time increment. Also the minimum time required to change the state of one cell from a non-distortion (uniform) state to a maximum distortion state. Note that four time-quanta are required to complete one cycle.

Figure 2.3: Bipolar oscillation in the form of sin(ωt)

If math (trigonometry) functions such as sin(ωt) or |sin(ωt)| are not a part of your everyday reality, do not be concerned. They are not particularly important to understanding the binary nature of disturbed vs. not-disturbed. I use them here only to demonstrate the wide range of simple as well as complex possibilities that AUO could employ to define this versus that and because the logical side of Mother Nature seems to be partial to sinusoids. That AUO, similarly to the primordial biological cells of our planet, somehow evolves to become dimly aware that it can affect changes in its state is the main message here. The details of how it changes state are not important to the conceptual Big Picture being painted.

AUO is now at a level that is analogous to the one-celled or few-celled organisms floating in the primordial soup that represents our planet's biological beginnings. In fact, in honor of this analogy, let's call this singular relative disturbance in AUO a reality cell.

As the Fundamental Process dictates, awareness, however dim, always creates ever more possibilities for itself to explore. Likewise, complexity, however simple, always generates greater possibilities for the evolving entity to investigate. Thus, as evolution would have it, AUO eventually discovers it can simultaneously create two disturbances relative to its seemingly infinite uniformity, then three, then four, then hundreds, then billions, then.... After all, an approximately infinite, practically unbounded oneness should easily manage and support quantity far beyond our comprehension. We ourselves are composed of billions upon billions of cells. Continuing our analogy with biological systems, AUO is now at the stage of a huge multi-celled but still very simple behemoth. Here a cell, there a cell, everywhere a cell cell ... (reality cell, that is), but no structure, no order, no specialization of function – yet.

Growth in the type and number of reality cells should be sufficiently challenging for a long time because each increment of growth creates new possibilities for new configurations of the larger system. Likewise, each new state of the system represents new possibilities and opportunities for growth. Awareness, complexity, and useful control grow with the number of potential states or possibilities AUO can profitably explore (reach through evolution). What happens next? AUO is about to get organized.

27

■■■

The Evolution of AUO:
Patterns, Symbols, Information,
and Memory; Motivation and
Evolutionary Constraints

■■■

If you were AUO, what could you eventually do with a trillion billion gazillion reality cells? For starters, you could begin arranging your local deformations (cells) into patterns. Then patterns of patterns, and groups of patterns of patterns – whatever your mind could hold. Would a good memory be helpful here? Isn't it neat how the imperative to implement the Fundamental Process creates evolutionary pressures that deliver whatever is most profitable to the evolving organism (mega-memory is on the way)? Where many choices can be profitable, the outcome is great diversity.

To get a glimmer of the potential of AUO organizing its cells into multiple levels of patterns, look at what William Shakespeare accomplished by arranging and rearranging only twenty-six letters of the English alphabet. Consider the contents of the Library of Congress, and this book you are reading: together they represent a tremendous output from simply rearranging twenty-six letters of one language into groups of patterns of patterns. If every word **ever** written or spoken in **any** language were stored utilizing binary reality cells as memory (using distorted vs. not distorted, in the same way computers use 0s and 1s to represent letters and numbers), AUO would have used up only an infinitesimal percentage of the available reality cells. Such is the nature of seemingly infinite unbounded oneness. It seems limitless; its capacity, relative to ours, **appears** infinite.

I do not say that AUO appears to go on endlessly and forever because applying our space and time constrained words and concepts to ideas far beyond their reach creates confusion and paradoxes. AUO cannot be conceived of in terms of space and time. Yet we 3D creatures of limited knowledge must use the tools and modes of conception and communication that we have – and stretch them to reach out to the unknown that lies beyond our horizon. It is important not to let our words and their implicit PMR conceptual limitations trap us into believing that reality is, by definition, fully contained within three spatial dimensions and restricted to what we can physically perceive.

By now, AUO is (or parts of AUO are) considerably less dim. Continuing with our biological analog, it is now time to diversify and specialize. Within biological forms and functions, diversification and specialization are primarily driven by two basic pressures: survival and propagation. Applying the Fundamental Process of evolution to biological systems creates these pressures as well as creates the various individual strategies that are designed to respond to these pressures. The survival (continuing existence) of a particular individual member of a species is not only significant to that individual, but also contributes to the profitability and continuance of the species, evolutionary experiment, and ecosystem. Each individual, besides being an autonomous entity, is an integral part of a larger system. Nothing stands alone, disconnected from the rest. To misquote John Donne: *"No man or bacterium is an island."*

▶ During the eighteenth, nineteenth, and first half of the twentieth centuries, humans, in a typical display of little picture self-centered arrogance, believed they stood alone above all else – particularly in the rapidly industrializing West. Many, whose economic dynamics are still at the front end of the industrial revolution, continue to feel and act that way. That is easy to understand. Industrialization is a process that in the short-run turns natural resources into wealth, power, and a higher standard of living.

Unfortunately, short term profitability often drives non-ecological utilization of resources. Rapid industrialization is a very difficult package to turn down for the sake of ecological responsibility – especially if you are one of the last looters to get to the scene of the riot. To update and urbanize an old maxim, "the early looter gets the best TV." Furthermore, the early looter is also the least likely to get caught and face the consequences.

It is an obvious fact that the easiest way to get some quick cash to support an immediate higher standard of living is to mug Mother Nature as she walks through her park. Fortunately, she is an exceptionally hardy and charitable sort and gracefully tolerates our abuse up to a point. However, to pass that point is to trade an endless supply of golden eggs for a single goose dinner. Even if you are extraordinarily hungry, that is a stupid trade.

As the bigger picture of a global ecosystem has come into view, some have realized that we have responsibility as well as rights of plunder by virtue of superior force. A viable and stable ecosystem must achieve and maintain balance. That we humans have the capability to seriously disturb that balance is the source of our responsibility.

Our natural environment does not constitute the only global ecosystem. Eventually, among the human population, we will discover (and learn the rules and dynamics of) global technological, political, social, and economic ecosystems. In global systems, individual players always have bit parts, yet all are vitally important, even from a system perspective. In general, the larger the system, the smaller the part any one participant plays. Each individual entity (including you) plays out its unique interactive part and absolutely affects the whole whether or not they are aware the whole exists. Some individuals and groups affect the larger system more than others and thus must assume a greater responsibility commensurate with their greater impact and influence.

A complex ecosystem can maintain balance only if a great ability to use, exploit, and destroy is tempered by an equally great responsibility to conserve, replenish, and protect. Ability must be balanced by responsibility, force with caring, and fear with love. With great responsibility comes great challenges and great opportunity. The bigger your perspective and understanding, the more effective and productive you can be within your system.

Your ability to take intelligent action depends upon the depth of your vision and the quality of your understanding. The smaller your perspective and understanding, the more likely you are to inadvertently shoot yourself in the foot. Low quality consciousness does not see the Big Picture and makes short sighted decisions for near term gain. To a being of low quality, feel-good appears more important than do-good which appears more important than be-good.

There is no rule that requires evolution to optimize profitability through only random trial and error activity. **We are allowed to use our brains.** No kidding, we actually are. I know there is little hard evidence to support that assertion but a bigger perspective and understanding of the larger system and our optimal interaction with it and responsibility to it is well within our intellectual capability.

Theoretically, we humans are intelligent and educable. However, let me remind you that intelligence and education are attributes of individuals, not groups – you cannot pass the buck or abdicate your **personal** responsibility (rely on somebody else to solve a shared problem) without becoming part of the problem.

Large ecosystems come in layers. To capture the point of this discussion, you must generalize the above thoughts to a much bigger picture. We are participants in an evolving consciousness ecosystem. The consciousness system in which we participate is the mother of all others. It is the largest, most complex ecosystem we can interact with. It supports all other ecosystems. Our physical universe is a small virtual habitat within this larger consciousness system. The same ecological issues, concepts, conclusions, and lessons-learned that we discussed earlier in this aside apply directly to you and your relationship to the consciousness ecosystem. Science is science, the principles are the same. Reread this short aside with each observation about us and our physical ecosystem being applied and reinterpreted to describe our interaction with the larger consciousness ecosystem – you will gain a new perspective. ◀

Any species, or any evolutionary experiment, continues to fulfill or actualize its future potential until there are no more significant potential states to investigate and the Fundamental Process grinds to a halt. The experiment is over, at least temporarily. This does not necessarily imply extinction, just that no future progress, growth, evolvement, or experimentation takes place until new external or internal conditions create new significant possibilities. In biological systems, the imperative or urge to implement the Fundamental Process is naturally energized and guided by the profitability of survival and propagation. For evolution to remain viable within a system, the system must maintain a **continuing** set of significant, useful, or profitable choices and possibilities. Specifically, for biological systems, evolution remains a viable process only if the biological organisms continue to survive and propagate. Nevertheless, survival and propagation are not the only test of evolutionary significance or profitability of biological organisms.

Both extremes of biological evolution are not explainable by positing survival and propagation (as we generally think of it) as the **main** motivators of choice. The first small groups of biological cells had no enemies (even the environment became friendlier over time) and they weren't interested in eating each other – not yet. Life was simple and good.

Toward the other end of the evolutionary spectrum, many humans are likewise no longer focused on survival issues on a daily basis. Technology intervenes in our behalf. For example, almost a fifth of us in the Western world have a genetic vision impairment that is correctable by technology (wearing glasses or contacts). Ten thousand years ago such a defect would have made us much less survivable. Are our modern bespectacled brethren still dropping like flies because of their inferior visual equipment? Is evolution weeding them out as genetically inferior? Does having to wear glasses or contacts make it more difficult to survive, find a mate, and propagate your genetic material? A little perhaps, but not as much as it used to.

Some futurists picture us as evolving into people sporting large brainy heads with spindly arms and legs – our physical weakness both created and overcome by technology. If survival and propagation were the only measures of evolutionary significance, why would we need such big brains? Have we not dominated our competition with the brain we have? We have only one natural enemy now – ourselves.

Perhaps we need bigger brains to avoid self-destruction. That proposition doesn't make us seem very smart. It is our brains that make us so destructive. A bigger brain, as the solution to the excesses of a bigger brain, is hardly a logical solution. I have read somewhere that we use only a fraction of our brain's capacity as it is. Bigger is hard pressed to justify greater evolutionary profitability. It is not a lack of intellectual capacity that is at the root of humankind's self-inflicted difficulties and dysfunctional behavior. The fundamental problem is the lack of quality in consciousness. Quality is the issue, not quantity or capacity. We obviously have more processing capacity within our consciousness than we have the quality, maturity, or wisdom to put that capacity to good use. As a species, we are out of balance – and that is not good.

Mother Nature, who is talented at evolving interdependent complex systems, always produces self-balancing systems. Natural systems are self-regulating because the evolutionary process of maximizing the profitability of the **overall** system must be a self-optimizing and self-balancing process in order to achieve and maintain stability. If a natural complex system is knocked out of balance beyond recovery, it self-destructs or regresses to a state where the unbalancing factor is brought under control. Growth toward an out-of-balance condition within a complex natural system will eventually be eliminated one way or another (future growth moves the system toward balance, the system regresses to a previous stable state, or it self-destructs).

Within biological systems, the most obvious example of an unbalanced system leading to self-destruction is a quickly growing cancer. In contrast, within consciousness systems, the most obvious example of an unbalanced system leading to self-destruction is ignorance, fear, desire, need, and ego – a lack of quality.

What is creating evolutionary pressure if we are no longer preoccupied with the traditional issues of survival and species propagation? We have become aware enough and capable enough that **self-improvement** is now our main goal. Most importantly, that means spiritual evolution, or equivalently, the improvement of the quality of our consciousness. Self-improvement could also mean the development of science and application of technology that might eventually result in spindly arms and legs, or merely developing a more civilized civilization. It could also mean something as quick and direct as human genetic engineering.

Self-improvement is the result of an internal pressure created by the Fundamental Process. Evolution expressed through a high level of sentience becomes the urge to grow (reduce entropy), the drive to increase profitability, and an inherent dissatisfaction with stagnation and decay (increasing entropy). Stagnation is at best an astable state for any life-form. Typically, if growth is halted and does not soon resume, decay sets in.

The internal environment produces the evolutionary pressure of self-improvement for the sake of greater individual and system profitability while the external environment specifies system constraints. Clearly, self-improvement represents the major evolutionary pressure driving change in contemporary humankind as well as the original clumps of cells in the primordial sea. Take note that inside environments can be a significant player in the evolutionary process and that survival and propagation are not the only important variables in the profit calculation supporting PMR evolutionary dynamics.

Profitability is a matter of dynamic evolutionary circumstance that is wholly dependent upon the nature of the inside and outside environments. Whether or not a driving evolutionary force leads to a more profitable or less profitable state for any particular self-modifying and evolving system depends on the collective choices made (path chosen) by that specific system.

> ▶ There is a bigger picture in which our overall profitability equation is shown to have additional terms beyond PMR related survival, propagation, and self-improvement that you will understand much better after you have completed Sections 3, 4, and 5 of *My Big TOE*. For now, keep your skepticism healthy, your mind open (free of beliefs), and realize that it is much too early to jump to conclusions – there will be plenty of time to do that later. ◀

Our level of awareness has delivered us to the point where we have within our grasp the potential to dramatically affect the direction and speed of our evolution. However, to use this potential to improve the profitability of our species within the larger system will require a dramatic increase in our ability to integrate technology with wisdom at the point of individual application. Without a doubt, improving the quality of our individual and collective consciousness is the most important and critical aspect of self-improvement (evolution) facing the human race as we move into the twenty-first century.

Balance is always important. If our technical know-how gets too far out in front of our ability to apply its results wisely, we will lose our balance and fall flat on our face – perhaps irretrievably. Ours is a particularly critical time. The choices we make during the next half-century will dramatically affect the outcome of the next half millennium.

Improving the quality of our consciousness is, and always has been, fundamental to our evolution but today it is also critical to our survival and to the continued success of the Homo sapiens experiment. If we accomplish a significant improvement in the quality of our consciousness first, if we can lead with our quality, the rest of our options will be guided by our wisdom and we will leap boldly ahead. If, on the other hand, the quality of our consciousness lags, and we do not accomplish a sizable measure of spiritual growth first, we will have the cart in front of the horse, so to speak, and it is going to be a wild and dangerous ride.

Isn't the evolution of consciousness a fascinating process? I suggest that we invest some serious effort in improving the quality of our consciousness. I also suggest that we fasten our seat belts.

We have been discussing our biological evolution because it is best to start with something basic that we at least think we understand. In doing so, we have defined the concepts of evolutionary pressure and specific criteria for evolutionary profitability. Having done that, it is obvious that survival and propagation are non-issues to an Absolute Unbounded Oneness. Instead, it is self-improvement, the reduction of system entropy, that provides the evolutionary pressure and profitability criteria that guide AUO's evolvement.

In order to understand the natural pressures that drive AUO's evolution we must first understand how consciousness improves itself by achieving higher levels of internal organization (entropy reduction). Let's review the evolutionary process. After the first step of exploration into **all** possible states, the second step is to assess which states are profitable or significant and to continue to explore those valuable states while letting the losers go.

Do not imagine that evolution, or an evolving entity, makes rational, cognitive choices using specific criteria that define profitability and significance (such as lower entropy, survivability, and propagation). Though I may use that language construction as a convenience, be aware that evolution must **begin** as a natural, not a cognitive or intellectual, process. Only after a certain level of awareness, competency, and tool use has evolved can evolution be influenced by individual intent.

Potential or possible states are continually explored. Those that happen to lead to reduced profitability, self-destruction, or dead ends are the losers. These losers either remain as they are or degenerate if there are no more unique possibilities or viable existences to explore that are also good investments. Every evolving complex system will eventually either keep growing (entropy decreases) or run out of evolutionary gas (entropy increases or stays the same). This is true of all large complex systems (consciousness systems, earth's ecosystem, the solar system, technological and organizational systems, computer systems, the internet, and biological systems including physical human beings).

However, keep in mind that evolutionary potential is dynamic. Investment opportunities come and go as evolution continually modifies the system upon which it operates. Change one thing and everything is affected, including the external and internal environments of the individual entities that make up the system. Change is constant ... and often chaotic. As long as there are large numbers of complexly interacting self-modifying entities, there will be evolving systems of those entities.

Survival and propagation represent the external pressures or constraints of a biological environment. Thus, if a particular complex system is biologically based and has constraining issues such as survival and propagation, choices relative to these constraints can put certain avenues of exploration out of business. On the other hand, where there are few external constraints and no competition is defined, individual systems, and systems of systems, simply continue (evolving) as long as they have someplace to go. Thus, with fewer constraints, evolution delivers more diversity because there is always someplace to go. For example, there were few constraints placed on offensive or defensive survival strategies or on modes of locomotion for biological life forms. Consequently, we observe many, many types of survival strategies and modes of locomotion among the creatures born to Mother Earth, as well as many variations within each type. AUO naturally has few constraints, and therefore is granted great freedom of form and function in solving evolution's profitability equation.

Winning evolutionary strategies are not based upon some **predetermined** specific criteria or profitability calculations, they just happen and persist. Losing strategies just happen and then fade away or stop progressing. No one performs an evaluation. I know this is difficult to fathom, but accountants and lawyers are not required to implement the Fundamental Process – it just happens. No doubt some lobbying organization is trying to figure out how to legislate mandatory legal and accounting services into the evolutionary process and then charge high fees, but so far, all life-forms continue to evolve, change, and grow without professional help.

▶ In fact, Mother Nature so abhors bureaucracy that even if she gets raped, she will not call the authorities. However, there is little comfort in that fact for any of us because if the abuse she suffers goes too far, she will eventually get even – count on it. And when she does, all within her reach will be equally punished regardless of culpability.

On the other hand, as long as we are respectful, she is willing to let us have our way with her whenever desire and indulgence peaks our insatiable appetites. She is an extraordinarily robust lady – at ease with poisonous snakes, killer bees, vampire bats, erupting volcanoes, tornados, and earthquakes – but shortsighted lobbyists and self-serving politicians scare her to death because together, like a malignant tumor, their destructive potential may overpower her capacity to regenerate. Greed kills. ◀

Optimal profitability, as it is constrained and prodded by internal and external environments, defines evolutionary success. Profitable being, growing, and evolving constitute the criteria for evaluating the success of sentient entities. The Fundamental Process iterates individuals and systems toward success by improving upon previous results wherever growth and investment potential exists. Because no management and no intellectual efforts are required to control or manipulate the evolutionary process, it remains efficient. System within system within system – the whole must be self-balancing, self-sustaining, and self-correcting, or it becomes self-eliminating.

Because survival and propagation do not constrain our timeless, immortal, space-less, apparently infinite AUO, it would seem to be free to pursue every possibility open to it. If you happen to be apparently infinite, spatially unrestrained, timeless, immortal, multi-dimensional, and aware, you have tremendous potentiality. With so few constraints, there is almost no end to what you could do to keep yourself busy and avoid becoming dead ended. (It should now seem more obvious to you why the less constrained NPMRs should evolve a more varied set of life-forms than the more constrained PMRs, but more about that later.)

A potential constraint on the capacity of a finite consciousness system might be the energy or focus that would be required to keep track of all the "gedanken experiments" in progress. To maintain and profitably organize all the information required to support a complex interactive virtual reality would require a good memory – or perhaps a big computer. The existence of limiting factors (because of AUO's actual finiteness) would inevitably lead a self-modifying computational system (digital organism) to set priorities and develop rules that optimize resource utilization.

Because there must be limiting factors associated with any form of actual or real finite existence, then "infinite" and "unbounded" do not accurately describe AUO. However, from the relatively tiny perspective of our local reality system (OS), AUO appears infinite and unbounded – there are no edge effects that we experience **directly**. Imagine how unbounded and infinite your brain would appear to a carbon atom stuck in the middle of it. We shall soon see that a **relatively** infinite Absolute Unbounded Oneness is sufficient for the purposes of generating all the reality that we can possibly be aware of – and much more.

It makes sense that evolutionary pressure operating upon a complex system of consciousness would encourage that system to invest in improving the extent and quality of its own awareness (the ability to profitably interact and organize). In other words, the Fundamental Process causes AUO to organize and configure itself to decreases (minimizes) its entropy. Equivalently, we could say the Fundamental Process causes AUO to improve and develop the potential of its being, the quality of its consciousness, the level, breadth, and depth of its potential.

That appears to be similar to **our** mission, **our** reason for being, doesn't it? Does AUO's motivation and evolutionary purpose flow down to us? Of course; we are manifestations of it, so how could it be otherwise? We will hear more about that later. For now it is enough to understand that through increased complexity in relation to itself, AUO escapes atrophy and puts its limited energy (ability to modify itself, to change its internal environment) to the most profitable use – continually redefining and improving its overall capacity, quality, and awareness. AUO develops an awareness of its **internal** states and learns how to modify them to decrease its overall entropy.

Other types of interaction and awareness related to AUO's **external** environments may also be evolving but they are not **directly** relevant to us; consequently, we will continue to ignore them because we cannot experience or understand their processes or their significance. AUO's outside environment is to us like our outside environment is to our intestinal bacteria. Those little entities that live in our gut are so immersed in their own limited reality that they simply do not appreciate what we go through to earn money to purchase food – much less the roles that farmers, sunshine, rain, transportation, and economic conditions play in the larger food cycle. Jeez, some of them don't know there is a larger food cycle – can you believe that? They think food is manna from heaven. Bullpucky! They should deal with your boss and the line at the checkout counter!

Let's wrap it up with a short summary. Devising and implementing ways to optimize the process of making self-improvements, as judged by AUO's immediate sense of profitability, leads to improvements in the quality of

AUO's consciousness. That is in line with what those tiny globs of cells were doing in the primordial soup a few billion years ago on our planet. They were engaging in simple self-improvement – exploring the possibilities – trying to find a better more profitable existence. The energy form and constraints are different, but the evolutionary process is exactly the same. AUO is constrained by its internal environment and the Fundamental Process to move toward a more profitable existence by decreasing its average entropy, or equivalently, by increasing its useful energy.

Self-improvement has become humanity's primary evolutionary motivator as well. The external environment for humans is essentially subdued; consequently, we have become our only major threat. The greatest challenge to our species today is to survive the self-destructiveness of our own low quality of consciousness. We must now learn to master the internal environment. Our success at gathering knowledge and making tools has placed a great capacity to destroy in hands animated by low quality, underdeveloped, immature consciousness. The need for rapid self-improvement has become critical. Will the individual conscious beings that collectively define humanity grow up (lower the entropy of their consciousness or equivalently raise their spiritual quality) enough to make the choices that will allow their species to prosper?

Might this maturing of the spirit or quality of mankind happen sometime soon or do we need to experience more pain before a significant number of eyes and minds begin to open? Remember, growing up is not a group or political activity, it is a personal activity. Groups raise their average quality level only as the individuals within those groups make a personal effort to increase their individual quality. Self-improvement of the species in general is up to you as an individual. Nobody has more potential to contribute than you do. Only individuals acting as individuals can make a difference.

Tough guys with big muscles have less real power and are less in control of their environments than brainy bespectacled nerds. Survival and procreation are giving way to self-improvement as the defining evolutionary constraint for human-kind. Genetic engineering and psychotropic drugs are a quickly growing reality. The control we can exercise over our physical bodies is rapidly increasing. If the maturation and quality of our consciousness were as precociously developed, it would provide grace, stability, and balance to our great leaps into the unknown. We are slowly taking the reigns of physical evolution into our own hands. Climbing out of the petri-dish and into the lab, we are becoming a co-designer – a partner in the evolutionary process. We are undoubtedly following in AUO's footsteps because the Fundamental Process is the same for everyone and everything, and because we, like AUO, are primarily manifestations of aware consciousness.

The fundamental process (which develops the potential of an individual entity or system of interacting entities by continually exploring the available states of profitable existence) applies equally well to humans, other beings and critters, consciousness, ecosystems, technology, governments, and all other sufficiently complex interactive systems. Systems are simply an organization of individuals whose synergistic interaction produces collective results. Systems of systems are developed in the same way.

All growing systems, including consciousness systems, evolve toward minimizing average entropy by generating more profitable levels of organization. Inanimate things such as rivers, mountains, rocks, atoms, and molecules change through an evolutionary process that moves toward increasing average entropy by seeking the lowest available energy state. Non-living physical matter, objects, and systems do not have the capacity for self-improvement or entropy reduction that sentient consciousness has because their choices, interactions, feedback, and the ability to make self-modifications as a result of their "experience" is either nonexistence or too limited.

It seems that we have derived a new and more general method for differentiating between living and non-living objects or systems (virtually all objects are systems). Living systems are sentient and exhibit consciousness – no matter how dim or unfocused. They have choices. Their choices are guided by intent and profitability – they evolve. Any system that can intentionally (act, react, interact) improve its present situation or configuration, or purposely (by making the appropriate choices) decrease (or maintain) its entropy in the face of the constant tug of the second law of thermodynamics, is a growing, evolving, living system. The attributes of a consciousness system are given more precisely at the beginning of Chapter 7, Book 2. For now it is enough to know that the capacity and capability to effectively self-organize toward some purpose (evolutionary profitability) is critical to forming and maintaining aware consciousness and all life as we know it. Does that make your government, the earth's ecosystem, a national or global economy, digital computers, and the internet **potential** life-forms? Stay tuned.

It is the fact that non-living and non-growing systems tend to move naturally (evolve) toward minimum energy states, along the path of least resistance, that is ultimately responsible for the truth of the second law of thermodynamics. We will see later that this fact of PMR existence is one of the rules in the space-time rule-set that defines the laws of physics in PMR.

Later it will become clear that we are an integral part of AUO's evolutionary process – that we are evolving consciousness.

Where is this AUO thing going, how do we fit into this picture, and what does AUO have to do with deriving physics, the meaning of life, our physical reality, or the Big Picture of the larger reality? Are we lost wandering aimlessly in the metaphysical desert? We are not lost and the answers to these questions and many more will be forthcoming. Be patient, there are many basic concepts that first must be introduced before the Big Picture can begin to take shape. It is better to let these questions slow cook a while before we get back to them. Before results can be discussed, we need to follow AUO's evolution to its logical conclusion.

That is it for the summary. I expect that questions are popping up in your mind like toadstools after a summer rain. To what end is AUO motivated to expend resources? What defines AUO's top evolutionary priorities? Mental capacity? Growth? Power? Curiosity? What turns AUO on – art, science, knowledge, benevolence, love, entertainment, investment strategy, leisure, pleasure, or just having fun? Interesting questions to be sure – but also hopelessly anthropomorphic ones. Avoid the habit of thinking of AUO in terms of human attributes; there is a connection, but attribution naturally flows from the parent to the child – try thinking of humans in terms of AUO's attributes.

28
■ ■ ■

The Evolution of AUO:
The Birth of the Big Computer (TBC)

■ ■ ■

Meet AUO – a gazillion reality cells more or less randomly changing state, oscillating, appearing and disappearing. These eventually evolve into patterns and groups of patterns-of-patterns as awareness and complexity increase. Some patterns are more interesting and profitable than others. Recall that higher levels of organization leading to lower average entropy define self-improvement within a consciousness system. The Fundamental Process in interaction with consciousness produces an evolutionary pressure that pushes all consciousness entities toward self-improvement.

The concept of an entity organizing itself into a more profitable ensemble of patterns and patterns of patterns returns us to an earlier discussion of how and why life-forms diversify and specialize. Bacteria, guppies, alligators, kangaroos, people, arms, eyes, legs, breasts, brains, electric automobiles, the internet, and representative government are just a few examples of the advanced biological world organizing itself into more profitable ensembles of patterns and patterns of patterns. If somewhere within the far reaches of your intuition the phrase "patterns of patterns" suggests some sort of undefined fractal process as the ultimate creator of complex structure, you are on the right track. Hang on, we'll get there eventually.

Some patterns might indicate a subsequent or a preceding pattern or define pattern interaction. Rules are themselves none other than knowledge-based or experienced-based patterns for the reliable definition, repetition, and interaction of other patterns. Rules defining the formation of patterns, as well as pattern interaction and relationship, would evolve naturally from the evolutionary pressure of self-improvement. With the concept of rules come the concepts of control and hierarchy.

For instance, binary patterns of 1s and 0s, on and off, or for AUO, uniform and non-uniform can be used to do arithmetic, store information, and move data around between groups of cells. Simple binary patterns, and the rules (instruction-set) defining relatively few operations, have **evolved** into today's computer technology.

Unquestionably, it is the patterns, the patterns of patterns (and the rule-sets that evolve to define, regulate, and order them) that constitute the basic ingredients of almost everything we directly experience. For just one example, imagine a human brain's pattern of cellular organization, and its patterns of neuron and electromagnetic activity. For other examples, think of the city you live in, the economy in which you work, and the political and cultural patterns that order your life. Civilization is about ordered patterns defined by profitability and constraints – so is everything else, including consciousness.

It may prove to be a useful concept to describe consciousness as made up of discrete fundamental units (quanta). Some minimum group of complex interactive reality cells would constitute a quantum of consciousness. Given that groups of reality cells are at the heart and core of consciousness and given that the simplest form of a reality cell is a binary unit, then logic dictates that computers have the **theoretical** potential to become conscious devices. After all, they are made up of basic binary units that are like the reality cells that led to the development of consciousness, memory, and pattern processing within AUO. Clearly, having a collection of binary cells is not enough. That these cells interrelate, use and share information (patterns of data), and modify themselves around some purpose or intent (regardless of how dimly perceived) is critical to the formation of a quanta of consciousness.

AUO could specialize a small part of itself into gazillions of tetra-tetra-tetra bytes of memory because that would be an interesting and useful thing to do. Indeed, very useful! In the last chapter we concluded that evolving consciousness may be constrained by accessible memory. Evolving a memory and processing section could lead AUO to invent its **own** form of mathematics – which is nothing other than patterns, patterns of patterns, rules, operations, and relationships – a self-consistent system of logical process.

This computational and memory function of AUO represents the primordial Big Computer. The Big Computer (TBC) is an important metaphor used throughout this model of reality. TBC's function and operation are described and discussed in more detail throughout the rest of *MY Big TOE* but especially in Section 4 (all), and Section 5 (specifically

Chapters 6 and 11 of Book 3). The Big Computer is just that – memory, processing, rules, operations, and content. It is not necessarily The Big Brain as we think of it in biological (discrete physical organ) terms. At this point, it is more of a memory-intensive computationally based process that provides improved organization to a relatively dim cellular mind. Think of TBC as a digital computational functionality (based upon discrete reality cells) that naturally evolved to improve organization, and thus reduce entropy, within the energy form we call AUO.

AUO itself now represents a form of digital consciousness based upon reality cells. AUO is able to reduce its entropy and brighten its awareness because it evolved gazillions of self-differentiated reality cells that eventually became organized into patterns of patterns, rules, and ordered processes – all maintained, tracked, and controlled by evolving groups of interactive binary memory cells whose actions and interactions are coordinated to facilitate a more highly organized and profitable system. Digital logic and memory are needed to apply the rules of interaction and to coordinate the whole toward greater profitability. Content sharing and intentioned manipulation evolves on the heels of digital logic, thus adding direction and purpose to the process. Purpose differentiates success from failure and provides the necessary rationale and direction to achieve lower entropy configurations that appear as system self-improvements.

Think of TBC as a special purpose digital processor and memory subset of a much larger digital consciousness. AUO is evolving specialized groups of cells in the same way and for the same reasons that biology-based physical critters did: The same Fundamental Process is universally applied to all interactive or intra-active systems complex enough to be capable of profitable self-induced change (growth). Nevertheless, the results of applying that simple process differ widely according to the capabilities and constraints that define each system. A system's capability is intrinsic to the nature of the system while its constraints are defined by its internal and external environments.

Just as evolving non-living, non-growing entities naturally move toward higher entropy, consciousness naturally moves toward lower entropy. Dimness gradually gives way to brightness as entropy is lowered. The quality of consciousness also increases as entropy is decreased – we call this growth of quality, spiritual growth. Just as **external** energy can **sometimes** drive non-living, non-growing entities to decrease their individual entropy for a time (they grow – like sand into sandstone, minerals into crystals, decomposing bio-mass into fossil fuels, or the fusing of hydrogen into helium), **internal** energy can **sometimes** drive consciousness to greater entropy and lower quality. More about this in the next section as we pit our favorite team, The Rats, against the Anti-Rats in the Reality Bowl.

▶ We now know almost enough to pull together a better understanding of the word "dimension." We have said the larger reality is a multidimensional reality and that PMR and NPMR represent two of those dimensions – but what does that mean?

Let's begin with what we know. I have used the term "three dimensional" or its abbreviation "3D" to characterize our PMR local reality. Some may be confused because they have been told that modern science uses a 4D space-time to model PMR. Indeed, space-time, as the term is used within general relativity, is referred to as a 4D continuum – three space coordinates (that are also functions of time), and one time coordinate (that is also a function of the space coordinates). There is mathematical justification for calling space-time four dimensional, but in the sense that I use the word "dimension," mixing time with the position coordinates does not constitute a new dimension.

Although time – the technology and process AUO will eventually construct for ordering events – is fundamental to defining and creating the larger reality, it is not particularly helpful to think of time as an independent dimension. It is more descriptively accurate to say that we humans directly experience a 3D time-ordered reality that appears to be the perception limited product of a space-time universe requiring four coordinates to specify individual events relative to one's frame of reference, wherein each possible reference frame is as fundamentally proper as any other.

Searching for a fourth and higher dimensions in terms of geometry is also not particularly helpful to the understanding of the larger reality. Reality is not fundamentally geometric. We think it must be geometric because our little picture view is centered in 3D geometric reality and we naturally tend to expand upon what we know. PMR is geometrically constrained by the space-time rule-set; however, the space-time rule-set is only a local rule-set and does not apply to the larger reality. This will become clear in Section 4.

What is this dimension thing – If it is not time and not geometric, what is left? Forget about all the sci-fi and fantasy movies you have seen, the dimensionality of reality does not function as the screenwriters for *Twilight Zone* or the *X-Files* would have you believe. However, it is true that most realities simultaneously exist within their own dimension and as a subset of a larger reality, and that travel between dimensions is possible – indeed, it is relatively easy once you know how.

We will discuss the concept of dimension in more depth later; for now, I want to peek ahead just enough to give you some sense of the nature of dimension without confusing you too much in the process.

Because the larger reality and the subset of the larger reality that serves as our local reality are constructs of consciousness, we could say metaphorically that they exist in mind-space or thought-space. Connect this with the idea that fundamental consciousness, in the form of AUO, is composed of reality cells and that reality cells may be employed as binary cells – cells that are either in this state or that state. Binary cells, like transistors in a microprocessor or the 1s and 0s on your favorite compact disk, are handy for creating memory, storing information, and supporting complex processing. Thus mind-space, in the form of digital consciousness, is beginning to look like a logical, rule-based, computational system – a generalized computer of some sort.

You will discover in chapter 30 of this book that the fundamental potential energy of consciousness (AUO) eventually evolves into brilliant digital consciousness as its dim awareness slowly brightens. Within digital consciousness, the creation of various dimensions is simply the creation of separate memory and processing subsets. For years, we have implemented partitioning in our commercial digital computers as well as figured out how to multitask and multiprocess. We can easily, for example, run multiple simulations and multiple instances of the same simulation (with differing initial conditions perhaps) simultaneously within our PMR mainframes. Think of each simultaneously running simulation as representing an independent reality within its own dimension and you will have a glimmer of the concept of dimension within digital consciousness, and within the larger reality. "Dimension" refers to a well defined processing subset within The Big Computer, a constrained thought-space or region of related content processing within the larger consciousness. A particular dimension or reality may be thought of as a digital simulation of a virtual world running in its own memory-space within TBC. The concept of dimension will become clear as these ideas are developed in later chapters. ◀

Now we must begin to contemplate things happening in sequence. There is an immense benefit to the organizational potential of a system if operations and content can be arranged in a specific order and sequence. AUO, in its pursuit of profitability, needs to "invent" time, thereby inventing ordered process. Like sea creatures needing to "invent" lungs and legs in order to crawl out of the oceans to exploit the resources available on dry land, AUO needs to invent time in order to exploit the increased order and organization (lower entropy) that comes with ordered process.

Time provides the indexing and sequencing scheme to support the next higher level of organization, awareness, and complexity within consciousness. With the possibility of indexing and sequencing interactive content, dynamics (time ordered causality) is born. The application of time to digital content causes the number of explorable possibilities available for the fundamental process to explode exponentially into a creative interaction of cause and effect.

Time is a digital technology that enables consciousness to organize its content (thoughts) more effectively. Improved organization implies reduced entropy and greater profitability for the system. The evolution of mind is about to shift into high gear as the potential of aware consciousness takes another great leap into the unknown.

29
■ ■ ■

The Evolution of AUO:
The Birth of Time

■ ■ ■

AUO is about to get natural rhythm. Time is as easy for AUO to invent (evolve) as it is for us to keep time by tapping our foot. To create time, our state flipping friend needs only to oscillate (repetitively change the state of) some individual or group of reality cells more or less regularly (uniform, non-uniform, uniform, non-uniform, and so on). These regularly oscillating reality cells become AUO's clock – like a metronome, they keep time for everything else. If the frequency of this group of clock cells is constant, it will be a more useful clock. The best clock would oscillate as efficiently, regularly, and quickly as possible (its natural frequency). Because "works better" is what drives evolution, we should expect that AUO would eventually evolve a process that produces a highly regulated constant frequency.

Time is a technology, a construct of a self-modifying evolving consciousness, an artifact of a system of energy improving its internal organization. When the potential energy of primordial consciousness (the potential to self-organize more profitably) evolves the ability to decrease its own entropy one infinitesimal smidgen, time is the byproduct of that internal change. Time separates the "before" state from the "after" state. Change creates the notion of time. Awareness of change necessitates the idea of a personal time. The concept of time is defined and created within the dim awareness of AUO when the Fundamental Process enables AUO to change something, to somehow modify its absolute oneness – even if that change is entirely random.

The initial modification may have been a quirky unplanned fortuitous event, or directly related to AUO's unknowable external environment – no one can know. We cannot with certainty specify the origins of the first bio-logical cells within PMR, much less the first reality cells within AUO; that was a long time ago and we were not there when it happened. As I said in Chapter 25 of this book: "...go ask your mother! It is not an appropriate question." Scrupulously avoid making assumptions and creating beliefs (pseudo-knowledge) to fill in for what you cannot understand.

Pseudo-knowledge is useless except as a pacifier for a needy ego. You and your intestinal bacteria must realize there are some things that you will never fully appreciate because they are, and will always be, beyond your limited reach. Appreciating your limitations is the first step toward obtaining wisdom. At the same time, creating apparent limitations where none actually exist by getting stuck in belief traps is a great waste of poten-tial. Read the previous two sentences again. Do you see the importance of discovering Big Truth, and why you should spare no effort to clearly understand the difference between actual and apparent limitations? Make a note: The ability to accurately assess one's fundamental limitations dif-ferentiates the wise from the foolish.

The incredible evolutionary profitability of time is immediately obvi-ous. Ordered events allow sequences to carry and propagate content. Complex interaction and causal logic chains evolve as the beat goes on. Entropy is reduced. Time acts as a catalytic agent. It dramatically enhances AUO's ability to self-organize, thus speeding up the interaction between the Fundamental Process and consciousness.

The evolutionary pressure of self-improvement moves consciousness toward higher quality and lower entropy states – which is equivalent to moving consciousness to brighter, more aware, and more highly organ-ized internal configurations. Lower entropy produces higher quality, which means that the consciousness system has more energy available to do work (to more profitably organize).

One divided by the frequency of oscillation gives the period of one cycle. The period of a cycle is the time required to change state and then change it back again. One period is often used as a handy measure or unit of time. For example, the period of the rotation of the earth on its axis is one day and grandfather clocks use the period of a pendulum to count seconds.

More possibilities and evolutionary potentiality can be generated if AUO's parts and patterns can communicate, if they can interact and be coordinated with each other (like the arms, legs, brain, tail, and eyes of a monkey trying to snag a banana). Coordinated activity can both propagate and regulate patterns of content. Signals and messages can be passed from cell to cell as fast as one cell can change state in response to an "adjacent" cell changing state. If the patterns encode meaning as our patterns of neurons, letters and words, gestures, or sounds do, soon AUO has parts of itself communicating and sharing data with other parts. Imagine something roughly analogous to a biological nervous system communicating between body parts using sequenced patterns of neurons.

▶ Do you find it an interesting concept that our central nervous system (CNS), which includes brain, nerves, neurons, synapses and electrical charges, mirrors consciousness in its information transfer processes? Contemplate the close connection between our central nervous system and our consciousness. The CNS is a highly constrained physical analog of consciousness functionality. The CNS hosts our consciousness as a computer hosts an operating system and applications. It serves as a transducer, a data port and bi-directional translator between the virtual experience of the physical body and the individuated nonphysical consciousness that defines your existence and motivates your intent within the larger reality.

It is reasonable that the mechanisms of data-processing and information-transfer that take place within the cell-based mind we call AUO are similar to information processing and communications used by the CNS. Imagine a sophisticated top-end mainframe computer being, among other things, connected through a simple interface to a bank of custom made sensors. Because the CNS evolved to be the interface between the perception of physical experience and the consciousness of the perceiver that it hosts, it is reasonable to expect the communications technology on both sides (physical and nonphysical) of the interface to be highly compatible – which usually implies some functional similarity. Our view from the physical side of the interface is no doubt severely limited, but after we more fully understand how the brain and CNS works, we will perhaps have a small, physical, highly tinted window through which we can peek at the mechanics of the processes within nonphysical consciousness – the same processes through which the larger reality is eventually expressed. ◀

The technology of AUO's clocks could get complicated. We know for sure only that AUO can make one terrifically good clock in order to produce, regulate, and integrate patterns, and patterns of patterns of patterns. Evolution, through the Fundamental Process, creates the optimal clock solution for AUO – whatever that is. The details are not that important. Do not be intimidated by sinusoids or by the mathematical expressions that were given as examples of oscillating functions in Chapter 26 of this book; all you need to know is that a cell-based digital AUO can readily evolve an adequate clock (regularly oscillating group of reality cells) to meet its evolutionary needs.

The upper limit on the speed with which a given message can be prop-agated is determined by how fast a single reality cell can change state. This maximum state-change speed is directly related to the minimum clock time of one half cycle or one quantum of AUO-time. (A full cycle would require a reality cell to change state and then change back to the original state.) In other words, the maximum speed with which a cell can normally change state provides the definition of the smallest unit of time our AUO clock can directly measure. This minimum time unit is defined as the fun-damental quantum of time.

I can see that many of the technoids in the reading audience have their hands in the air. If the state-change is smooth and continuous (in the form of $\sin(\omega t)$ for example), the smallest practical unit of time can be reduced to the smallest discrete **portion** of a state change ($\Delta\omega t$) that AUO can consistently and accurately measure (be aware of). However, that is a technical detail that is of little importance to the Big Picture.

Above, we have been using words such as "adjacent" and "speed" which denote distance or space, but space is not yet defined. These words are only metaphors – do not take them literally or you will be thinking anthropomorphically, back in habitual 3D concepts, believing that AUO takes up space and exists "out there" somewhere, somehow, in a different place apart from us. Consider the speed of your thoughts, the space between consecutive or adjacent ideas, or the patterns of thought in your skeptically open mind. Think about multiple, simultaneous, or regularly occurring thoughts and about having thoughts simultaneously exist in the foreground and background of your mind. Great big thoughts and little tiny thoughts are not spatially large or small. We must guard against imposing our extremely limited 3D conceptual patterns (as well as our sense of time and causality) on AUO.

The constant evolutionary pressure to maximize profitability by reduc-ing entropy, made AUO progressively more complex and self-aware; bio-logical organisms went through a similar process. The more awareness and complexity an individual entity or system creates through evolution, the more potential states and possibilities there are to explore. Learning, growing, and evolving are often accelerating processes. The actualization of a given potential gives birth to a greater potential that gives birth to an even greater potential that ....

Because the birth-survival-propagation-death process, which absorbs an enormous amount of our time and energy within PMR, is not part of the consciousness evolution process, the acceleration of the evolutionary process is much greater for a consciousness system than a biological one.

Without a body to drag around and care for, AUO travels light and moves fast within a much larger set of possibilities.

For example, education and learning is a bodiless process that obviously accelerates. Given a constant level of intelligence, the more someone knows and understands, the more quickly and readily he or she can know and understand additional related material. The rapid increase in the complexity, value, power, and pervasiveness of technology provides another clear example of a bodiless evolutionary process (the expansion of knowledge and technical expertise) that clearly demonstrates evolutionary acceleration.

▶ The rate of technological evolution has been increasing for hundreds if not thousands of years. As always, each generation believes the pace of technological change must be about to slow down – since almost everything they can imagine has been invented. Hah! Those closer to the edge of knowledge know better. Forward vision is always clouded by limited imagination. Our science and technology have **barely** scratched the surface of the possibilities – we have only now begun to pull back on the throttle and get our training wheels off the deck – "Uhh oh ...hey...how do you steer this thing!? Oh jeez, it's picking up speed! Hey! There is no way to get off, nothing to steer with...and no breaks! Criminy! Now what do I do?"

What we need to do is obvious: We must learn very quickly how to guide our rapidly accelerating technical know-how with some hastily gained and applied wisdom before the opportunity to do so is lost. Trying to halt or suppress innovation, discovery, and the development and application of new knowledge is like trying to permanently stop the flow of a major river – it is not a realistic option. Social and economic forces (religions, governments, unions, corporations, and various social movements) have never been successful in slowing technological progress by very much or for very long.

The bottom line is that high speed far ranging change guided by immature and inexperienced social dynamics over totally unfamiliar territory depends, for the most part, upon good luck to avoid disaster. Depending upon good luck to avoid a multiplicity of disasters that each have the potential to be catastrophic is not a clever plan. The only way out of this predicament is to quickly develop clear long term vision and execute good planning based upon high-quality judgment (wisdom) **before** the speed increases too much (system goes irretrievably unstable), or luck runs out – Splat!

Troglodytes, Ludditites, religions, homicidal wackos, and governments have all tried from time to time to dramatically slow the pace of innovation and technology – all have failed, are failing, and will continue to fail because that is the wrong approach. Combating unwise applications of knowledge and technology by extolling the virtues of selective self-imposed ignorance is a losing strategy that will never work. Typically, this strategy is not even effective as a delaying tactic. From the smashing of labor saving machinery in the seventeenth century to the outlawing of stem-cell and cloning research in the twenty-first century – all attempts to control the application of knowledge will necessarily fail.

Attacking a specific result (particularly research and products that cannot be practically controlled) will never defeat the Fundamental Process: Cut off one head and two more will pop up in its place. Focusing energy on a failed strategy simply makes the situation worse – attention is directed away from the real problem while the available time for implementing an effective solution is squandered. A head in the sand always leaves an unprotected butt waving in the air.

Great potential is a two edged sword. We are all passengers in this local reality rocket where the technological manipulation of our internal and external environments may soon produce more dramatically accelerating change. We must depend upon the **quality** of our political, ethical, economic, technical, and philosophic institutions to grasp the opportunities and deliver the advantages, while avoiding the pitfalls.

Before you begin lamenting the incompetence of your public institutions you should understand that quality, understanding, and wisdom are individual attributes. The quality of the individuals within a society defines the quality of that society's institutions. There is no one to whom you can pass the buck – collectively, the citizens of planet earth more or less get what we deserve. The average social, economic, educational, or government institution reflects the quality of the average individual that produces and populates it. You individually are either an integral and active part of the solution or you are a part of the problem – there are no innocent bystanders. The onus is on everyone to substantially raise the quality of their personal consciousness.

Compelling a solution by the application of external force is usually counter productive and never a good long term solution.

The point is that the evolution of consciousness, as all big system evolution, is an accelerating natural process. To make that concept and some of its attendant issues more intuitively understandable, I have simply pointed to the evolution of technology as a well-known example. ◀

Nonphysical mind can change (grow, evolve) more quickly than the physical body because it contains more degrees of freedom and fewer constraints. There is, for a long time, a steady acceleration in the growth and development of consciousness. This means the rates of growth continually increase. This acceleration allows each newly evolving expression of consciousness to be more efficient and productive more and more quickly. Learning, like any other cumulative function, cannot experience large positive acceleration forever, but you would be surprised at how far consciousness can progress before the Fundamental Process begins to channel the greater part of its energy toward only the better opportunities.

The phenomenon of accelerating learning and accelerating evolution-ary process applies to the evolution of both biological and consciousness entities. In the biological realm, with the coming of cloning and genetic engineering (a result of our computer and other technologies), expect the biological evolution of certain sentient entities to make discontinuous hops through the available possibilities to accelerate the potential (posi-tive or negative) of their species relatively quickly. In the consciousness realm, the acceleration effect represents a steeper and smoother function of self-improvement vs. time as brightness increases its capacity to learn as well as the quality and depth of its understanding.

▶ I have painted a picture of how sentient beings with aware consciousness evolve. However, I do not want you to let this understanding limit your vision as to how a par-ticular subset of beings might have ended up populating a given dimension of reality like OS or PMR. The facts of consciousness evolution as they apply to communities within $NPMR_N$ do not logically preclude an implant of sentient beings or an implant of additional sentient capability within existing beings. Modifying existing OS entities through evolution, adding new beings to OS, or directly modifying selected OS entities represent three ways to change the OS consciousness sub-system. Because these are not mutually exclusive operations, existing collection of sentient beings may be the result of all three processes working together to optimize the whole. ◀

As awareness masters and refines its evolving mental capabilities, a new, more complex motivation arises as a result of, and in conjunction with, the imperative to implement the Fundamental Process. The com-plexity and interactive properties of the mental processes being evolved eventually produces the functions of intention, feedback, interaction, syn-thesis, and integration. As these important second-order functions begin influencing and driving the evolutionary process, the potential number of profitable states dramatically expands.

Earthbound mammals and many insects can provide countless exam-ples of second order attributes. The slogan, "Homo sapiens do it better" (found etched on the rump of a prehistoric horse) makes the point that because of our ability to think and process information, we declare our-selves to be the current mental synthesis, integration, and interactive feedback champions of all earth-bound biological evolution. Even if Flipper and Shamu, with their significantly larger brains, disagree with the preceding statement, humanity has evolved an extraordinary poten-tial that is primarily fed by an impressive array of second order con-sciousness functionality. The AUO consciousness-system-thing (now also a digital-thinking-being-thing) has the right stuff to one day be many orders of magnitude better at these second order analytic functions than we are. Perhaps there are fourth, fifth and higher order functions we can't imagine.

The choices and complexities available to AUO are now staggering. The sounds that people can make and hear likewise represent a staggering selection of possibilities, though infinitesimal in depth and breadth compared to the possibilities available to AUO. What do we people do with the available sounds? Language and music are two applications that immediately come to mind. The first holds great practical value in direct response to the external demands of the Fundamental Process; the second provides for our internal well-being, our pleasure and enjoyment. "Just for fun" does **not** imply useless, or that no evolutionary profit is produced. Music evokes emotion, reduces stress, motivates and bonds people, communicates feeling, and increases milk production on progressive dairy farms.

Look at what we have been able to accomplish with only three primary colors, twenty-six letters and a limited array of sounds. All of our communications, art, literature, collective memory, science, and technology rest upon specific combinations, sequences (in both time and space), arrangements, and patterns of this relatively small set of fundamental variables – and we have only scratched the surface of what is possible. Can you imagine what AUO might be able to cook up without our severe constraints? No, of course you can't, but we can imagine that AUO would have a gazillion times more variables to arrange within a huge manifold of multi-dimensionality. Simple fact: We cannot even vaguely imagine how far beyond our comprehension AUO's possibilities are. Imagine your intestinal bacteria speculating about the larger organism within which they live.

It is these second order processes within consciousness that are responsible for the eventual development of values. When awareness and the complexity of choice reach a sufficient level, the concepts of enjoyment, aesthetics, ideals, and quality begin to modify our expression of the Fundamental Process and our motivations in partnership with it. These comprise a set of third order functions that subsequently influence the outcome of the Fundamental Process of evolution. Given enough awareness and complexity, we have fun. We make music. We produce art. We are the creator and the consumer. We have preferences, likes, and dislikes. Good and bad become defined. We develop values and make moral choices. Birds sing and soar; dogs fetch tennis balls and chase Frisbees.

Play is widespread among highly evolved creatures of all sorts. If having fun wasn't profitable to Big Picture consciousness evolution, it wouldn't come so naturally or be so popular. Sentient critters have inside environments as well as outside environments to pay attention to and interact with. In fact, the more sentient we become, the greater our quality, the more important our internal environment becomes to our evolution.

It is only reasonable and logical that AUO would have the potential to evolve values, compassion, purposeful choice, play, communications, music, mathematics, computer science, creativity, humor, and so on within a system that has billions of trillions of gazillions times more native richness, selection, complexity, memory, and awareness than we humans do.

Wow! Don't you wish you could have bought stock in this binary state-flipping baby before it took over the reality market? This Creative-Supercomputer-Being-Consciousness-System-Thing (with emphasis on the "Thing") is evolving values. Additionally, it has some extraordinary potential that goes far beyond our comprehension. If people evolved second and third order functions that influenced their subsequent evolution, why would AUO not be able to do likewise? After all, the Fundamental Process and the nature of consciousness are the same in all of their various manifestations. Values, choice, play, communications, music, mathematics, compassion, computer science, and creativity are a few of the natural results of the Fundamental Process being applied to consciousness.

Simply having these attributes of consciousness is not enough. In order to effect self-improvement, AUO needs a process and feedback mechanism that can accurately deduce what is profitable from what is not – and another to move the entire system toward a lower entropy existence. We will discuss these processes and feedback mechanism (of which we are a part) in Sections 3 and 4.

There is the outrageously limiting anthropomorphic temptation to make this AUO being-thing into a bigger and better super-cool spooky humanoid. [Ahhh... just like us, how comforting. Beings that are truly great, significant, and powerful must be sort-of like us... inside, I mean... even if they look a little weird on the outside... right? I feel better now.] Resist that temptation. It is not at all like us, although we may be a tiny little bit like it.

You will soon be able to logically support the astonishing idea that AUO's consciousness and existence is fundamental while our consciousness and existence is derivative.

30

■■■

The Evolution of AUO:
The Birth of AUM
(AUO Evolves into AUM)

■■■

By now AUO (Absolute Unbounded Oneness) is ready to make space-time, physical matter, you, me, and begin several experiments in the evolution of consciousness. Each experiment is developed and evolves within a specialized part (memory and computation-space) of AUO. We perceive each of these special parts (unique mental spaces within AUO) as separate dimensions, separate realities. There may be dimension within dimension, reality within reality, like a set of Russian Matryoshka dolls or perhaps the concentric layers of an onion. For example, our beloved PMR universe is one of a very large group of both physical and nonphysical reality subsets – each within its own mind-space dimension of the larger digital consciousness. These realities are contained within, as well as derived from and dependent upon, the much larger, more general, less constrained (more degrees of freedom) reality of $NPMR_N$. Likewise $NPMR_N$ is one of a dozen or so subsets of NPMR.

> ▶ If the use of subscripts is confusing, simply think of the $NPMR_n$ as being mem-
> bers, subsets, or separate portions of NPMR (like neighborhoods, states or countries
> represent social, political, and geographical subsets on earth). The following is a list of
> some of the subsets of NPMR: $\{NPMR_1, NPMR_2, NPMR_3, \ldots NPMR_N, NPMR_{N+1},$
> $NPMR_{N+2}, \ldots\} = \{NPMR_n\}$. Using subscripts such as $NPMR_N$ is a convenient way to
> refer to some portion, dimension, or neighborhood of NPMR which contains and sup-
> ports OS, which in turn contains and supports PMR. Using a similar notation, we will
> sometimes refer to multiple PMRs as the PMR_k (where $k = 1, 2, 3 \ldots$). If the use of a

subscript notation bothers you, just forget about it – it is not that critical to your over-all understanding. A general idea of what is intended is all that is necessary. ◀

Using our digital simulation analogy (see the aside on dimension at the end of Chapter 28 of this book), we can easily envision subroutines within subroutines, partitioned memory and calculation space that is further sub-divided into smaller pieces where certain subsets (such as PMR) of the overall simulation are processed. We can imagine more general realities containing more constrained sub-realities, each in their own calculation space, mind-space, or dimension. Do not think of a solitary onion or a single set of Matryoshka dolls, there are many. For you couch potatoes with digital TV tuners, reality and dimension are somewhat analogous to picture within a picture within a picture – displaying or running multiple TV programs in their own sub-space of the larger TV screen simultaneously.

However the consciousness pie is divided up, however many realities may be running as simulations or as sub-sets of larger simulations, all are connected through (and are a part of) the One Source: AUO consciousness. AUO is the foundation of everything, because everything exists in the relation of AUO to itself. Consciousness is The One, while the many, the great diversity of realities and the entities that populate those realities, are specialized subsets of consciousness within their own thought-space or dimension. The process and purpose of subdividing consciousness into both dimension and individuated units of awareness is discussed in Sections 3 and 4.

When AUO eventually grows up and evolves into an extremely complex and highly ordered set of specialized reality cells performing specialized functions, it becomes an entirely different type of entity. Consequently we are going to give it a new name: The Absolute Unbounded Manifold (AUM).

AUM appears to us to be absolute and unbounded. For that matter, AUM is still an Absolute Oneness as well, but now also a manifold (one into many) of sequences, patterns, realities, dimensions, and existence. AUM is a more complex, lower entropy manifestation of AUO; no new substance or assumptions are added. At AUM's core is the same basic AUO consciousness energy sporting a more evolved level of awareness, lower entropy, and greater functionality.

There is no clear dividing line between AUO and AUM. The distinction is entirely arbitrary. The extent to which AUO grows up and develops structure, organization and complex communications, as well as content, meaning, self-awareness, memory, value, and purpose is what allows AUO to emerge renamed AUM. It is more a matter of degree than it is a matter of developing new fundamental capabilities – evolution, not revolution. Because the awareness, function, ability, and purpose of AUM is so different – more resembling the consciousness we are used to, than the consciousness we call dim awareness – I decided to give it a new name, reminiscent of how we call people "people" instead of upright naked monkeys with short arms.

Think of AUM emerging from AUO as the natural consequence of digital consciousness purposely evolving a highly-parallel, multitasking operating system and interactive application software. That concept should not be too difficult to understand: We humans may likewise soon begin to modify our software or firmware (relative to our physical systems) as our ability to apply genetic engineering to ourselves matures and we become better at manipulating the biochemistry of our mechanisms of conscious perception. Human genetic manipulations and psychotropic medications are at their infancy. We haven't seen anything yet – we cannot imagine what is coming – these fields will impact humanity with every bit as much force as the digital revolution in computer and networked communications technology.

We live at the dawn of a potentially explosive evolutionary and cultural transition. The pace of change is dramatically accelerating. Ahead lies a unique and powerful potential for an incredibly accelerated progression, regression, or self-destruction. After 250 years of the Industrial Age comes the genetics engineering, cloning, psychotropic drug, computer-networked communications, digital information age – all at once! Oh Jeez! Get ready! Put on your helmet, batten down the hatches and fasten your seatbelts – this baby is lifting off the launch pad.

The point is: Once a complex system is capable of directly programming itself (developing or modifying its original source code – which includes genetic engineering), the pace of evolution dramatically accelerates. The intellect, aided by the products of its increasing awareness (digital and other technology), replaces random mutation and natural selection as the primary driver; consequently, evolution accelerates from a very slow paced process to an ultra-fast one.

Exactly how much AUO-AUM's evolution accelerated as it gained the tools to become self-directing is unknown. Looking at the evolution of biologic systems we can foresee processes that would normally take hundreds of thousands of years being compressed into a hand full of decades or only a few years through genetic manipulation. Faster evolution may seem like a good idea, but speed is speed whether it is in the positive (lowers entropy) or negative (raises entropy) direction.

If the direction turns out to be negative the question is: Has the evolutionary process changed too much too quickly to be turned around before the overall system self-destructs? Wisdom would say to go slowly until one knows for sure what the pudding tastes like. Is there enough wisdom with enough influence to have a significant impact on the quality and far-sightedness of our collective decisions? If not, we need to start the process of generating some because the day of decision is not far off!

The nature, quality, stability and balance of any self-programmable system determines if evolutionary acceleration will eventually cause that system to take giant leaps forward or backward. Great opportunity and great risk travel together down the road of self-design and chemical manipulation. Of course, digital consciousness does have some major advantages over biological systems. If the resulting cumulative profitability assessment goes negative, it can always preserve (save) previous states and then punch the undo or reset button (while retaining lessons learned) – one of those cool digital tricks that make carbon based systems envious.

I know what you are thinking: You are coveting the degrees of freedom contained within digital systems. You desperately want your spouse, mother-in-law, and the neighbor's dog to have undo and reset buttons. Be careful of what you wish for, you might get it before you understand all the ramifications. You will learn in subsequent chapters that you, your spouse and his or her mother as well as the neighbor's dog are, at the most fundamental level, individuated sub-sets of digital consciousness. More amazing yet, you will clearly understand the how, why, purpose, and inter-workings of this Big Picture digital reality model. No, no, no, that is not true – you are being pessimistic. Such an understanding will not be a delusion, or serve as proof that I have driven you insane – it is not as far-out or as difficult a concept as it first appears. Some very well respected hard-science types are in my corner on this one and I will introduce a few of them to you in Section 6 (Chapter 19, Book 3).

▶ There is more to an operational consciousness than an on-off switch. You also have reset, pause, record, rewind, fast-forward, playback, slow-motion, instant replay, edit, picture in a picture, and repeat buttons – so pay attention to this AUM Dude and discover how to operate your consciousness fully. It would be a shame for your consciousness to sit there idly flashing zeros in its display for a lifetime because you never bothered to learn how to use the controls.

"Here comes AUM ladies and gentlemen! The One, the Only – the Source of All That Is, the generator of reality! All right! Let's give AUM a big round of digital applause! Get those digits moving folks!

Ladies and gentlemen and distinguished members of the press, this is the moment we have all been waiting for. As the highlight of our program tonight, AUM – the omniscient digital consciousness dude from the beginning – has agreed to answer one question from the human gallery. This is an unprecedented moment in the history of existence ladies and gentlemen – before us lies the answer to any of the great questions of our time – past, present, or future.

"Not all at once please! Quiet! Quiet please! Yes, Ms. Gumwrapper from the Seattle Sunshine, what is your question? Shhhhh! Quiet everyone! I cannot hear the question. Huh? What is AUM's favorite color? Come now Ms. Gumwrapper, don't you think that is a tad shallow – quickly, let's take another question! OK, Ms. Anchordesk from the Evening Views, what is your question? Does AUM wear briefs or boxers? Oh, good grief! OK, let's get a question from somewhere other than the press box – Uh oh ... AUM's getting up... he's walking away shaking his head.... come back.... sir... we are not all from the press...we can do better.....its, its,... just that , well, sir, to be honest, people want to know... sir... Sir? What's the answer sir? Briefs or boxers? You promised sir, you promised! Don't go! Please sir ...briefs or boxers? Give us a sign!!

"He is gone folks. Well, you saw it. The Big Dude was here and left without saying a word. Not a single word. What do you think, Johnny?"

"Well Dan, when AUM walked off I thought I saw his shoulders bobbing up and down. Do we have that instant replay yet? See that, see that little jiggle there! Can we get a close-up of that? Look at that Dan – definitely bobbing up and down!"

"All right folks, there you have it – now pick up those phones and call in your opinion – That's 1-900-$$$-0000. Was AUM laughing or crying when he walked away shaking his head? Let's run that playback again Johnny.... Yep, that's a definite jiggle there! What does our studio audience think? Laughing or crying ...that is the big-dollar question for tonight!" ◀

All right, enough silliness, let's settle down and get back to work. You get the picture: The digital consciousness AUO is renamed AUM when the degree of complexity and opportunity (possibilities) evolves sufficient awareness and mental function capable of creating, evolving, storing and manipulating self-modifying content, process, value, and purpose. In the next chapter, we will see how time generates space and how they both together generate space-time – all so we can experience. Why? Because as everyone knows, experience is the best teacher.

31
■■■

The Birth of Space-Time
How Space is Created by Enforcing
a Constant Speed Limit in PMR

■■■

As I will demonstrate, space and time are closely interrelated; accordingly, we will refer to them as a single entity called space-time. Space-time, in this context, is a construct of consciousness. It is not a physical substance or a thing – it is not a physical construct – it is created by imposing a set of constraints upon a subset of the larger reality. PMR scientists describe space-time as a continuum in which events or physical objects with associated times appear to be located or moving relative to some observer. It is also described as a manifold which is sometimes time-like and sometimes space-like, depending on how one interacts with it

Space-time, from the point of view of *My Big TOE*, is a particular pattern of constraints applied to the energy transfers between individuated consciousnesses. Space-time exists within the digital media that supports the rule-set that defines our perception and thus our physical experience. It has a structural component (space-like) and a dynamic component (time-like). Space-time is the construct within which our fleshy bodies appear to live and interact. It is a consciousness interface filter that defines the perception (experience) of Physical Matter Reality (PMR) to participating sentient conscious entities. The experiences of PMR space, PMR time, as well as PMR mass, energy, and gravity are all derived from the space-time constraints placed on interacting consciousness. (These goofy sounding statements are explained in detail in Section 4. By then they will seem much more reasonable and credible than they do now.)

When I say "AUM invented space-time," or "AUM... (followed by any action verb), I mean in the evolutionary sense, the way fish invented lungs and legs with which they turned themselves into amphibians.

Don't get anthropomorphic on me here and postulate AUM as a little old man with a long white beard making people out of space-time clay on day seven. That is a perfectly nice metaphor, but it is not where this discussion logically leads. This is an effort to improve science and model reality, not to expose and follow threads of Big Truth that turn up in various religious metaphors, though it may accomplish both simultaneously.

AUM utilizes a particular subset of its consciousness digital energy, a portion of its organizational potential, a chunk of thought-space, in which a uniform set of constraints are impose on all energy transfers between individuated subsets of consciousness that inhabit that particular chunk (virtual reality dimension). If the constraints are represented by a rule-set that defines the properties of space-time, the virtual reality dimension created is one of the PMR_k – perhaps our PMR. Thus, space-time is a special perceptual construct defined within a dimension or subset of AUM's consciousness. The space-time rule-set delivers a consistent experience to interacting individuated units of consciousness. Huh? Is this English? I know this description of space-time is somewhere between difficult and impossible to understand right now, but if you hang with me through this chapter and Section 4, what now appears to be off the wall and confused will eventually become both reasonable and crystal clear.

I decided to jump right in and tell you what space-time is before I developed the background necessary for you to understand it because I think that having some idea of where we are going will help you synthesize the concepts required to get there. The experience of space-time is produced by a consciousness-construct that constrains interactions between individuated chunks or subsets of consciousness. The point or purpose of space-time is to produce a specialized consistent virtual experience to individual constrained subsets of consciousness called conscious entities or beings. Don't worry; these concepts should be difficult to comprehend at this time. As always, open minded skepticism defines the correct approach. Be patient: Believe it or not, there is a coherent and logical process that leads to these descriptions but it may be a while before we get to it and through it.

Let's go back to building a logical model from the bottom up. AUM, under pressure to improve itself, must evolve profitable internal environments and processes that methodically reduce the entropy of consciousness, that is, the entropy of its own system. Space-time is **one** such environment. Within the space-time structure, the PMR rule-set defines the processes that make us and our space-time uniquely profitable to AUM.

Digital simulations, like those run on our mainframes or within TBC, generally model what appear to be analog events at the macro level. Likewise, we will develop a macro model of how AUM might conceptualize digital space-time in terms of space-time cells and the time required to pass information between those cells. This should be more satisfying and more helpful than simply stating that space-time and the PMR ruleset constitute an optimized design solution for a virtual reality simulator that serves as an interactive multiplayer consciousness-quality development trainer for units of individuated consciousness.

Let's start by conceiving space-time as a construct of space-time cells. Remember, these space-time cells are conceptual – the result of a *gedanken* experiment in the mind of AUM. We will show that space-time cells must be uniform in form, function, and makeup in order to produce the underlying structure for a simple isotropic experience-space (reality) that can be used to improve AUM's evolutionary profitability.

To help make this metaphor more concrete, let's say that these space-time cells reside in the space-time part of the mind of AUM. Next, let's drop down one more level of detail and separate space from time. The **structural** basis of this model is space-like, and provides the spatial concept or space-part of AUM's *gedanken* experiment, while time provides a dynamic basis for this conceptualization that leads to the possibility of ordered change and therefore growth. Space-time subsequently becomes the fundamental media for a uniquely dimensioned sub-reality or virtual reality within the larger consciousness system. It would appear that space-time is more profitable, useful, or advantageous to AUM if the space-part functions as a simple 3D isotropic experience-space for interacting consciousness because that is how it has successfully evolved. It should be relatively easy to picture a three-dimensional matrix of uniform isotropic space-time reality cells in your mind – which is what I imagine AUM started with, but that was only the beginning.

(No need to grab your dictionary for the scientifically challenged. "Isotropic" is one of those $5 cool-sounding techno-speak words with a ten cent meaning that we technoids love to use to impress the masses of business majors who make more money than we do. It simply means that conceptual space-time is not directionally unique; that within the consciousness of AUM, it is (reacts, interacts, propagates, behaves) the same irrespective of how AUM "looks" at it, applies it, thinks about it, or interacts with it.

Keep in mind that we are talking about the concept or idea of space-time within the digital mind that is AUM. Within a spaceless consciousness, "direction" has no meaning. As the concept of space solidifies around its defining constraints, "isotropic" provides a simpler more straightforward conceptualization of a virtual space. That the **implementation** of the space-time rule-set (governing PMR time and energy as well as 3D space) has non-Euclidian consequences presents no logical difficulty.

The relativity buffs are probably choking on this description of an isotropic Euclidean conceptualization of space. However, the preceding assertions create no conflict with the relativity of our perception in the PMR subset where all coordinate systems may be moving arbitrarily relative to each other, each being as fundamental as any other. Nor does it conflict with the chunky non-homogeneous distribution of mass/energy that interacts by the rules of gravitation. The idea of an isotropic space begins with the definition of light speed as the primary constraining constant.

Although we are describing the space-part of AUM's consciousness with simple Euclidean geometry, PMR space will appear to be curved (non-Euclidean) to a well instrumented high-tech perceiver experiencing physical reality within PMR. The bottom line is that as long as there is no fundamental physical inertial frame within a chunky PMR, curved space-time defined by general relativity continues to represents an elegant model of our perception **within PMR** – even if we assume a simple Euclidian frame of reference for conceptualizing virtual space in the mind of AUM. Our PMR space-time experience is a derivative of, or is based on, the constraints of the space-time rule-set that orders our particular reality. You will see later that the space-time rule-set resident within TBC defines the details of the constraints that define our physical reality and thus our physics.

If you are not a relativity guru, and don't have a clue what the previous two paragraphs are all about, forget about it, it is not important. Physicists, having long ago buried Euclid in their physical big picture, tend to be a little slow in giving up old thought patterns. That the perception (from within PMR) of a curved **physical** space could be derived from the **concept** of an isotropic space is not that difficult to understand, you merely run the traditional paradigm in reverse.

Recall that each reality cell exists as a duality, a condition relative to some different condition, each condition existing only in relation to the other. Conceptually adjacent space-time cells communicate by changing state in sequence thus enabling a distortion or non-uniformity to propagate through the matrix. It was the concept of a pass-it-on communications technique (sequential cellular interaction) that led AUM to develop the idea of space. A cell or group of cells can be specialized to keep time with their constant oscillations in order to set the pace for controlled cell to cell propagation. They may be independent of AUM's main or fundamental clock and can be set to any frequency as long as it is less than AUO's fundamental frequency.

The smallest time increment, DELTA-t, in space-time (one quantum of space-time time or equivalently one quantum of PMR time) must be some positive non-zero integer (n) times the smallest time increment fundamental to AUM. The smallest time increment fundamental to AUM is called the "fundamental time quantum." It is the smallest time quantum possible within the larger reality. DELTA-t is also the minimum time required to change the state of a **space-time** reality cell. All space-time will subsequently march to the beat of DELTA-t.

Distortions can appear to move through space-time at a maximum velocity of one space-time cell per DELTA-t. Keep in mind that a space-time cell is in non-geometric, distanceless thought-space. We are generating only the **concept** of space within the space-time part of AUM's consciousness. This space-time concept is implemented by defining the constraints that bound it. Once the constraints are defined within the PMR rule-set, the consequences (properties of space-time) can be easily computed. Let me say this once again because it is an unusual and important concept. We are **not** creating a **physical** 3D space or a **physical** 4D space-time out of consciousness reality cells. Physical space, and your experience of it, is an illusion, a trick of your individuated mind, a virtual reality within the actual reality of your consciousness. I **am** developing the existence of a **concept** or idea of space within AUM's consciousness – an idea that will evolve to provide the experience of space to an individuated consciousness. Space as a mental construct, not physical space itself; there is no such thing as physical space!

"Are you kidding, no physical space? What is this all around me? I learned to calculate volumes of simple 3D shapes in sixth grade." Making that outrageous statement ("there is no such thing as physical space") is not as obviously dumb as it may first appear; you will hear that same exact statement directly from Albert Einstein and other knowledgeable top-scientists in Section 6 (Chapter 19, Book 3). Do not jump to any conclusions.

We have measured the upper limit on information transfer in PMR as "C," which is the symbol commonly used by scientists to represent the speed of light. "C" is approximately 186,000 miles per second or 3×10^8 meters per second. In less precise terms for you technophobes, the speed of light is "exceptionally quick," "almost instantaneous," "like greased lightning," "smokin'," or "haulin' ass" depending on your socioeconomic and generational affiliation (the degree of degeneracy you take pride in). At least that is the view from PMR.

From my experience, and that of many other NPMR explorers, communications are **seemingly** instantaneous in spaceless NPMR and not restricted by the relatively pokey transmission rate of light-speed as they are in PMR. For this reason, it would seem safe to assume that the integer value of **n** is an exceedingly large number. [Where, as you recall, **n** is the number of AUM's fundamental time increments (fundamental time quanta) that tic-tock away during one (very much larger) time increment of the space-time clock (one quantum, DELTA-t, of PMR time)]. For the record, there are also many fundamental time quanta (smallest chunk of time on AUM's fundamental clock) ticking away during one increment of the independent clock defining time within NPMR (a quantum of NPMR time).

You will learn in Section 5 (Chapter 7, Book 3) that **n** needs to be a large number so that the statisticians in NPMR have plenty of NPMR time to compute probable reality surfaces between successive DELTA-t. Likewise, AUM sets up NPMR with a larger time quantum than its own, enabling AUM to process data between NPMR time increments. Remember, whoever iterates with the smallest time quantum is usually in the driver's seat.

It is easy to study, manipulate, or observe beings, objects, and energy that move in super slow motion relative to yourself, as long as you do not get bored. AUM evolves (chooses) the optimum **n** to suit its needs (easy to study and collect results without getting bored). From my experience and the experience of others, an enormous number of increments (quanta) of NPMR time pass during each quantum of PMR time. We will make good use of this concept in Section 5 where past, future, and para-normal communications are discussed.

Information transfer also **seems** instantaneous here in PMR (over short distances) because light-speed is exceptionally fast relative to other natural PMR velocities. It would seem that you must be careful in using your direct experience to determine what is or is not instantaneous. For large distances, such as the distance from earth to its **nearest** star (4.5 light-years to the Alpha-Centauri triplet), even light-speed seems agonizingly slow.

In NPMR thought-space, individual things are not separated by physical distance and information does not have to be transmitted through space in order to travel between the sender and receiver. Nevertheless, within NPMR, information must propagate from the sender to the receiver (but not through space – there is no **spatial** distance between them). Thus, it requires some **NPMR time** for the information to make the trip between the unique digital mind-spaces of the sender and receiver; time is needed to flip the cell states that represent content within the receiver. Think of this process as analogous to display time, or similar to how your computer shuffles data within its core memory.

I know, this is starting to get weird and I can see your eyes beginning to glaze over with information overload. Clarity will come – collect the big ideas and let the details go for now. Let us do a quick review of the high points and go on.

AUM's time is the most fundamental because it has the smallest time increment (quanta) and is used to define all the others. Imagine, for the sake of putting some concrete meat on these highly abstract bones, that AUM's fundamental quantum of time is ten nano-nano-nano-nano-nano-nano-nano-nano-nano-seconds (10^{-80} s), while NPMR's is 10^{-62} s, and PMR's is 10^{-44} s. Each is a billion, billion (10^{18}) times larger than the previous one.

Using these numbers, it follows that DELTA-t, which in our example is 10^{-44} seconds and represents PMR's quantum of time, is **defined by AUM** to be 10^{36} fundamental quanta ($\mathbf{n} = 10^{36}$). That is, for every 10^{36} tics of AUM's (fundamental) clock, one quantum of space-time time is incremented in our dimension of reality (PMR). After 10^{80} tics of AUM's fundamental clock an entire second of our PMR time has dribbled by.

Talk about slow motion! Just as there are many **fundamental time-quanta** in one quantum (increment) of NPMR time, likewise there are many of these **NPMR time-quanta** in one **quantum of PMR time**. The relatively huge magnitude of one quantum of PMR time (one quantum of space-time time) is exactly the time required for one **space-time** reality cell to change its state from non-distorted to distorted (**or** vice-versa).

The upper limit on propagating distortions in **space-time** is thus one space-time reality cell per quantum of space-time time. We define that upper speed limit as "C," a constant whose value has been evolved by AUM and which has been experimentally measured in PMR to be 3 x 10^8 meters per second. C, therefore, **conceptually** defines the virtual size or conceptual spatial extent of a space-time reality cell. Thus, the virtual width of one space-time-cell divided by DELTA-t (which is defined as one quantum of PMR time) would equal C.

▶ Let's use the values given in our arbitrary numerical example above to calculate the space-time reality cell width. The virtual width of one space-time reality cell = (C)•(PMR time-quantum DELTA-t) = (3 x 10^8m/s)•(10^{-44}s) = 3 x 10^{-36} meters, which is about the size of Planck's length (16×10^{-36} m) – a measure of the point at which some of the world's best physicists say that our 3D space becomes granular (is composed of non-continuous discrete cells).

I purposely made up the numbers in the preceding example to be simple round numbers and to force the width of a space-time reality cell to be near Planck's length. They are for illustrative purposes only – do not take the actual values too seriously.

I know that this is clear to you, but let me remind some of the other readers to set aside their habituated PMR concepts and keep in mind that AUO's tick-tocking clocks are not actually ticking off fractions of our seconds. It is ticking in mind-space, within an aware consciousness that can differentiate between this way and that way, flip-flopping atoms of consciousness called reality cells whose state can be manipulated at will and with regularity. These atoms of consciousness in turn produce molecules of space-time.

The tick-tock of AUM's clock represents the fundamental time-piece, the primordial clock, a mental process within consciousness from which our PMR clocks are derived. Our time, measured in seconds – fractions of the periodic revolutions of the heavenly bodies or more recently some number of atomic oscillations – is a shadow of Fundamental Time; it is our sensory perception of a specific constrained and limited implementation of the more fundamental time defined by AUM-consciousness. ◀

In the example above, information can travel much faster than C (the speed of light in PMR) in NPMR because the quantum of NPMR time is a billion, billion (10^{18}) times smaller than a quantum of PMR time. As I mentioned earlier, OS contains physical (PMR) and nonphysical ($NPMR_N$) components that are interactive with each other. **Between** time increments in PMR (time stands still in PMR between increments), things continue to happen (distortions, patterns, and information continue to propagate) because the clock keeps on ticking in $NPMR_N$. In other words, while time appears to stand still in PMR, $NPMR_N$ continues to race along through 10^{18} more time increments worth of activity. And, between each $NPMR_N$ time increment, while time is standing still in $NPMR_N$, AUM has another 10^{18} fundamental time units in which to conduct business as usual.

▶ If this "time standing still between increments" thing has you buffaloed, forget your habitual notions of continuous time and consider how a complex dynamic simulation might increment time within various subroutines. Time appears to stand still in a given subroutine until the next time that subroutine is called and the local time variable is again incremented. A clear description of time-loops within simulations is given early on in Section 5. Unless this concept is driving you crazy, it can wait until you get to Book 3. ◀

Trust me, 10^{36} or a billion, billion, billion, billion (1,000,000,000,000, 000,000,000,000,000,000,000.0) is a really big number and **could** represent a relatively long time for AUM to wait for one PMR DELTA-t to come and go, depending on how long AUM **perceives** a fundamental time quantum to be. To **our view**, AUM **is capable** of moving in super fast motion. Imagine watching all the movies ever made in a fraction of a second. That represents some serious fast-forwarding. On the other hand, AUM can pace itself however it wishes and often seems to take the long view exercising plenty of patience. **AUM's view** of us may be like our view of some sluggish bacteria growing in a petri dish.

Imagine what it would be like if we each aged one year every 100,000 years (we would have a life-span of about eight million years) and had brilliant nearly perfect memories and minds that were kept busy with many important things to do and think about. We could watch rivers and mountains come and go as well as study mutations in successive generations of quickly breeding fruit flies. If you can imagine this, you have a minute glimmer of AUM's perspective. AUM does not seem to be getting bored or to be in any hurry. AUM's perception of the passage of time (that AUM itself creates by regularly flipping states in order to organize and orchestrate its activity) is very different from ours. Do not anthropomorphically project your sense of the passage of time to AUM. Imagine how subroutines within a digital computer, or the computer itself, might perceive the passage of time.

The existence of multiple levels of quantized time is why information transfer in NPMR seems near instantaneous compared to poky light speed in PMR's space-time construct. From NPMR, PMR would appear to be running in slow motion. Nevertheless, NPMR has its own speed limit, as does AUM itself, because it requires a finite time to change the state of any cell from uniform to not-uniform; that is how we defined the concept of time in the first place.

AUM can define (evolve) as many clocks as necessary for each group of specialized cells that define a unique dimension of reality. Our space-time reality (PMR) is implemented by one such group of specialized space-time cells. This collection of specialized cells existing as a sub-group within the larger group of NPMR provides the computing resources (memory, structure, rule-sets, and processing) required to actualize (compute the consequences of) that subgroup as a unique virtual reality within NPMR. Visualize a reality dimension (like PMR) within a larger reality dimension (like NPMR) within a larger reality dimension (like AUM). There may be many sub-groups that define unique dimensions of reality within NPMR. We will see in Section 5 how the various sizes of time quanta (all derived as integer numbers of AUM's fundamental quantum of time) each in their own dimension can be directly related to nested time loops within a simulation. What a bizarre thought! Reality as a layered digital thought-simulation within AUM – hang onto that concept and we will explore it in detail later. The significance of multiple levels of quantized time will become clear and seem less arbitrary after we have completed Section 5.

Here is a quick summary of the concept of time within NPMR. Keep in mind that NPMR has no space and therefore no distance – it exists outside of PMR's space-time. Without space and distance, the propagation time for information takes on a different perspective. Because AUO and AUM can flip states relative to itself only so quickly, thus there is an upper limit on the speed with which distortions can be propagated. It is a much larger upper limit than we can imagine with our relatively snail-like light speed that sets the upper limit in PMR.

Time, or equivalently, frequency is a fundamental attribute of AUM, whereas the notion of space is derived from time by specifying a constant velocity of propagation of information. That is why the citizens of space-time must live with C as the celestial speed limit. Time is fundamental; space is derived from time by specifying the constraint C.

For those who occasionally visit the PMR physics fringe, the fact that we might be clever enough to take a space-time shortcut through a "wormhole" does not change the fact that C remains the upper speed limit on information propagation through space that **defines** our local experiential space within AUM's consciousness. Likewise, if data transfer rates seem to exceed light-speed in certain peculiar situations; this implies only that the defining rule-set has a level of generality that allows special cases to **appear** to violate the speed limit C.

The reality in which we interact with each other is a virtual classroom or learning lab designed to help us reduce our individual entropy and grow the quality of our consciousness. As consciousness, that is what we do; that is how evolution challenges us. That many implications of our rule-set await our discovery (the physics of the future) simply makes that classroom more interesting, challenging, and educational. New discovery creates better understanding as well as new opportunities to learn.

How did AUM come up with the constant C? By occupying all the possibilities and building on the best results, by trial and error, by evolution. It was derived by applying the Fundamental Process on a scale and at a pace that is difficult for us to comprehend. Keep in mind that AUM has no body to feed, does not take up space, and is not preoccupied with perfumed AUMettes.

AUM's evolutionary experiments are roughly analogous to our or *gedanken* experiments or computer simulations, and thus can be done in great variation relatively quickly. With the aid of its specialized binary computing part, AUM can evolve at an incredibly fast pace compared to biological systems. The Big Computer (TBC) and the Even Bigger Computer (EBC) discussed in Section 5 (Chapters 6 and 11 respectively of Book 3) are actually only tiny subsets of AUM's computing part. If you enjoy torturing and abusing the English language as much as I do, you have my permission to describe AUM as a consciousness-system-digital-being-thingamajig.

Reality cells, memory cells, binary cells – everything seems to come down to cells. Cells are discrete units of state-specific **relational** content, and represent both information and organizational substance (not necessarily physical matter). Awareness, form, function, content, and purpose all flow from the possible interactions of reality cells – the basic building blocks of aware consciousness.

All cellular and digital creations exhibit granularity at some level of detail. Both our reality and our perception of it are granular at the root. At the bottom layer of organization within reality, one will find discrete units relationally formed and arrayed into constrained dynamic patterns of relationship. The complexity and organization of these patterns are progressively developed within a primordial undifferentiated potential energy (unaware dim consciousness) by the iterative and recursive operation of the Fundamental Process. The mechanics of evolution naturally act upon any entity that possesses a substantial number of self-generated alternative choices and possibilities. The process is simple – maintain the winners, discard the losers – more or less random permutations and combinations are applied statistically to systems that have a significant array of potential outcomes. The winners continue to evolve while the losers fade away or maintain the status quo.

Sometimes an evolving consciousness system may in time develop terrific complexity and seemingly endless potential as the Fundamental Process iterates upon itself repetitively, eventually evolving into something that begins to mimic its source. When the wheel turns full circle and the successful product of the evolutionary drive toward self-improvement begins to take on the characteristics of its source, it becomes a partner in the process of consciousness evolution.

Imagine this. An individuated constrained high entropy fragment of consciousness eventually evolves (profitably self-organizes) to low entropy wholeness. As a part of the source from which it was cleft, it lowers the entropy (increasing the quality, furthering the evolution) of the whole by the amount of its personal growth. This individual contribution to lowering the entropy of the entire consciousness system constitutes the up-stroke the consciousness cycle. The down-stroke is represented by the creation of individuated consciousness by uniquely bounding subsets of undeveloped (raw) consciousness (of relatively high entropy) that are capable of eventually evolving toward lower entropy states.

Are you beginning to sense the great cycle of consciousness evolution of which you are a part? A vague understanding of how and why the consciousness cycle operates to sustain the ecology of the larger consciousness system is your first peek at the Big Picture. The consciousness cycle describes a mechanism that allows consciousness energy to continuously organize itself within the larger consciousness ecosystem. You are an important player in a consciousness cycle that drives system profitability, capability, operational power, and brightness upwards as it exhausts entropy. We will pursue these concepts more fully in Chapter 24, Book 2.

Let's pull it all together. The constant upper limit of C (speed of light) defines the concepts of both distance and space within the space-time subset of AUM's consciousness. Each so-called space-time cell, by definition, now has the **conceptual** attribute of extent. Thus AUM invented (thought-up, or evolved) the **concept** of space by imposing the constraint of a constant maximum velocity of propagation of information within its space part. Using the previous numerical example to add a sense of concreteness, DELTA-t is the smallest unit or quanta of time **within space-time** – it is one tick on AUM's **space-time** clock, (but 10^{18} tics on AUM's NPMR clock, and 10^{36} tics on AUM's fundamental clock). Each space-time reality cell now has the conceptual attribute of spatial extent. It is (C m/sec)•(DELTA-t sec) wide – about 3×10^{-36} meters (approximately Planck's length).

The science, engineering, and math types need to chill out. I know that I am about to drive you crazy with repetition, but most of the rest of us are only beginning to get comfortable with powers of ten and C notation, the concept of interrelated time quanta, and the calculations of space-time cell width. Take care not to burn out your clutch or overheat your engine – this is a good time to lie back and coast a little.

To say the same thing in the opposite direction: If an imagined row of adjacent PMR space-time cells, each of width (C)•(DELTA-t), uniformly propagate a distortion by changing state consecutively, one each DELTA-t, the distortion propagates at the velocity C. Thus the cells in the space part of AUM now have the **attribute** of size. This is not to say that they have size, or begin to take up space; they have the **concept** of size. You could say they carry the attribute or property of size, that they have virtual size, or that they simulate or model size.

These space-time reality cells are a part of AUM and exist as thoughts exist – without space. Because AUM's evolution of the space-time rule-set found optimal profitability within an experiential isotropic space, the functional propagation of distortion in any imagined direction is the same throughout this uniform space-time matrix of reality cells.

To maintain a constant propagation velocity in all directions, it is convenient if these space-time reality cells are **conceptually** spherical – 3D solid geometry becomes a concept, an attribute of the space-part – and any propagation in any virtual direction will find the virtual distance to any neighboring cell to be the same. More succinctly: The spherical diameter = the conceptual width of any cell in any direction = $(C) \bullet (\text{Delta } t)$. The **concept** of space (distance and direction), and the **concept** of time are interrelated through the constant C, and merge conceptually as space-time. Don't worry about the voids that exist between spheres when packing spheres in a 3D matrix – that is an issue in PMR space-time but not an issue in digital thought-space where space-time is created and defined. Similarly, energetic interactions among various forms of energy and the invariance of reference frames within the experience of PMR reality are not in conflict with the Euclidean frame of mind of AUM.

Our PMR space-time (within which the experience of matter in our universe is created – see Section 4) represents only one uniquely constrained space-time application existing within **a** space-time part (as opposed to **the** space-time part) of AUM. There are other space-time parts (or space-time dimensions) of AUM corresponding to the other PMRs (mentioned in Chapter 4, Book 3). From our point of view, these other PMRs exist in nonphysical worlds within other dimensions. From our perspective, every subset of specialized reality cells in AUM defines another dimension of existence – another reality, or, if you prefer, another virtual reality. The specialized parts of AUM are to AUM as systems of thoughts are to us – a rough analogy even if we had super memories. These specialized subsets of AUM represent separate experiments in consciousness evolution propagating their way to whatever comes out of them.

Digital space-time is implemented by a basic rule-set that defines the profitability criteria required to evolve the content of a given dimension. Each virtual reality with self-modifying content automatically begins to evolve its own uniquely profitable configurations as its possibilities are explored. Patterns of interaction within the PMR space-time sub-system will eventually evolve to contain the attributes of, content, information, and substance – as patterns of light, sound, and neurons within our biological systems or as patterns of stars, comets, galaxies and solar systems within our universe.

As a direct result of the space-time rule-set, a few billion years ago clumps of biological cells began a series of similar experiments in specialization. Specialized subsets of cells became the food-section (digestion), the sensor-section (eyes, nose, skin, ears, taste buds), the motion-section (tail, fins, flippers, legs, wings), and the control-section (central nervous system, brain). Then, communication among the various specialized parts was established, followed by communication between individual entities.

Thus AUM sprouts reality systems as the earth sprouts species of plants and animals, each contained in its own dimension or piece of thought-space within TBC, and all on the same "network." AUM creates dimensions and manipulates their content similarly to how we create ideas and write them down as paragraphs of patterns of symbols. AUM's creative thoughts and use of dimension to separate specialized parts of itself is roughly comparable to our creative writing and use of paragraphs, books, or documents to separate and bound specialized chunks of content.

Note that we generally do not refer to higher or lower dimensions. Higher and lower have no meaning relative to non-geometrical dimensions. Dimensions, and their corresponding realities, are different in the same way books are different. Some may be simple or complex; some may be more or less useful to the consciousness system. However, all are specialized in response to evolutionary pressures to carry out their particular function. All specialized functions contribute to the self-improvement or entropy reduction of the whole. You see, this consciousness system is not that weird or mystical and works the same as any evolving complex system. For example, it must develop a balanced ecosystem (system of relationships) among its large number of interacting, interdependent parts.

You now have the top-level hand-waving description of the origins of space-time and the nature of dimension. This is only the beginning of a more in depth discussion that will continue through the next three sections and two books. Before long, you will appreciate space-time as a rule-based consciousness-construct that constrains energy exchanges between individuated subsets of consciousness (beings) in order to produce a specialized virtual experience where they can profitably interact – and that description will make sense.

By the end of Section 4, all these scattered bits of theory will begin to pull together into a high resolution Big Picture. Keep in mind our earlier discussion of belief and "spin." The logical solidity and reasonableness of this discussion may not be the only, or the major, factor that leads you to your conclusions. To optimize the return on your investment, your analysis should be independent of belief-based paradigms. If your approach is open minded, you will find that the evaluation process itself is usually more valuable than the final conclusions reached.

▶ All great sages know this one Big Truth: "You can lead a jackass to water and, if you are clever enough, induce it to drink, but you cannot make it do the backstroke, or gargle and spit the water back out."

That is why this trilogy is strictly for open minded humans. If you see a jackass with a copy, please confiscate it immediately before he or she gets any Big ideas. But, please be careful! It is also well known by the great sages that: "A little Big Truth rattling about within the small mind of a jackass can be a dangerous thing."

That is everything I know about common horse-sense. Thus, as always, you are on your own at the watering hole of Big Truth. ◀

Before temporarily leaving the subject of space-time and ending this chapter, let's make an effort to bridge the gap between the fundamental view of the binary reality-cell space-time part of AUM's consciousness and the digital systems view of the implementation of space-time within TBC. AUM, aware consciousness, and therefore space-time (our physical reality) is ultimately based upon the existence of reality cells within consciousness. Equivalently, one could say that space-time is a construct of consciousness. Some may be tempted to say that space-time is constructed of consciousness, but that statement is likely to spread more confusion than illumination. Think of consciousness as a digital media rather than a building material. At the root, TBC (memory, patterns, logic, and processing) is conceptually based on the binary property of reality cells.

Let us recap the evolutionary road from AUO to AUM. Primordial AUO is a relatively simple, uniform, high entropy, energy-form that is the basic foundation of consciousness. Reality cells are created by the relative existence of a this way and that way pair – a distorted or non-uniform existence existing in relation to a non-distorted or uniform existence. The proliferation of reality cells and the interaction between reality cells creates complexity and a greater potential for self-organization that eventually leads to a more comprehensive lower entropy self-awareness that in turn leads to intelligence, values, personality and purpose. In scientific terms, a lower entropy consciousness system has more power – more energy available to do work – a higher, more useful level of organization. In common terms, a lower entropy digital system commands more usable energy (more profitable organization) and, therefore, becomes capable of creating greater and more profitable configurations of itself. Additionally, a lower entropy consciousness eventually develops the ability to use directed conscious intent to reduce its entropy further. The **rate** of evolutionary progress increases as the system pulls itself up by its bootstraps (evolves) to actualize lower and lower entropy configurations.

The specific nature (physics) of our reality is defined by the space-time rule-set which defines the constraints that limit what is possible. The space-time rule-set is a collection of patterns or algorithms within TBC that defines the limits and relational properties of our physical experience. The space-time rule-set subsumes our physics. It is implemented at the lowest level by constraining the interaction between individual and groups of reality cells and at the highest level by constraining individuated subsets of awareness.

Reality cells are roughly analogous to the transistors on a computer processor chip. They come in very large numbers and are the most basic active units of the processor and memory. Like reality cells, each transistor is a thing that can be on or off, a 1 or a 0, this way or that way, distorted or undistorted. At the next higher level of generality, is the processor's basic instruction-set that defines operations and processes for storing, retrieving, and performing arithmetical and logical operations. In our analogy, the processor's basic instruction-set is analogous to basic cognitive functioning within AUM. At the next level of abstraction, we get to the space-time rule-set which is analogous to algorithms written in assembly language. Our experience is generated at the next higher level of abstraction by an AUM-TBC to individuated-consciousness interface which is analogous to a simulation programmed in object oriented C^{++} where we are the objects. AUM is the computer, the programmer, and the operating system. We sentient conscious beings are, as individuated subsets of consciousness, a bounded subset of highly organized, evolving, interactive reality cells.

As an analog to space-time, consider a custom designed special purpose processor such as a Digital Signal Processor (DSP) chip. Understanding the rules (patterns) governing the transfer of energy to and from transistors in a special purpose microprocessor would provide some understanding of the most basic relationships in the processor's design, implementation and capacity. Likewise, understanding the rules governing the transfer of information between space-time reality cells should produce some of the most fundamental relationships of physics. In Section 4, you will see how that works.

Physical experience is generated when the perception of an individuated consciousness (sentient being) is constrained to follow the space-time rule-set. Imagine a specialized space-time virtual reality trainer (operating within a subset of digital calculation-space called a dimension) that is constrained by the space-time rule-set to provide a causally consistent operational experience that enables an individuated consciousness to evolve to lower entropy states by exercising its intent through free will choice. The specific relationships defining AUM's space-time instruction-set constitute the laws of space-time physics (PMR physics).

Applied mathematicians, scientists, and engineers have a tendency to define their reality in terms of its constraints expressed as physical constants. For example, C (the speed of light in a vacuum) defines the speed limit of matter in PMR. Think of C as one of several local PMR space-time constants that constrains our physical reality to a certain experience-set. Likewise, it is reasonable to assume there are constants that constrain the bigger picture as well. For example, given that a finite growing digital consciousness system cannot create an infinite number of reality cells and that the information contained within that digital consciousness system is limited by the capacity of the system (an upper limit on the total number of reality cells perhaps), then, after the system's native technology has stabilized, the ratio of the size of the system to the amount of information it contains would tend toward a constant as the system matures. Picture a growing AUM where new information and new reality cells are constantly created and recycled while the entropy of the system evolves toward greater profitability by more productively using and organizing that information. The point is: Real finite systems must always deal with constraints and the AUM-digital-system-thing is no exception.

What does AUM do when it is done (reached capacity limitations)? Being digital, it can always purge enough of its least productive bits to continue on, or purge even more than that and start over. Consider that AUM may be a contributing player in a larger consciousness ecosystem. Just as we iteratively cycle subsets of our individuated consciousness through the PMR learning lab to help drive the consciousness cycle, AUM may recycle its own consciousness in a similar manner to drive a higher level of consciousness organization that is beyond our grasp. AUM may regularly upload lessons learned and then recycle itself or it may simply continue to improve itself gradually as it continually and forever moves toward an absolute zero of system entropy. In either case, we come to the same conclusion: An evolving digital dude is never done.

A few low-hanging observations need to be plucked from the preceding discussions and then we can pack it in. You may find it interesting to take a Big Picture look at the conceptual flow that is unleashed by the concept, implementation, and evolution of time.

AUO evolves the exceptionally useful organizational catalyst we call time by maintaining a regular beat (a constant rate of oscillation). The ability of time to sequence patterns and enforce consistency allows AUO to create ordered and disciplined process and thus lower its entropy. Time enables simple existence to generate complex evolutionary potential from the explosion of new patterns, sequences, and forms that suddenly become available with the invention of dynamic process. Time generates new degrees of freedom for consciousness to explore. Time allows dim consciousness to become brilliant. Order, consistency, and regularity enable the creation of precise multi-frequency clocks, the big computer, and space-time as individuated specialized patterns of information and content within AUM.

Because the attributes of space-time provide the logical conceptual structure for our experience of PMR (mass, energy, space, and hence biology), it is clear that our existence is enabled by the invention of time. It is time that allows AUO to get organized – to create, store, and use information interactively – to evolve self-ware purpose and develop proactively.

The concept of time within the dim awareness of AUO is a byproduct of a potential energy system finding profitability in improving its self-organization. As an incredibly effective engine for entropy reduction, time becomes an evolutionary inevitability. The Fundamental Process could not help but find time (an artifact of change) on the path toward greater profitability. Thus time evolves naturally within consciousness – it delivers the fundamental organizing technology that enables the decrease in entropy (winds up the digital spring) that fuels, runs, drives, and enables everything else within an advanced AUM digital system.

Time is fundamental to the existence of our reality while space is a virtual perception based upon time and the constraint C. As consciousness evolves, its energy-spring continues to wind up as its entropy decreases. In contrast, within our PMR sub-system, the energy-spring (energy that is organized, structured, and able to do work) must slowly unwind as the experiment runs its course. Physicists refer to this natural PMR structural disintegration as the second law of thermodynamics. The second law is hailed as very bad long-term news for our local reality because traditional scientists have only little TOEs.

That music is universal to all cultures (and most creatures) and evokes a deep resonance within us seems reasonable enough when you consider that our consciousness, our being – undeniably, our entire reality – is constructed of rhythm and pattern.

Take a moment to ponder the deep connection we have with our reality. Try to think a few big thoughts (your choice) – go ahead, I'll wait. You might toy with the idea of having an original insight toward developing your personal Big TOE. Take your time. Then when you are done, heave a deep sigh of silent resignation in appreciation of your limitations. But don't give up. Both you and AUM have to start from wherever you are and pull yourself up by your own experiential bootstraps – that is simply how consciousness evolution works.

Consciousness evolution does not progress through a process of successive epiphanies. Significant entropy reduction is accomplished through an iterative process that slowly accumulates a large number of nearly infinitesimal profitable choices to produce significant growth. Trying to grow your consciousness in great leaps impedes progress by distracting you from the hundreds of small profitable choices you have the opportunity to make every day. Your consciousness quality rises and falls based upon the intent that animates your everyday interactions.

32

■■■
An Even Bigger Picture
■■■

Will AUM ever exhaust all the possibilities? Can it grow indefinitely? Will it one day reach an unchanging stable equilibrium, still viable forever but no longer evolving? Are there other AUOs or AUMs or is reality big enough for only one? And if there were two, how would they interact? That would dramatically raise the level of complication and create new possibilities for the Fundamental Process of evolution to work with. It certainly did for us.

What if AUM splits in two, employing a process analogous to biological cell division, enabling it to interact with itself in an entirely new way? Biological cells figured out how to do it. Do you think they are smarter or luckier than AUM? A self-replicating AUM could build up a new consciousness-thing out of AUM-cells, each existing within their own digital dimension. Would each AUM-cell function as a single brain cell (or consciousness cell) within a stupendous group-mind, or would a different and unique creature emerge? Cloning, reproducing, repairing, expanding, and merging are particularly straightforward processes within a digital medium – ever copy a floppy? Where does the pursuit of profit lead a brilliant finite digital oneness? Groups of AUM cells could very well specialize and form a much more complex thought-system-thing-being, and then.... and then... AUMamoebas and AUMamabobs thinking around in primordial mental swamps!

The biological cells of a larger bio-organism mature, die, and are replaced. In contrast, digital AUM-cells may simply mature and maintain some optimal joint profitability with a larger organism or perhaps occasionally recycle themselves by uploading their accumulated products of evolutionary profitability along with all other useful communicable results of accumulated experience and then reboot. AUM, like us, may serve as a cog in a much larger entropy-reduction engine that is engaged in driving an even larger manifestation of the consciousness cycle toward ever lower entropy states.

Big picture this: consciousness systems (like future digital computers), derived from consciousness systems (like humankind), derived from consciousness systems (like TBC), derived from consciousness systems (like AUM), derived from consciousness systems (an even larger system in which AUM is only one of many contributors) – all exhibiting the same fundamental structures and processes while hierarchically supporting each other at various levels and scales. Did you notice that the terminology used to describe interconnected interdependent consciousness systems at various scales and levels is similar to the terminology used to describe fractals? Consider the conceptual elegance of a consciousness-evolution fractal and hold that thought until we will get back to it toward the end of Section 5.

While you are in the mood for big thoughts, imagine this: our entire local reality (OS, containing a portion of $NPMR_N$ as well as our PMR universe), evolving on its merry way as if it were a self-contained colony of bacteria existing within a small remote corner of the space-time-part of just one of the apparently infinite number of apparently infinite AUM-cells, inhabiting the gut of an AUMosaurus.

It may be fun to let a few of the possibilities that might describe AUM's **external** environment run wild in your imagination, but all we need to build a complete theory of everything is a simple one celled monolithic singular AUO and its internal environment. Logically, all that is required is a finite primordial-consciousness-potential-energy-thing to exist along with the Fundamental Process of evolution. From only those two assumptions, I intend to derive physics, the nature of your existence, your physical universe and experience, and provide a comprehensive working model of the larger reality – all self-consistently contained between the knuckle and nail of My Big TOE. That should be enough! I'll publish the definitive work on AUMosaurus-beyondgraspus-outofmindus, which is its proper Latin name, next year – look for it at your local asylum bookstore in the humor section.

▶ Watch out for that AUMosaurus folks! …Oh no! … It's beginning to squat! Hang on … this baby could blow a thousand universes (including ours) out of its Anterior Sub System in one mighty blast of digital flatulence!

The roar of a billion suns exploding simultaneously violently shakes the foundations of reality!

Existence shudders and quakes in uncertain terror.

"Are we still here?"

"I think so, but I'm not sure? How can you tell?"

"Whew, that was a close call!"

"Yeah! Wow! That really makes you proud to be an intestinal bacterium, doesn't it?" ◄

Seriously folks, do you see how important it is to appreciate your fundamental limitations? If you do not, you run the risk of being unable to discriminate between silly and serious. Insisting that we, the magnificent crème de la crème of existence, could not possibly have such limitations simply adds a layer of obfuscating illogical arrogance on top of what is already beyond comprehension. With regards to the Even Bigger Picture, the best conclusion is no conclusion: Open minded skepticism requires no closure, and thus, accepts its limitations. It does, however, require that you put aside your normal knee-jerk responses (which have been conditioned by your ego, beliefs, and fears) in order to recognize all the possibilities.

Never fear to let your mind run free, but at the same time be aware of the innate limitations of your perspective or you may get lost wandering along the mystical shores of Never-Never land believing that what you see is what is there.

33

■■■

Infinity Gets Too Big for Real Britches

■■■

In this chapter, the concept of, and necessity for, a **finite** AUM will become clear. You will see that AUM does not need to be infinite or anywhere close to infinite to generate all the reality we can comprehend.

In the biological world of PMR, large biological cells must seem infinitely big to atoms. Let's translate that comparison of scale to our universe. If our entire universe was like a single atom in an apparently infinite cell of something much bigger, we actually couldn't care less because from our minute perspective, the really, really big stuff isn't that important to us. Whether that cell is actually infinite or not is not an issue. If it is relatively infinite to us, that is good enough to account for everything we can know.

From the smallest thing that we think we know exists (sub-atomic particles) to the largest thing we think we know exists (the universe), about 100 orders of magnitude (10^{100}) are spanned. The numbers 10 and 100 are not particularly big numbers. If there were some big thing, as much bigger than our entire universe as our universe is bigger than a sub-atomic particle, then this big thing would be only 200 orders of magnitude bigger than one of our sub-atomic particles. If this big thing were itself to be the relative size of a sub-atomic particle to something even bigger and if that even bigger thing was to be the relative size of a sub-atomic particle to something even bigger yet ....

Are you following me here? **Our** entire universe would be as a single electron to a universe that is also as an electron to a universe that is also as an electron to a universe, (four nested universes, one inside the other, each being at a size-ratio of 10^{100} to the next). I think you will agree with me, that final universe is really, really big. This colossus really, really big thing is only 400 orders of magnitude bigger than one of our own tiny electrons. And guess what? That's only 10^{400}, and everyone knows that 10 and 400 are not big numbers.

Already we have slipped beyond the far edges of your ability to comprehend. What about $10000000000^{10000000000}$ ($10^{100 \text{billion}}$)? That is a 1 with a hundred billion zeros between it and the decimal point times bigger than an electron. That much magnitude would allow a billion nested universes existing one within the other – each being the relative size of a single electron to our universe, to the next larger universe. I can write these numbers in a few seconds taking up only a few inches of paper – are we close to infinity yet? No way, these are still relatively infinitesimal numbers compared to infinity. Nevertheless, we have gone far beyond the size that represents something your imagination can begin to begin to comprehend. What about a trillion-trillion zeros ($10^{\text{trillion trillion}}$)? And still, we are not yet a tiny miniscule fraction of the way to infinity yet. How many zeros could you write in your lifetime? How many times could you write the word "trillion"? Even at that, we wouldn't be close to infinity – we could always take that number and raise it to an exponent equal to itself.

Do you get the idea of how **unnecessarily** big infinity is when you are talking about a **real** thing? **AUM is a real thing**, an **apparently** infinite something, but actually quite finite. All the PMRs and NPMRs are real things. Reality is a real thing. Infinity is far too big for real things. You see, AUM doesn't need to be infinite; in fact the concept of infinity brings with it all kinds of logical inconsistencies such as infinite processes that require infinite time and infinite energy which are always unavailable to anything real. Consequently, it is sufficient for AUM to be only relatively infinite, apparently infinite. That is enough to suit our purposes. In your mind, let the word "infinity" be a metaphor, not a defined mathematical abstraction. "Infinite" makes a handy mathematical concept but a very misleading adjective in front of a real, extant, noun.

While we are on the subject of big real things being small relative to the abstract concept of infinity, let's talk about time and infinitesimal things. It is the same drill. For the sake of comparison, let's resurrect the numbers we made up in Chapter 31 of this book. I bet you didn't know there have been less than 10^{18} of our tiny little seconds that have ticktocked away since the Big Bang formed our universe. In case you were wondering, those 10^{18} seconds would consume only about 10^{62} PMR DELTA-t time-quanta (recall that one DELTA-t = 10^{-44} s). Break a second into a billion pieces and you get a nano-second (ns). Less than 10^{27} nanoseconds (ns) have come and gone since the Big Bang went kaaaboom!

Break a nano-second into another billion pieces and you get a nano-nano second (n-ns). There have been less than 10^{36} (n-ns) since the Big Bang, and less than 10^{45} billionths of a billionth of a billionth of a second (n-n-ns) ticked away since our universe began. Is it surprising that a ten n-n-n-n-ns long DELTA-t time increment (about 10^{-44}s) could be small enough to make our gigantic PMR nanoseconds seem absolutely continuous and that the number of them that has ticked away (for much longer than our universe has been forming) remains a relatively tiny number compared to infinity? No doubt a trivial number for an apparently infinite AUM to track.

There is another important point here besides the fact that AUM is finite and real and maintains a huge excess capacity that allows it to do, think, create, and be much, much more than we can imagine. You need to realize that we exist in, and have the capacity to comprehend, only a tiny, tiny, minute, infinitesimal fraction of the possibilities for existence. We have seen above that many entire universes each progressively larger than ours (by the same amount that our universe is larger than an electron) can coexist with us, within our finite 3-D space-time reality. Likewise, in the opposite direction, many realms may exist that are each progressively smaller than ours.

These scaled up and scaled down universes would not evolve carbon based humans and critters resembling us. Our physical matter (composed of the elementary particles, atoms, and molecules that we are familiar with) is nicely suited to our own scale and ill suited to drastic changes in scale. However, that is not to say there could not exist enough weird stuff (totally unlike our matter) that has evolved forms and structures appropriate to its own scale that have enough complexity, memory and processing power to evolve intelligent life-forms. **Why**? Because Mother Nature is one aggressive babe! **Why not**? Because you do not have the capacity to conceive of it? Why would a rational person (who wasn't hopelessly optimistic about the completeness of their knowledge) believe that our personal and collective ignorance and limitations should logically constrain the possibilities of creation?

Our contemporary objective knowledge-base sets the limits on what we can collectively imagine, much less comprehend, and it is unlikely that our little picture science can ever hypothesize more than a minute fraction of the possibilities of creation. Regardless of how hard we try, all we can conjure up are various versions of ourselves because that is all we know. There is little point in speculating beyond the limits of your vision. Appreciating your inherent limitations and applying open minded skepticism to your logical and scientific processes constitutes the only approach to exploring the Big Picture that makes sense and produces results. Any other approach will eventually lead you to paint yourself into a corner with broad strokes of belief and arrogance.

We can barley comprehend, or even wildly imagine, only a very small slice of the potential 3D space-time possibilities for existence within our own 3D space-time – much less existences in other 3D space-times within other dimensions – much less existences outside 3D space-time but within $NPMR_N$ – much less existence outside of $NPMR_N$ but within NPMR. Would the possible realms that lie beyond our comprehension be populated? Could they have evolved consciousness, critters, objects, energy patterns or other structured stuff? No one says they, their matter, their environments, or their governing rule-sets (physics) must necessarily be like us, our matter, our environment, or our rule-set.

In a digital consciousness reality, anything that can be conceived is possible. Anything with a rational structure (rule-based) and with enough potential and complexity will eventually evolve to a more highly organized (lower entropy) system of systems. We are not alone – reality is teaming with intelligent life-forms. In fact, we humans and nonphysical entities of OS are relatively minute – like one small school of fish in a gigantic ocean of sentient life. When you learn to move your awareness between dimensions, you will be amazed at the diversity of life-forms that share our consciousness ecosystem.

What difference does the existence of other reality systems make? Until one or more of these realities interact with your reality, the answer is none whatsoever. Absolutely none. It is a fact that OS is only one of many evolving reality systems but this particular fact is of no **practical** importance to your current task of reducing your entropy within the PMR learning lab. It may be nice to know that you are not alone, and interesting and educational to explore realms outside OS, however, such exploration can do little by itself to improve the quality of your consciousness. Activities that do not contribute significantly to the positive evolution of your consciousness are not important.

The Fundamental Process of evolution combined with the potential of sufficiently complex digital systems to self-organize generates all the reality that is within our capacity to comprehend. In contrast, our space-time universe and small blue planet represent only one special-case application of that process. It is worth noting that the dynamic interaction of a simple evolutionary process with the fundamental energy of a self-organizing digital consciousness spawns individuated sentient awareness (thinking beings) through a multi-leveled self-generating progression of recursive process that is reminiscent of how a simple geometric relationship generates an intricate fractal pattern. An interesting similarity: In both consciousness and fractal systems, each part of the pattern carries the blueprint of the whole.

The critters and things of the earth along with our beloved planet, solar system, and universe inhabit only that sliver of 3D space-time and nonphysical reality that is appropriate for our kind and our purpose. Every reality evolves its own compatible systems and ecosystems. Palm trees do not grow on high mountain tops for similar reasons.

The space-time rule-set is only appropriate for a tiny subset of reality. Other rule-sets define consistent causalities elsewhere that are unimaginable to the residents of PMR. Consciousness and evolution have few limits placed upon their combined creativity. If any system or subsystem is profitable (can lead to self-initiated entropy reduction), it probably exists. Why would you believe that reality systems like OS are the only ones likely to be profitable when your mind can comprehend no more than an infinitesimal subset of the possibilities?

Do not let your beliefs and the limitations of your current knowledge limit your notion of what is possible. Letting your ignorance define the limits of an acceptable reality is bad science; unfortunately, it is also the norm. That is why young scientists make most of the dramatic breakthroughs. When you **believe** that you know, but do not, you cut yourself off from the possibility of ever knowing. The knowledge that lies outside the possibilities allowed by your core beliefs is beyond your intellectual reach – entirely invisible to your self-limited vision. You simply cannot see beyond the walls you have constructed regardless of how hard you are trying to do exactly that and no matter how strongly you believe that your vision is clear and unimpeded. To see a bigger picture, to view what lies beyond, you must first tear down the wall or at least some portion of it. Human cultures are little more than communities of shared belief where common belief-blindness leads to erroneous conclusions that are universally held as obvious truth.

Energy-forms (matter and light for example) and physics within other reality niches (including other 3D space-time realms) may be vastly different from our PMR because each dimension of existence (separate reality) functions under its own rule-set. Nature (the natural manifestations of evolution within each reality) tends to leave few empty places and has a way of evolving something (not necessarily carbon based biology) to populate whatever can be populated. Even the environs around high temperature thermal vents, under huge pressures and in total darkness at the bottom of the oceans, produce life. Not as we are used to perhaps, but life just the same. The fundamental evolutionary process seems to work everywhere – life or conscious awareness or individuated sub-systems of consciousness are merely the result of a purposeful, self-interacting complex system with memory, evolving its way through a large and diverse set of environmentally constrained possibilities.

A complete set of the possible forms that sentient life could take are beyond our knowing. AUM is one member of that set and we are another. Bacteria and flat worms are two more. Evolution produces life-forms that are suited to their particular environment. That is how we and all the critters (including one celled critters) and plants turned out as we are – we fit (are efficient and effective in) our environment. An environment beyond our imagination will evolve forms and functions beyond our imagination to suit itself. Everyone should agree that a digitally simulated interactive virtual reality has few intrinsic limitations.

It is a generally accepted idea among scientists that if we (or at least something vaguely like what the earth has produced) can not exist, grow, and evolve within some postulated reality or host environment, then it is not possible for sentient life to flourish within such a place. The belief that any life-forms that might exist "out there" must be similar to the life-forms of earth is a product of little picture thinking. Without a doubt, we have a very limited view from where and what we are and thus should be doubly careful not to constrain the possibilities we can grasp merely because we do not already know the answers. Such arrogance creates the walls of its own conceptual prison.

Our PMR time appears to us to be continuous (non-granular or non-quantized) because the smallest times we can measure are vastly huge compared to one quanta of our time. You do not notice the granularity in a slab of steel or a pane of glass unless you can measure distances down to the size of an atom or molecule. The glass, steel, or wood tabletop you set your drink on appears to be solid and continuous although we know it is made up of discrete tiny particles with vast regions of empty space between them – the granularity is imperceptible from the macro view. Time is the same way. From the macro view of our everyday experience, time appears to be continuous.

You may find it profitable to visit this topic again after you have read Chapters 9 and 10 of Book 3, where parallel probable universes are discussed. The bottom line is that all the time in all the past and present worlds that you might imagine is not a big deal for AUM to track. In time, as well as space, we see that apparently infinite (but actually finite) is much, much more than enough to accomplish everything we have laid at the feet of a real AUM and a real TBC. It is reasonable to assume that AUM and TBC have multiple gazillions of margin (extra capacity) left over to grow into and play with. Although AUM is a Big Dude with a lot to do and keep track of, being infinite is not a prerequisite for the position.

34

■■■

Section 2 Postlude
Hail! Hearty Readers,
Thou Hast Shown Divine Patience
and Great Tenacity

■■■

I know it has been a wild ride and that you are wondering what to make of all these new concepts and ideas piled one upon the other upon the next like food on the plate of a teenage boy at an all-you-can-eat junk food buffet. What's worse, most readers probably have little experience that can help them evaluate the truth of what you have just read. That is the nature of Big Truth. It is either trivially obvious or totally opaque.

There is no need to make judgments or jump to conclusions. Do not **believe** anything, for or against. Maintain an open mind and realize that you are only at the beginning of this journey. If everything made sense early on, it wouldn't be a particularly complex exposition and a trilogy would not be required. Because I am taking most of you on a trip far beyond your wildest musings, you should expect (this early in the unfolding) to feel somewhat ambivalent, lost, and – please – always skeptical.

If you have little experience systematically exploring the larger reality of inner space, what you read here will no doubt seem abstruse, unsubstantiated and beyond knowing. It is not. It only seems that way from the perspective of your culture and your self-limited experience. Consider how a five-year-old child, or your favorite pet critter, views and understands the larger world it lives in.

Many things will seem absolutely beyond anyone's possible knowing when they are actually only out of sight of a limited vision and understanding. Believing that your vision is less limited than it actually is reflects a natural trait of high entropy consciousness that is constrained to an individuated unit of independent action. (Section 4 will clarify this concept.)

Although what you have read in Section 2 may seem remote from your sense of reality, it was necessary to introduce some of the basic ideas you will need to bring the Big Picture into focus. Everything will fit together more smoothly later on. If the discussion of the life and times of AUM was tough slogging and prompted you to yawn a few ahhh-ummms of your own, take heart, this next section – Section 3 – is all about you.

Because it is about you, it is bound to be exceptionally interesting – how could it be otherwise? In Section 3 ("Man in the Loop") we will make the first tentative connections between all the weird off-the-wall concepts in Section 2 and what they could possibly have to do with you and your physical and mental reality. I think you will like this next section more than the previous one, because it will give you some things to think about that you **do** have the experience to evaluate and it will be less abstract.

If you have made it this far and still have the desire and gumption to go on, award yourself four beautiful gold stars for your intellectual tenacity and inquisitiveness. Paste them inside the front cover of this book so that everyone will know that you are a dedicated, committed, serious seeker after something extraordinarily important even if you are not sure at this point exactly what it is.

Find the other two books of the *My Big TOE* trilogy:
http://www.My-Big-TOE.com
http://www.lightningstrikebooks.com
Phone orders: 1-800-901-2122